303
CIRCUITS

Elektor Electronics (Publishing)

A WOLTERS-KLUWER COMPANY

Elektor Electronics (Publishing)
Down House • Broomhill Road • LONDON SW18 4JQ
Telephone 01-877 1688 • Telex 917003 • Fax 01-874 9153

First printed 1988
This 2nd impression 1989

Copyright © Elektuur B.V.

Printed in the Netherlands by TULP B.V. Zwolle.

ISBN 0 905705 26 2

WARNING!
ELECTRICITY CAN BE DANGEROUS!
The electronic projects in this book are, to
the best of the author's knowledge and
belief, both accurately described and safe.
None the less, great care must always be
taken when assembling electronic circuits
which carry mains voltage, and neither the
publishers nor the author can accept
responsibility for any accidents which may
occur.

Because electricity is dangerous, its use,
application and transmission are subject to
rules, regulations and guidance. These are
laid down in numerous laws, Electricity
Generating Board regulations, British Stan-
dards, and IEE recommendations. Some of
these may be obtained from your local
electricity showroom, but most, if not all,
should be available for reference in your
local library.

contents

001   AUDIO-CONTROLLED MAINS SWITCH

It is often useful for audio or video equipment to be switched off automatically after there has been no input signal for a while.

The function of the on-off switch in such equipment is then taken over by switch S_2 in the accompanying diagram. It remains, however, possible to switch off manually by means of S_1. Automatic switch-off occurs after there has been no input signal for about 2 minutes: this delay makes it possible for a new record or cassette to be placed in the relevant machine.

The audio input to the proposed circuit may be taken from the output of the relevant TV set, amplifier, or whatever. The input earth is held at +6 V with respect to the circuit earth by potential divider R_1-R_2-R_3-R_4. The two 741s function as comparators: the output of IC_1 goes high when the input signal is greater than +50 mV, whereas the output of IC_2 goes high when the input signal becomes more negative than —50 mV. Resistors R_6, R_7, and R_8 form an OR gate that drives transistor T_1. If the output of either IC_1 or IC_2 is logic 1, T_1 conducts.

The 555 operates as a retriggerable monostable, whose period is determined by R_{10} and C_1. The device is triggered when its pin 2 is earthed by the closing of S_2. Its output, pin 3, then remains high for 1 to 2 minutes, depending on the leakage current of the 555. The monostable resets itself as soon as the potential across C_1 exceeds a certain value. As long as there is an input signal to the circuit, T_1 conducts and C_1 remains uncharged. As soon as the audio signal ceases, T_1 switches off, and C_1 charges until the potential across it is sufficient to reset the 555. The monostable may also be reset by closing S_1, which connects pin 6 of the 555 to +12 V.

When IC_3 is reset, C_1 is discharged via its pin 7. Resistor R_{11} serves as protection, because without it T_1 could short-circuit the supply lines.

When the output of IC_3 goes high, T_2 conducts, the relay is energized, and the relay contacts switch on the mains voltage as appropriate. To counter the induced potential when the relay contacts close, which could damage T_2, diode D_1 has been connected in parallel with the relay coil.

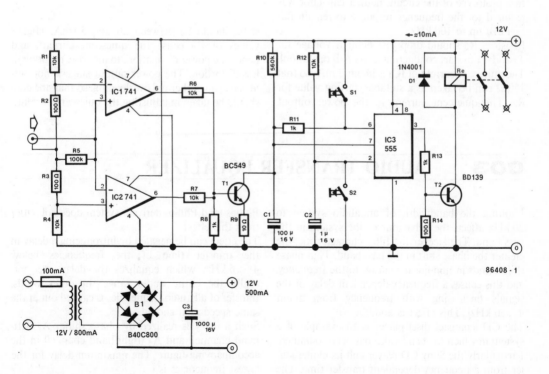

86408 - 1

Integrated operational amplifiers are not always suitable for applications where a high signal level ($U_o \leq 10$ V_{rms}) is required for driving a relatively low impedance ($Z = 50$—600 Ω). The amplifier described here is eminently suitable as a high dynamic range line driver or power buffer in public address systems and AF distribution amplifiers.

The input amplifier of the line driver is formed by a low noise opamp Type OP-37 from PMI. This ensures the following technical specification of the line driver: $U_o = 70$ V_{pp} max.; $I_o = 400$ mA_{pp} max.; $D_{tot} = 0.01\%$ at $U_o = 10$ V_{rms}, $Z_L = 50$ Ω and $S/N \geq 90$ dB.

Regulators T_1-T_2 bring the supply voltage for the OP-37 down to ± 15 V. The complementary power output stage is formed by T_3-T_4. The amplifier has a standard negative feedback circuit R_1-R_2, which results in a voltage gain $A_V = -(R_2/R_1)$. A local feedback R_3-R_4 has been included to keep the output voltage of the opamp within safe limits, while capacitors C_1-C_2 serve to improve the stability. It should be noted that the value of C_1 and C_2 depends on the construction of the line driver: typical values are 680 pF for C_1 and 22 pF for C_2. In a prototype of the circuit, neither capacitor was required for the frequency response to remain flat (± 1 dB) up to 100 kHz.

Resistors R_B should drop just enough voltage for T_3 and T_4 to start conducting (class A-B operation). The quiescent current of IC_1 is about 3 mA, so that 150 Ω can be taken as a suitable starting value for R_B. The quiescent current in the power output

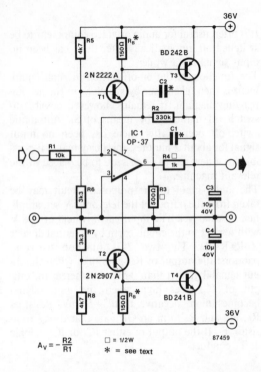

$$A_V = -\frac{R2}{R1}$$

$\square$ = 1/2W
$*$ = see text

stage should be between 20 and 50 mA. Higher values of R_B cause the quiescent current, and hence the power dissipation, to increase, resulting in less distortion. The power output stage is not protected against thermal overloading, so that due dare should be taken in adjusting the quiescent current.

003 AUDIO TRANSFER EQUALIZER

Limiting the bandwidth of an audio system to 20 kHz affects the behaviour of the system in the pass band. The steeper the filter characteristic, the greater the phase shift in the pass band. That phase shift stands in non-linear relation to the frequency, and this causes a frequency-dependent delay of the signals (increasing with frequency from about 4...6 kHz). This effect is audible.

The CD (compact disc) player is an example of a system in which the bandwidth has been so limited. Particularly the Sony CD player and its clones suffer from a frequency-dependent transfer time. The

Philips (and Philips-derived) system does not suffer from this effect.

The effect can be negated by introducing a delay in the transfer time of the frequencies below 4...6 kHz, which equalizes the delay over virtually the entire audio range. In other words, transfer of all audio frequencies is carried out at the same speed as it should.

Such a delay is realized by phase shifter A_2 (left-hand channel) and A_4 (right-hand channel) in the accompanying figure. The maximum delay for the lowest frequencies is

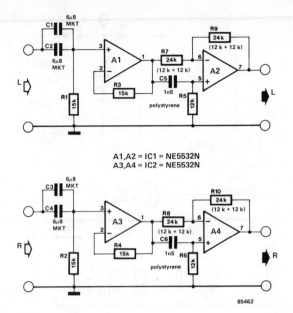

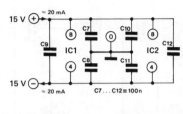

$$2R_5C_5 = 2R_6C_6 = 36 \ \mu s.$$

The circuit is connected between the output of the CD player and the AUX or CD input of the main amplifier.

004   COMPRESSOR

This versatile circuit serves to raise the average output power of an AF amplifier. Its simplicity makes it suitable for applications in intercom systems, public address and discotheque equipment, and also in various types of transmitter.

Compression of music and speech essentially entails reducing to some extent the dynamic range of the AF input spectrum in order to drive an AF power amplifier with a fairly steady signal level just below the overload margin, thus increasing the average output power of the system. However, some distortion is inevitably incurred in the process of amplifying the relatively quiet input sounds and attenuating the louder sounds. It is evident, therefore, that the control of the amplifier/attenuator function in the compressor determines to a large extent just how much distortion is introduced by the circuit.

Before inserting any type of compressor in an AF signal path, due consideration should be given to the *attack time* i.e., the time it takes the circuit to detect and counteract a sudden increase in the amplitude of the incoming signal. Allowing for personal preference and the character of the input signal (speech, popular music, etc.), the attack time of a compressor generally lies in the range from 0.5 to 5 ms. The *release time* of the compressor is the time it takes the circuit to return to the settings that existed before the rise in amplitude occurred. Contrary to the attack time, the release time is usually of the order of seconds. If it is made too short, the compressor's attenuating action may cause interference with the lowest components in the frequency spectrum. On the other hand, too long a release time (10-15 s) is also undesirable as this will give rise to an unrealistic and unpleasant effect caused by the output sound remaining completely muted long after the increase in input ampli-signal amplitude. In practice, the release time of a compressor will need to be adapted to meet the demand of the particular input signal; speech generally requires a longer release time than music. Some compressors have a provision for the setting of the release time, but the one proposed here is an auto-ranging type, that is, it arranges for the release time to change automatically with the instantaneous

11

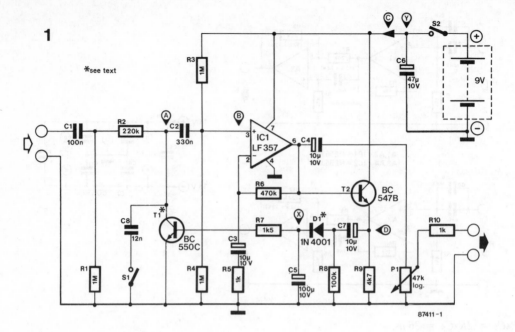

1

*see text

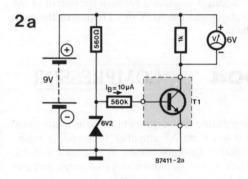

2a

b

amplitude of the input signal.

Figure 1 shows the circuit diagram of this compressor. Despite its simplicity, the design responds adequately to a good number of contradicting requirements. As to its dynamic characteristics, an input signal change from 25 mV$_{pp}$ to 20 V$_{pp}$ ($\triangleq$58 dB) is compressed into an output signal change from 1.5 V$_{pp}$ to 3.4 V$_{pp}$ ($\triangleq$7.1 dB). For a less extreme signal change, e.g., from 25 mV$_{pp}$ to 2.5 V$_{pp}$ ($\triangleq$40 dB), the compressed output signal changes from 1.5 C$_{pp}$ to 2.25 V$_{pp}$ ($\triangleq$3.5 dB). The circuit has an extended frequency response from about 7 Hz to 67 kHz nominally, thanks to the use of a fast opamp, the Type LF357 (IC$_1$), which is set up here to provide an amplification of about 471 [(R$_6$ + R$_5$)/R$_5$]. Capacitor C$_3$ blocks the direct voltage at the inverting input of IC$_1$, and with R$_5$ sets the low-frequency roll-off of the opamp alone at about 16 kHz.

Resistors R$_3$ and R$_4$ bias the non-inverting input of the opamp—and hence its output—at half the supply voltage, ensuring optimum linearity. Capacitor C$_2$ feeds the input signal to the opamp while blocking the bias voltage at pin 3. Its value is not critical, but it has some effect on the low-frequency response of the compressor. The attenuator section in this circuit is essentially composed of R$_2$ and T$_1$. The collector of this transistor is held at 0 V with the aid of R$_1$ and R$_2$. In this way, T$_1$ is always operated in its saturation region, and its collector-emitter junction acts as a variable resistance con-

trolled with the current fed to the base. The higher this current, the lower the c-e resistance, and the higher the instantaneous attenuation of the signal fed to IC$_1$. The controlling rectifier is composed of D$_1$-C$_5$-R$_7$. Transistor T$_2$ functions to provide the charge current for C$_7$ so as to avoid distortion otherwise incurred by too heavily loading the IC_1 output. The rectified voltage across C_5 is a direct measure of the output signal amplitude, and forward-biases the base of T_1, which regulates the attenuation as discussed. The use of a diode with a low internal resistance, D_1, and a buffer, T_2, ensures fast charging and slow discharging of C_5, and thus a short attack time and a long release time, respectively. As C_5 is discharged via R_7 and the base resistance of T_1, the release time of the compressor is the product of the value of these three components. When the base bias is reduced, the base resistance of T_1 increases, lenghtening the release time. This is a most welcome feature, especially with speech signals.

The output of the opamp is fed to C_4-P_1-R_{10}, which provide DC insulation and level adjustment.

Two compressors are readily combined to make a stereo version by feeding them from a common battery and connecting points X and points Y (never X to Y!). In this case, T_1 and D_1 in both compressors must be matched types to ensure proper operation. Figure 2 shows two simple test circuits for selecting transistors and diodes with matching DC characteristics. The basic method is to start with noting the voltmeter reading for a particular device, and then find a matching type from an available lot by inserting devices until one is found that gives the preciously noted test voltage. In the diode test circuit, the LED lights to indicate the absence or reverse connection of a diode under test.

A = 0 V	
B = +4.5 V	
C = 6 mA	
D = 3.9 V	

All values are typical and within 10%.
All voltages measured with respect to ground with a DMM ($Z_{in} = 1 M0$).

Provision has been made to use the circuit as a noise suppressor. Referring to Fig. 1, closing S_1 connects C_8 across the regulator transistor to form a low-pass filter in conjunction with R_1 and R_2. The cut-off frequency of this LPF is a function of the current sent into the base of T_1. The overall effect thus obtained is an effective elimination of noise from quiet passages in the programme. For louder passages, the suppression of noise is not so important, as it is then virtually inaudible.

Finally, when using this compressor, make sure that your amplifier has ample cooling provision, because it may well be continuously operated at the top of its power rating. For the same reason, check whether the loudspeakers can handle the available power.

005   CURRENT CORRECTED AF AMPLIFIER

The majority of modern AF power amplifiers drive the loudspeaker(s) with a voltage that is simply a fixed factor greater than the input voltage. It is fairly evident, therefore, that the power delivered by such amplifiers is inversely proportional to the loudspeaker impedance, since the cone displacement of a loudspeaker is mainly a function of the current sent through the voice coil, whose impedance may vary considerably over the relevant frequency range. In multiway loudspeaker systems, this difficulty is overcome by appropriate dimensioning of the crossover filter, but a different approach is called for when there is but one loudspeaker.

This amplifier is based on current feedback to ensure that the current sent through the voice coil remains in accordance with the input signal. The current through the voice coil and R_7 develops a voltage across the resistor. A negative feedback loop

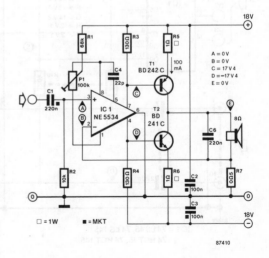

is created by feeding this reference voltage to the inverting input of IC_1. The overall amplification of the circuit depends on the ratio of the loudspeaker's impedance, Z_L, to the value of R_7. In the present case the amplification is 16 times ($Z_L/R_7 = 8/0.5 = 16$).

The connection of the opamp's output to ground is slightly unusual, but enables the base current for output transistors T_1-T_2 to be drawn from the supply rails, rather than from the opamp. Capacitor C_6 functions to set the roll-off frequency at about 90 kHz. The quiescent current of the amplifier is of the order of 50 to 100 mA for class A operation,

and is determined by R_3-R_4 and R_5-R_6. The complementary power transistors should be closely matched types to avoid fairly large offset currents (and voltages) arising. Some redimensioning of either R_3 or R_4 may be required to achieve the correct balance for the power output stage. The emitter current of T_1 and T_2 is about 500 mA when the amplifier is fully driven.

The harmonic distortion of this amplifier is less than 0.01% at $P_o = 6.25$ W and $U_b = \pm 18$ V.

Source: *Texas Instruments Linear Applications*.

---

006   DIGITAL AUDIO SELECTOR

Switching audio signals digitally could be done with the aid of CMOS analogue switches or multiplexers. Simple as this may seem, there is, however, an inevitable loss in the quality of the sound due to the noisy nature of CMOS switches. Furthermore, the high on-resistance of these devices together with the large parasitic capacitances generally present in

CMOS circuits causes a high susceptibility to crosstalk. The circuit given here is a novel way of selecting one out of ten audio signals digitally without any of the foregoing drawbacks.

As shown in the circuit diagram, the ten input signals numbered 1-10 are applied to the bases of transistors T_1-T_{10} via capacitors C_1-C_{10} respect-

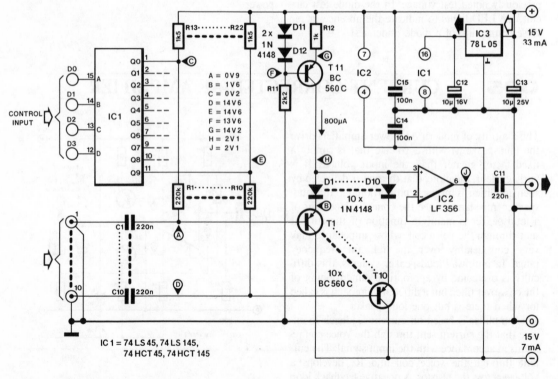

IC 1 = 74 LS 45, 74 LS 145,
74 HCT 45, 74 HCT 145

87443

ively. The bias voltages for the transistors are obtained with the aid of R₁-R₁₀. Depending on the binary state applied to IC₁, one of its outputs Q₀-Q₉ goes low. For example, if the input code is 0010, Q₂ goes low, pulling the base of T₃ to 0 V, while the bases of all other transistors are raised to nearly +15 V. Therefore, T₃ works as an emitter follower while the other transistors are effectively reverse biased. The output rail of the transistor array is connected to voltage follower IC₂, which provides the output signal of the digital audio selector.

Voltage regulator IC₃ is required only if a + 5 V rail is not available. If the number of channels required for a particular application is less than 10, the relevant components can be omitted. If a mute facility is required, simply short one input to ground to silence the output on selection of the corresponding channel.

This circuit can handle input signals up to 4 V_{rms}. The total distortion does not exceed 0.01% for frequencies up to 20 kHz. The crosstalk incurred in this circuit is less than —80 dB. This value can be attained by paying due attention to the layout of the practical circuit, the decoupling of the supply lines (fit C₁₄ and C₁₅ direct to the relevant pins of the opamp), and the use of good quality components.

The measuring values indicated in the circuit diagram were obtained in a prototype. All voltages are measured with respect to ground with the aid of a DMM (Z_{in}=1M0). The channel selected was number 1.

---

007 DIGITAL VOLUME CONTROL I

This digital potentiometer circuit is a hybrid analogue and digital design offering push-button controlled programmable attenuation as well as high to low impedance conversion by means of a single active device. Digital noise is eliminated as effectively as possible through galvanic isolation of digital and analogue parts in the input attenuator. At the heart of the digital control section is a Type 2716 EPROM, which can be programmed either as shown in Table 1 or to individual requirements, as will be detailed below. At power-on, debouncer bistables N₁-N₂ and N₃-N₄ force logic low levels onto EPROM address lines A₅ and A₆ respectively, selecting a programmed address range that supplies the digitally coded, initial volume settng. R-C network R₁₆-C₂ causes gates N₇ and N₈ to generate a clock pulse for IC₂, which latches the 8-bit word from IC₁, passes this information to driver IC₅, and thus determines which relay(s) is/are energized, thereby fixing the attenuation before the AF signal is applied to opamp IC₆. Depression of S₁ (up) or S₂ (down) causes the corresponding address line A₅ or A₆ to go low, selecting a certain address range in the EPROM. The exact address location is determined by the value last latched into IC₂ after either key has been released. It is readily seen that the five available databits at the Q₁...Q₅ outputs of IC₂ allow 32 (2⁵) simulated potentiometer settings.

The digital control section has been designed to of-

Table 1

0000	00	01	02	03	04	05	06	07	08	09	0A	0B	0C	0D	0E	0F
0010	10	11	12	13	14	15	16	17	18	19	1A	1B	1C	1D	1E	1F
0020	00	00	01	02	03	04	05	06	07	08	09	0A	0B	0C	0D	0E
0030	0F	10	11	12	13	14	15	16	17	18	19	1A	1B	1C	1D	1E
0040	01	02	03	04	05	06	07	08	09	0A	0B	0C	0D	0E	0F	10
0050	11	12	13	14	15	16	17	18	19	1A	1B	1C	1D	1E	1F	1F
0060	0E	0E	0E	0E	0E	0E	0E	0E	0E	0E	0E	0E	0E	0E	0E	0E
0070	0E	0E	0E	0E	0E	0E	0E	0E	0E	0E	0E	0E	0E	0E	0E	0E
0080	00	01	02	03	04	05	06	07	08	09	0A	0B	0C	0D	0E	0F
0090	10	11	12	13	14	15	16	17	18	19	1A	1B	1C	1D	1E	1F
00A0	00	00	00	01	02	03	04	05	06	07	08	09	0A	0B	0C	0D
00B0	0E	0F	10	11	12	13	14	15	16	17	18	19	1A	1B	1C	1D
00C0	02	03	04	05	06	07	08	09	0A	0B	0C	0D	0E	0F	10	11
00D0	12	13	14	15	16	17	18	19	1A	1B	1C	1D	1E	1F	1F	1F
00E0	0E	0E	0E	0E	0E	0E	0E	0E	0E	0E	0E	0E	0E	0E	0E	0E
00F0	0E	0E	0E	0E	0E	0E	0E	0E	0E	0E	0E	0E	0E	0E	0E	0E

fer an auto-repeat function when either one of the step control keys is kept depressed; oscillator gate N₆ then provides a clock pulse train to N₇-N₈, and so causes successive addresses in IC₁ to be scanned automatically, until either the lowest or highest possible volume setting is reached, at which moment the circuit forces itself to a hold state, which can also be selected at any time by simultaneously depressing the up and down key.

S₃ enables the user to select a further address block, programmed with another set of volume steps; the circuit as shown, along with the data from Table 1 arranges for 3 dB steps.

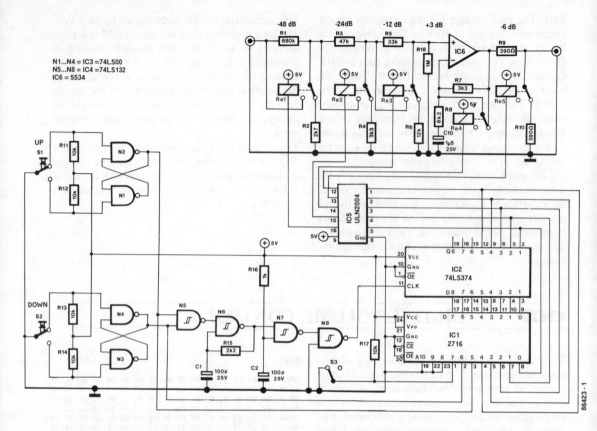

N1...N4 = IC3 = 74LS00
N5...N8 = IC4 = 74LS132
IC6 = 5534

86423 - 1

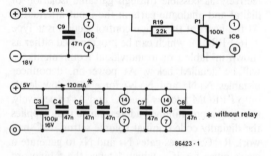

86423 - 1

The analogue section of the circuit is basically a four-section, relay-controlled attenuator composed of resistor networks to achieve a signal attenuation in 3 dB increments, as defined with the relevant bit pattern at the $Q_1...Q_5$ outputs of IC_2. Re_4 (Q_5), if deactivated, enables IC_6 to amplify its input signal by 3 dB. The inset resistor and preset combination may be used take over the function of C_{10}, since the latter should be a high stability foil type, which may be a rather difficult to obtain part. Both circuit alternatives function as click suppressors when stepping through the available range of volume settings. The preset, if used, should be set for zero offset voltage at pin 6 of the opamp; replace C_{10} with a wire link.

It is suggested to use miniature DIL relay types in the $Re_1...Re_5$ positions, while all resistors in the attenuator are preferably close tolerance (1%), high stability types. Also observe that the supply voltages to analogue and digital section are kept well apart and decoupled so as to preclude introducing switching pulses and digital interference in the sensitive attenuator sections as well as the opamp output stage.

Finally, Table 1 offers a suggestion for programming the EPROM with data to achieve circuit operation as set out above.

16

Many of today's hi-fi amplifiers feature a "clicking" volume control, but this is only rarely a real stepped attenuator based on a wafer switch. In nearly all cases, this expensive system is based on a normal potentiometer, whose spindle is fitted with a mechanical construction to simulate the stepping movement. A normal rotary switch is not suitable for adjusting the volume of an amplifier because it briefly

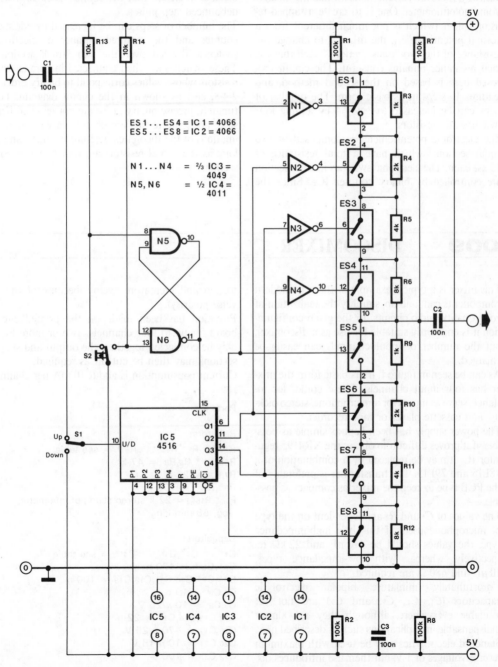

disconnects the input from the signal source when operated, and so readily gives rise to clicks and contact noise.

Different problems crop up when designing an electronic volume control. Of these, distortion is probably the hardest to master, but reasonable results are still obtainable, as will be shown here.

Basically, there are two methods for making an electronic potentiometer. One is to create a tapped resistor ladder (which is not much different from a normal potentiometer), the other is to change the resistance of the two "track sections" such that the total resistance remains constant. The circuit proposed here is based on the second method, and features 16 steps in its basic form. The number of steps can be increased to, say, 64 by adding four switches and resistors.

The electronic potentiometer is composed of two equal sections, which have a total resistance of 15 kΩ each. The electronic switches in each section are controlled by binary counter IC_5. Since the switches in section ES_1-ES_4 and those in ES_5-ES_8 are controlled in complementary fashion, the total resistance of the potentiometer remains constant. Resistors R_1-R_2 and R_7-R_8 serve to keep the potential at the input and output at 0 V so as to preclude clicks when the step switch, S_2, is operated. Switch S_1 is the up/down selector. Gates N_5-N_6 form a bistable to ensure that the counter is clocked with debounced step pulses.

The number of steps can be increased by adding a counter and the required number of electronic switches, divided over the two "track sections". These switches are then connected in parallel with resistors whose values correspond to binary order 1-2-4-8, etc., as shown in the circuit diagram. Fortunately, precise binary ratios are not required here, since adequate results are obtainable with approximations of the theoretical resistance values, and as long as the actual resistors are kept equal in both sections.

009   DISCOMIXER

This mixer is a typical example of the way modern components can, and do, simplify the realization of good quality audio circuits. In the given configuration it is eminently suitable for use as a discomixer, but the number of input channels can easily be enlarged.

As can be seen in figure 1, in its basic form the mixer has four input channels. These could, for instance, serve as inputs for a microphone, stereo pickup, and cassette player or tape recorder.

The power supply has been kept as simple as possible; if it proves difficult to obtain the XR4195 regulator IC, it may be replaced by a combination of a 78L15 and 79L15. The transformer is preferably of the PCB type to keep the mixer as compact as possible.

The values of C_1 and R_1 are dependent on the type of microphone used. If this is a high-impedance type, the values should be 470 nF and 22 kΩ respectively, whereas with low-impedance types, 10 μF and 680 Ω are required.

Unfortunately, miniature bipolar electrolytic capacitors (C_1, $C_{1'}$, C_9, and $C_{9'}$) are not yet available everywhere, although they are almost indispensable in applications such as described here. Standard electrolytics may be used with maximum reverse voltages of 1 V, but their use introduces distortion and premature ageing (because of the reverse polarity).

Provision has been made on the printed circuit board for up to four channels. Two or more PCBs may be connected together; the output and supply sections may then be cut off as required.

Current consumption is about 10 mA per channel.

Parts list

Resistors:
$R_1^*\ldots R_5^*, R_{1'}^*\ldots R_{5'}^*$ = see table
$R_6^*, R_{6'}^*, R_8, R_{8'}$ = 47 k
$R_7, R_{7'}$ = 22 k
$R_9^*, R_{9'}^*$ = 100 k
P_{1a}^*, P_{1b}^* = 22 k stereo slide potentiometer, log, 58 mm long

Capacitors:
$C_1^*\ldots C_4^*, C_{1'}^*\ldots C_{4'}^*$ = see table
$C_5^*, C_{5'}^*$ = 470 n
$C_6^*, C_7^*, C_{10}, C_{11}, C_{18}, C_{19}$ = 100 n
$C_8, C_{8'}$ = 10 p
$C_9, C_{9'}$ = 10 μ/25 V
$C_{12}, C_{13}, C_{14}, C_{15}$ = 22 n
C_{16}, C_{17} = 470 μ/25 V
C_{20}, C_{21} = 10 μ/16 V
C_{22}, C_{23} = 100 p

Semiconductors:

$D_1 \ldots D_4$ = 1N4001
D_5, D_6 = 1N4148
IC_1* = NE5532 or LM833
IC_2 = TL072
IC_3 = XR4195

Miscellaneous:

Tr_1 = mains transformer, secondary
 $2 \times 15V/100$ mA
F_1 = fuse, 50 mA, delayed action
S_1 = DPST on/off switch
Single-hole fixing chassis phono socket — 2
 per channel
PCB 85463

*One of each required per channel.

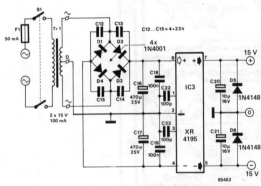

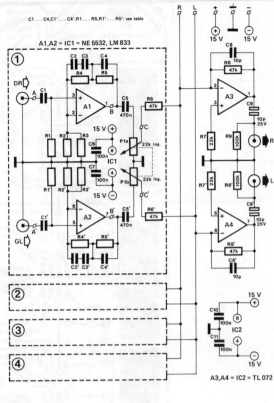

Table 1.

	C1 C1'	C2 C2'	C3 C3'	C4 C4'	R1 R1'	R2 R2'	R3 R3'	R4 R4'	R5 R5'	
pick-up	220 n	1n5	1n5	3n3	47 k	2k2	2k2	100 k	1 M	
tape/cassette	***	***	***	***	***	***	***	***	***	see Note 1
microphone (high impedance)	470 n	***	***	10 p	22 k	1 k	***	o—o	100 k	see Note 2
microphone (low impedance)	10 μ/ 25 V	***	***	10 p	680 Ω	1 k	***	o—o	100 k	see Note 2

Note 1. Wire links A—B and A'—B' required; IC_1, C_6, and C_7 not required.

Note 2. With mono microphones, use input R; do not connect P_{1b}; wire link C—C' required; all accented components not required.

o—o = wire link
*** = not required

19

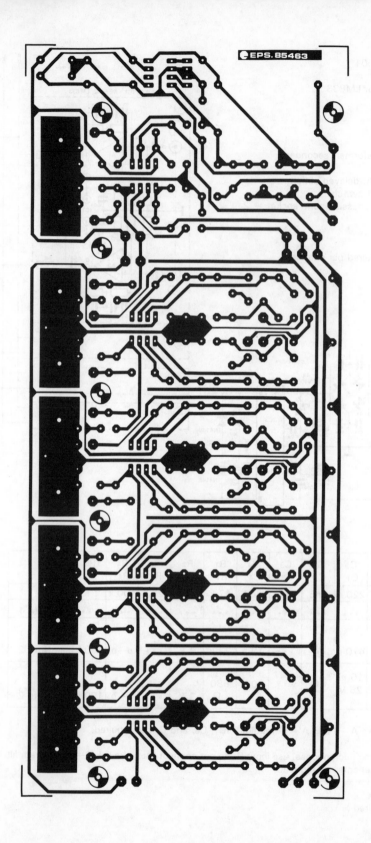

EPS.85463

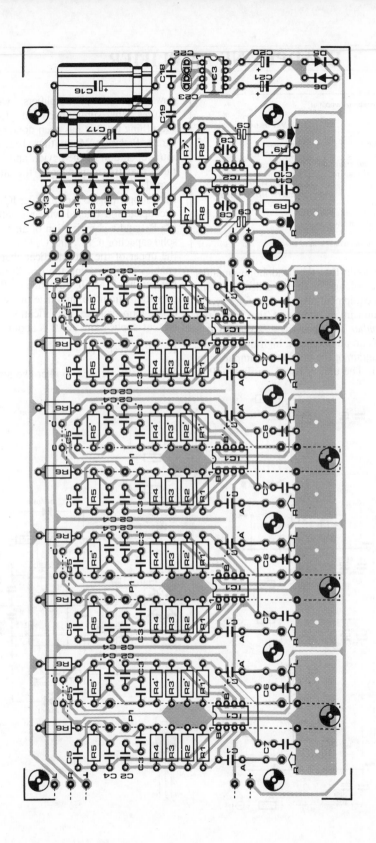

21

OP-50 Power operational amplifier

Features:

- Open-loop gain: 10^6 V/V min.
- Input offset voltage: 25 µV max.
- Input bias current: 5 nA max.
- Offset voltage drift: 0.3 µV/°C max.
- Common mode rejection ratio: 126 dB min.
- Power supply rejection ratio: 126 dB min.
- Noise level: 5.5 nV/√Hz (f = 10 kHz)
  4.5 nV/√Hz (f = 1 kHz)
- Output current: ± 50 mA
- Drives capacitive loads up to 10 nF.
- On-chip thermal shutdown circuit.

Data taken from manufacturer's data sheet.

There is little doubt that the headphone amplifier described here belongs in the so-called *high end* class of audio equipment, and is, therefore, perfect for incorporation in, or adding to, the *Top-of-the-range Preamplifier* described in [1], although it is also suitable as an autonomous, high quality, unit. The circuit diagram of the headphone amplifier appears in Fig. 1. The unit is based on Type OP-50

power operational amplifiers, whose technical features are summarized in Table 1. Clearly, everything feasible has been done by the manufacturers, Precision Monolithics Inc., to ensure optimum operation of the device, and it is with this in mind that the remainder of the amplifier was designed.

Both supply rails to the amplifier ICs are adequately decoupled and filtered with a small series resistor, (R_4-R_5) and a combination of an electrolytic and a solid capacitor (C_4-C_2 and C_5-C_3). With reference to the upper of the two identical channels, preset P_2 enables compensating the (small) offset voltage at the output of the OP-50, while C_1-R_3 forms a compensation circuit to minimize overshoot for a given closed-loop voltage amplification, A_{VCL}. In the present application, A_{VCL} is about 6, since

$$R_1 = R_2/(A_{VCL} - 1)$$

When it is intended to alter the amplification, R_2

1

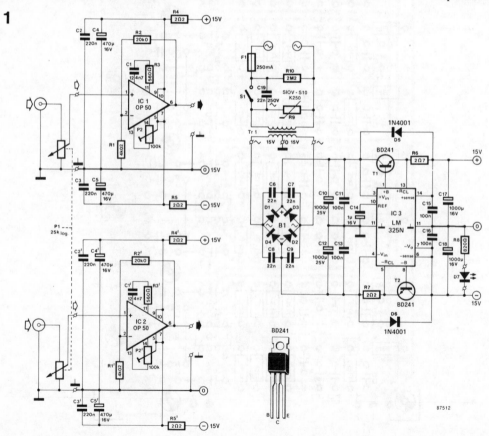

should be left at 20 kΩ. Also observe that the indicated values for R_3 and C_1 are valid when A_{VCL} is between 5 and 20, while $R_3 = 3.3$ kΩ and $C_1 = 1$ nF when A_{VCL} is between 20 and 50. No R-C compensation is required when A_{VCL} is greater than 50.

The +15 V supply for the headphone amplifier is a relatively extensive circuit based on a precision regulator Type LM325, which features excellent noise suppression whilst ensuring smooth and simultaneously rising output voltages at power-on. Mains-borne interference and clicks from S_1 are suppressed in varistor R_9 and high-voltage capacitor C_{19}. The four diodes in rectifier bridge B_1 are bypassed with rattle suppression capacitors to ensure minimum noise on the supply rails to the opamps.

The headphone amplifier can function optimally only if great care is taken both in the choice of the components and in the construction on PCB Type 87512, details of which are shown in Fig. 2. As already stated, the headphone amplifier is suitable for building into the Top-of-the-Range Preamplifier. This makes it possible to feed the ±15 V regulator from the raw voltage across C_9 (+) and C_{10} (−) of the existing ±18.5 V supply, while the inputs of the volume control of the headphone amplifier are driven direct from the outputs of IC_4 (R) and IC_4' (L).

Opamps IC_1 and IC_2 should be soldered direct onto the PCB, and are preferably fitted with a DIL-type heatsink. Provision has been made to screen the amplifiers and the supply on the board by means of two sheets of brass or tin plate, which are mounted vertically onto the dotted lines, and secured with three soldering pins each. Series regulators T_1 and T_2 can do without a heat-sink. When the board is complete, its underside should be thoroughly cleaned with a brush dipped into white spirit or alcohol to remove any residual resin. Next, the track side is sealed with a suitable plastic spray.

When possible, use insulated sockets for the stereo input and output of the amplifier. At the input side, few problems are expected to arise when using gold-plated phono sockets mounted onto a separate ABS or epoxy plate. When a good quality, insulated, 6.3 mm, stereo headphone socket proves unobtainable, the nearest alternative is a non-insulated type, whose common tag is connected direct to the ground point on the PCB, between C_{17} and C_{18} to effect central earthing. Mains transformer Tr_1 is preferably a toroidal type fitted behind a metal screen to ensure minimum hum and other interference picked up by the amplifier inputs. Presets P_2 and P_2' are trimmed for minimum offset voltage at the respective amplifier output—this is likely to require a very sensitive DMM. The headphone amplifier can be terminated in 100 Ω to 1 kΩ, and is therefore perfect for use as a high-quality line driver also. The outputs are short-circuit resistant.

Finally, a brief summary of the amplifier's expected performance at $V_o = 6$ V_{rms} and $A_{VCL} \approx 6$:

Total harmonic distortion: 0.0025% (100 Hz); 0.003% (1 kHz); 0.011% (10 kHz).
Signal-to-noise ratio: ≥ 80 dB.
Response flatness: ±0.4 dB from 10 Hz to 20 kHz.

Literature references:
[1] Top-of-the-Range Preamplifier. Elektor Electronics, November and December 1986, January 1987.
[2] Linear and Conversion Applications Handbook (1986). Precision Monolithics Incorporated.

Parts list

Resistors (±5%):
$R_1;R_1'$ = 4K02F*
$R_2;R_2'$ = 20K0F
$R_3;R_3'$ = 560R
$R_4;R_4';R_5;R_5';R_6;R_7$ = 2R2
R_8 = 820R; 0.5 W
R_9 = SIOV S10 K250 varistor (Siemens; ElectroValue (0784) 33603).
R_{10} = 2M2
P_1 = 25K logarithmic stereo potentiometer.
$P_2;P_2'$ = 100K multiturn preset.

Capacitors:
$C_1;C_1'$ = 4n7
$C_2;C_2';C_3;C_3'$ = 220n
$C_4;C_4';C_5;C_5'$ = 470µ; 16 V; radial
$C_6;C_7;C_8;C_9$ = 22n
$C_{10};C_{12}$ = 1000µ; 25 V; radial
$C_{11};C_{13};C_{15};C_{16}$ = 100n
C_{14} = 1µ; 16 V; tantalum
C_{19} = 22n; 250 VAC

Semiconductors:
$D_1 \ldots D_6$ incl. = 1N4001
D_7 = LED red
$IC_1;IC_2$ = OP-50 (Precision Monolithics Inc.) +
IC_3 = LM325
$T_1;T_2$ = BD241

Miscellaneous:

F1 = 250 mA delayed action fuse plus panel-
mount holder.

Tr1 = 2×15 V; 15 VA (≈2×0.50 A) toroidal
mains transformer, e.g. ILP Type 03013.

DIL-14 heat-sink for IC1 and IC2.

Mains entrance socket.

PCB Type 87512

S1 = SPST miniature mains switch.
Stereo 6.3 mm headphone socket, preferably
insulated.
2 off phone input sockets.
Suitable metal enclosure.

* See text

2

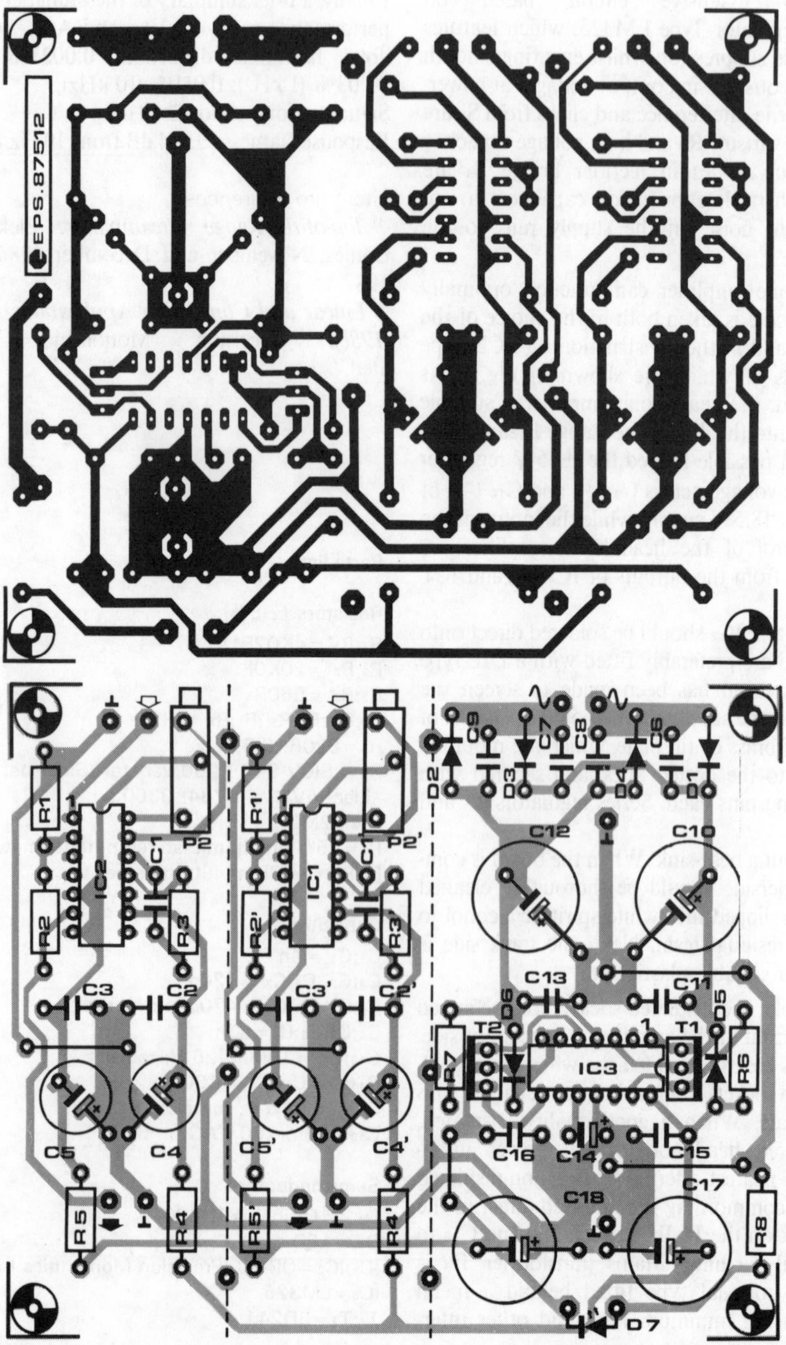

● EPS.87512

This 1-watt amplifier lends itself *par excellence* for use as driver for a low impedance headphone or as output stage in a hi-fi preamplifier driving an active loudspeaker. Many preamplifiers do not permit long, unscreened leads to be connected to them, but the present amplifier accepts these happily.

The circuit — figure 1 — consists of an opamp type LF 356 and a push-pull transistor output stage. Low-pass filter R_1/C_2 at the input limits the slew rate of the input signal. In conjuction with the relatively fast LF 356, this results in very low delay distortion. The fixed quiescent current of 30 mA drawn by the output transistors, and set by diodes $D_1 \ldots D_4$ in conjunction with emitter resistors R_7 and R_8, ensures very low crossover distortion.

Feedback resistors R_3 and R_4 fix the gain at about 15 dB. The consequent overall distortion with a — 3 dB bandwidth from 10 Hz to 30 kHz is only 0.1 per cent.

The amplifier delivers a maximum power of 1 watt into 8 Ω for an input signal of about 500 mVrms. High-impedance headphones and 4 Ω loudspeakers may also be connected without detriment.

The amplifier is best built on the printed circuit board shown in figure 2. To enable it surviving a short circuit at the output, the two transistors should be mounted on heat sinks — do not forget the insulating washers and the heat conducting paste!

The power supply need not be more than a simple affair, consisting of a mains transformer with a centre-tapped, 6 . . . 8 V, 0.5 A secondary, a suitable bridge rectifier, and two 1000 μF/16 V electrolytic capacitors in a conventional arrangement.

To drive high-impedance headphones at high volume, you need a ± 15 V regulated power supply: in some cases, this may be derived from the pre-amplifier supply. In this arrangement, care must be taken not to short-circuit the output terminals.

Parts list

1

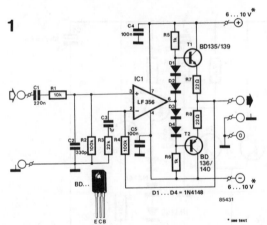

Resistors:
$R_1 = 10$ k
$R_2, R_4 = 100$ k
$R_3 = 22$ k
$R_5, R_6 = 1$ k
$R_7, R_8 = 22$ Ω

Capacitors:
$C_1 = 22$ n
$C_2 = 330$ p
$C_3 = 1$ μ

$C_4, C_5 = 100$ n
$D_1 \ldots D_4 = 1N4148$
$T_1 = $ BD 135 or BD 139
$T_2 = $ BD 136 or BD 140
$IC_1 = $ LF 356

Miscellaneous:
PCB 85431
Heat sinks for T_1 and T_2

2

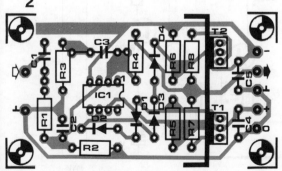
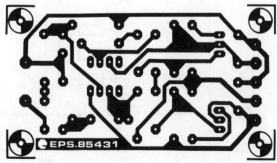

A mixer is expected to have low-noise and high dynamic performance. Most standard mixers use inverting operational amplifiers. Unfortunately, the noise figure of many opamps is poor, and opamps with a good noise figure are normally not suitable for operating with large signals.

The noise factor of standard circuits is often made even poorer because the source and amplifier are not properly matched.

The characteristics of a mixer can be greatly improved, therefore, by the use of buffers at the input stages, and the constructing of operational amplifiers from good-quality transistors. This has been done in the accompanying circuit. The input is buffered by T_1 and T_2. The input impedance of T_1 can be ignored, so that the source merely needs to be matched with P_1

The opamp is formed by transistors T_3 to T_8 incl. Good-quality RF transistors have been used in differential amplifier T_3-T_4-T_5. These transistors have

a better noise figure at a greater bandwidth than AF types.

The proposed circuit has a frequency range (—3 dB points) of 10 Hz to 80 kHz; third harmonic distortion of not more than 0.05 per cent at 10 kHz and an output voltage of 9 V_{pp}; and a signal-to-noise ratio of 100 dB.

The signal-to-noise ratio applies to an output signal of 9 V_{pp} with open-circuit input, and a bandwidth of 20 kHz. The maximum value of the output signal is about 12 V_{pp}, measured across a load impedance of 560 ohms. If the mixer is terminated by a higher impedance, the output voltage will be greater.

A further advantage of the circuit is that the popular valve sound may be realized in a simple manner. To this end it is necessary that T_1 and T_2 commence limiting at a slightly lower level, i.e. 12 V_{pp} input, than the composite opamp. The supply voltage of T_1 and T_2 must then lie between

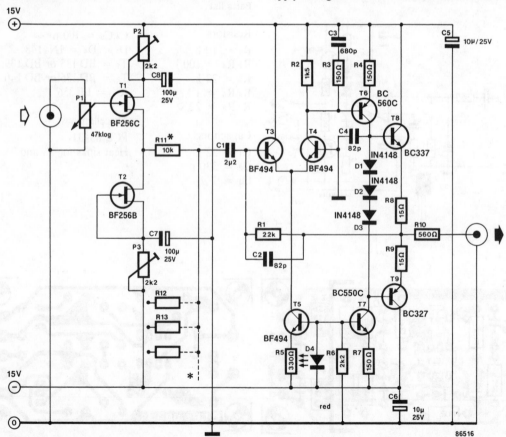

±6 V and ±9 V. Since T_2 is connected as a current source, the exact supply voltage can be set with the 2k2 preset at the wanted clipping level.

If desired, the output off-set may be zeroed by inserting a 50 kilo-ohm preset in the base circuit of T_4. This base should also be decoupled by a 1 μF, 63 V capacitor.

The current consumption of the opamp is about 35 mA and that of the buffer stages not more than 10 mA. If, therefore, ten buffer stages are used, the power supply should be capable of providing 150 mA at ±15 V.

013   INTEGRATED STEREO AMPLIFIER

The Type TDA1521 from Valvo/Mullard is an integrated HiFi stereo power amplifier designed for mains fed applications such as stereo TV. The device works optimally when fed from a ± 16 V supply, and delivers a maximum output power of 2×12 W into 8 Ω. The gain of the amplifiers is fixed internally at 30 dB with a spread of 0.2 dB to ensure optimum gain balance between the channels.

A special feature of the chip is its built-in mute circuit, which disconnects the non-inverting inputs when the supply voltage is less than ± 6 V, a level at which the amplifiers are still correctly biased. This arrangement ensures the absence of unwanted clicks and other noise when the amplifier is switched on or off. The TDA1521 is protected against output short circuits and thermal overloading. The SIL9 package should be bolted

onto a heatsink with a thermal resistance of no more than 3.3 K/W ($R_L = 8$ Ω; $V_s = \pm 16$ V; $P_d = 14.6$ W; $T_a = 65$ °C). Note that the metal tab on the chip package is internally connected to pin 5. The accompanying photograph shows that this high quality stereo amplifier has a very low component count, and is readily constructed on a piece of Veroboard.

The following technical data are stated as typical in the datasheets for the TDA1521 ($R_L = 8$ Ω; $V_s = \pm 16$ V):

Distortion at $P_o = 12$ W:	0.5%
Quiescent current:	40 mA
Gain balance:	0.2 dB
Supply ripple rejection:	60 dB
Channel separation:	70 dB
Output offset voltage:	20 mV
3 dB power bandwidth:	20-20,000 Hz

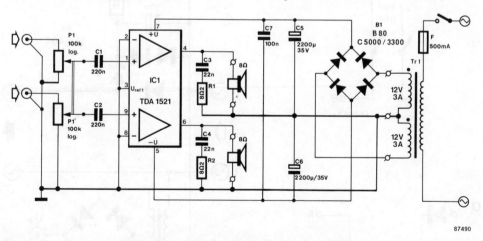

87490

014   LOUDSPEAKER PROTECTION I

There are many ways of protecting loudspeakers against the switch-on 'plop': many of these rely on a clamp circuit across the power amplifier input to

hold this at 0 V for a few seconds after switch-on. Others, like the one suggested here, depend on a relay to switch off the loudspeaker(s).

1a

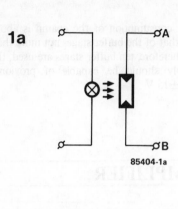

85404-1a

b

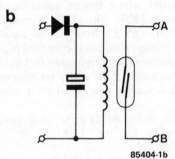

85404-1b

c

ON/OFF

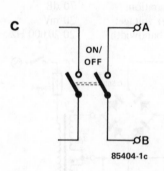

85404-1c

d

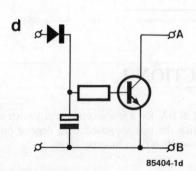

85404-1d

e

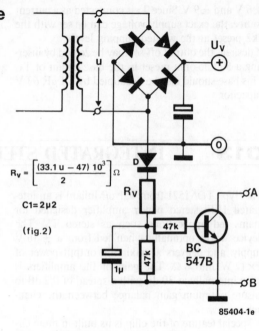

$$R_v = \left[\frac{(33.1\,u - 47)\,10^3}{2}\right]\Omega$$

C1= 2μ2

(fig.2)

U_v

47k

47k

1μ

BC 547B

D

R_v

85404-1e

f

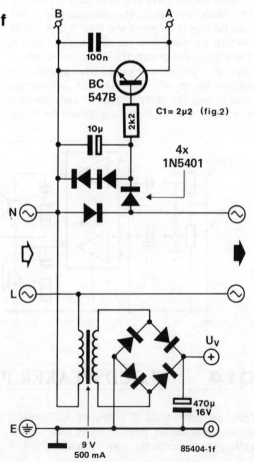

100n

BC 547B

2k2

10μ

C1= 2μ2 (fig.2)

4x 1N5401

N

L

E

9 V 500 mA

U_v

470μ 16V

85404-1f

28

Terminals A and B of the circuit in figure 2 are connected to one of the sensing circuits in figures 1a...1f, of which the pros and cons will be discussed shortly. Whichever of these circuits is used, A is shorted to B immediately the power is switched on. This cuts off transistor T1 instantly, which causes capacitor C1 to charge. After a few seconds, the voltage across C1 causes zener D2 to break down. Transistor T2 and T3 then conduct; the relay is energized, and the loudspeakers are connected in circuit.

When the power is switched off, T1 conducts and this causes C1 to discharge very rapidly. The voltage across C1 quickly drops below the breakdown level of D2; transistors T2 and T3 are cut off, and the relay returns to its quiescent state, which disconnects the loudspeakers.

Input circuit 1a relies on a light-dependent resistor (LDR) fitted close to the mains on indicator lamp. When the lamp lights, the resistance of the LDR drops sharply, so that terminal A is virtually shorted to B.

The input in 1b relies on a reed relay connected to the secondary winding of the mains transformer. As soon as the mains is switched on, the relay contacts close.

The third possibility, shown in 1c, is that the mains on/off switch has a third contact that connects A to B when the mains is switched on.

A further option is illustrated in 1d, where a transistor is connected to the secondary of the mains transformer via a diode and resistor. The transistor conducts when the mains is switched on.

The inputs in 1e and 1f also provide power for the protection circuit. That in 1e has a bridge rectifier connected across the secondary winding of the mains transformer. When the mains is switched on, the BC 547 conducts and shorts A to B.

Finally, the circuit in 1f is connected direct to the mains. Here again, as soon as the mains is switched

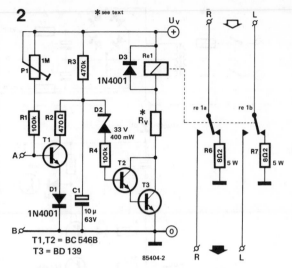

on, the BC 547 conducts and terminal A is shorted to B.

Whichever of the input circuits is used depends on circumstances and/or individual preferences. If one of circuits 1a...1d is used, a separate power supply is required for the protection circuit. As suggested, the output voltage, U_v, of this should be 40...60 V d.c. For lower values of U_v, the rating of D2 must be reduced accordingly.

Resistance R_v depends on the relay used, and is calculated from

$$R_v = [(U_v - U_r - 2.5)/I_r]\ \Omega$$

where U_r and I_r are the operating voltage (in volts) and current (in amperes) of the relay used respectively.

The relay contacts must be able to carry a large current: 10 A is not unusual in many amplifiers.

The rating of R_v is $[U_r I_r]$ W.

If the 'plop' is still heard, increase the value of R3 as required — in reasonably small steps.

015   LOUDSPEAKER PROTECTION II

This is an all-transistor design for incorporation in AF amplifiers that produce nasty clicks in the loudspeakers when turned on or off, jeopardizing the voice coils by passing a large current surge.

Assuming that AF amplifier and protection circuit are off, C1 and C2 are empty of charge and Re is deactivated. At power-on, D1 rapidly charges C1. Provided both the negative and the positive supply voltage are present and at the correct level, T2 and

T3 conduct, while T1 is off, enabling C2 to be slowly charged via R4. If the voltage across C2 is sufficiently high for T4 to conduct, T5 will draw base current and energize Re, which connects the loudspeakers to the amplifier outputs. Zener diode D4 fixes the voltage across the coil of Re, so that differently rated relays may also be used in the circuit, provided D4 is changed accordingly. However the relay coil current should not exceed about 50 mA,

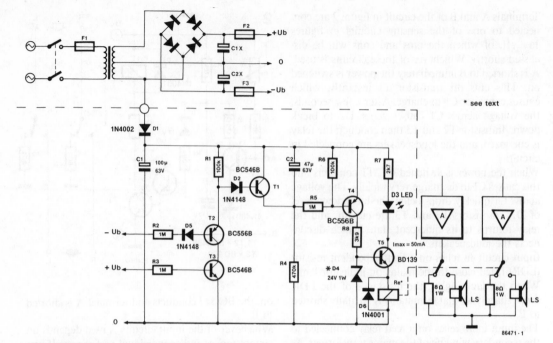

while the changeover contacts should be rated in accordance with the amplifier output power and impedance; for a 2 × 100 W at 8 Ω type, for instance, the relay contacts should be rated at least 8 A.

Should either one or both supply voltages (−U_b; +U_b) disappear for some reason or other (amplifier malfunction, short-circuited smoothing capacitor, etc.), the relevant transistor T_2 or T_3 will be disabled, causing T_1 to receive base current via R_1; C_2 will be discharged forthwith and Re is deactivated in consequence since T_4 and T_5 are turned off. The amplifier channels can now produce clicks they like;

the output is safely applied to two resistors matching the output impedance.

The protection circuit is fed off the voltage across C_1, which is purposely rated at only 100 μF to enable Re to be deactivated almost immediately after the amplifier has been switched off. Power-off clicks, if produced, will therefore end up in the dummy resistors rather than the expensive loudspeaker voice coils.

The protection unit is most readily fitted on a piece of veroboard, while Re should be mounted close to the loudspeaker output terminals to keep contact losses as low as possible.

---

016   LOUDSPEAKER PROTECTION III

Many modern AF power output stages are capable of delivering considerable power levels in the supersonic frequency range. When the loudspeaker can not handle that power, the voice coil is rapidly overheated, and causes a short-circuit. If the power output stage is not properly protected, it breaks down and supplies a direct current that effectively destroys the loudspeaker.

The present loudspeaker protector is composed of three sections: a measuring amplifier, a detector, and a relay driver. Four channels are shown here as an example. Potential divider R_1-R_2 determines the

sensitivity of the protection circuit, while D_1-D_2 protect the input of A_1. Opamp A_5 is set up as a low pass filter with a cut-off frequency of 0.5 Hz, so that it can function as a DC detector. The second section of the circuit is composed of four detectors A_9-A_{12}. A_9 compares any negative direct voltages to a reference set with R_8-R_9, while C_3-R_7 determine the delay time. Opamp A_{10} has a similar function for positive direct voltages. The circuit is actuated when

$$\frac{V_{in}R_2}{R_1+R_2}-0.65 > \frac{15R_2}{R_8+R_9}$$

Comparators A_{11} and A_{12} function as the power limiter. Positive and negative peak voltages are rectified in D_3-D_4 and averaged with the aid of R-C combinations R_{36}-C_{33} and R_{26}-C_{23}. The relatively long periods of these networks precludes erroneous triggering of the circuit on peaks in the input signal. The power limiter is actuated when

$$\frac{V_{in}R_2\sqrt{2}}{R_1+R_2} - 0.65 > \frac{15R_{28}}{R_{28}+R_{29}}$$

This equation is also valid for the positive detector set up around A_{12}. The stated component values result in $P_{max} \approx 30$ W in 8Ω.

When the input signals are all right, the open collector outputs of A_9-A_{12} are in their high impedance state, so that the output voltage is $+15$ V via R_{40}. When a fault condition exists at one or more of the inputs, junction R_{40}-R_{41} is pulled down to -15 V.

The central part in the relay driver is bistable FF_1. Gate N_1 is a resettable power-up delay circuit which clocks FF_1. The logic high level at the D (data) input is only transferred to output Q when the R (reset) input is logic high. It is seen that a reset pulse

can originate either from the mains detector N_3-N_4, or from the fault detectors A_9-A_{12}.

The loudspeaker protector is conveniently fed from the amplifier's symmetrical supply, but care should be taken to dimension D_{48} and R_v such that the indicated voltage across C_{44} and C_{45} is not exceeded. If the amplifier supply delivers less than 28 V, IC_6 may be omitted, and the loudspeaker relay, Re, replaced with a 12 V type fed from the $+15$ V rail. Voltage divider R_{43}-R_{44} should then be redimensioned such that the input of N_4 is held at about $+13$ V when $R_{43}+R_{44} \approx 100$ kΩ.

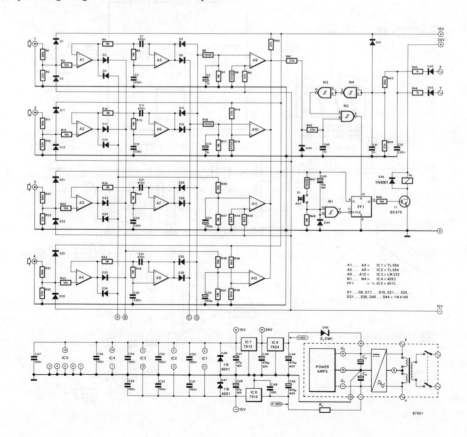

This high quality phono preamplifier is based on the Type HA12017 integrated circuit from Hitachi. The principal technical data of this chip are summarized in Table 1. The circuit diagram, Fig. 1, shows that output off-set correction is provided by integrator IC₂. The output signal of IC₁ is first passed through low-pass filter R₇-C₉, then integrated in IC₂-C₈. The error signal is fed to the inverting input of amplifier IC₁ via 47 kΩ resistor R₆. The amplitude of this signal is always such that the off-set voltage at the output of IC₁ is virtually nought. The off-set correction used here enables the preamplifier to drive a power amplifier direct.

The correct capacitive termination of the pick-up cartridge can be selected with the aid of S₁. The in-

put impedance is 50 kΩ, but can be altered by redimensioning R₂-R₃. The output impedance of the preamplifier is 510 Ω, i.e., low enough for driving a relatively long cable.

The RIAA equalization filter in the negative feedback circuit of IC₁ is fairly complex, which was necessary to meet the required IEC specification (note the use of high stability capacitors and resistors).

The regulated power supply for the phono preamplifier is shown in Fig. 2. This is once again a relatively extensive circuit which, in combination with the low-pass filters on the ± 24 V lines to IC₁ and IC₂, gives excellent suppression of RF signals, hum, rectification noise, and mains borne interference. Presets P₁ and P₂ serve to adjust the out-

1

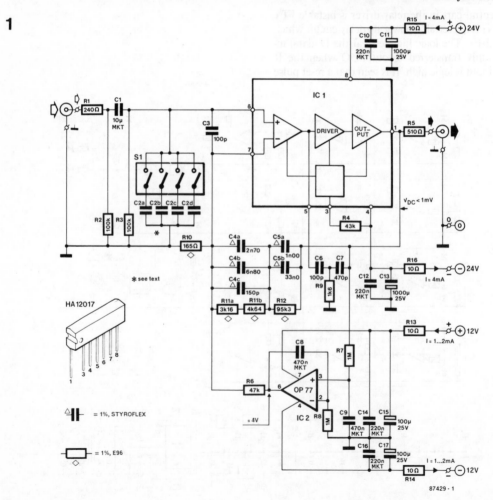

Table 1. HA12017 Low noise preamplifier

Features:
- Low noise: $V_{n[in]} = 0.185\ \mu V$ typ. (measured in IHF-A network, $R_g = 43\ k\Omega$, IEC RIAA). $V_n = -95\ dB$ relative to $V_o = 1\ V_{rms}$.
- Wide dynamic range: $V_i = 235\ mV_{rms}$ max. $(V_{cc} = \pm 24\ V,\ f = 1\ kHz,\ THD = 0.1\%,\ A_v \approx 100 \hat{=} 40\ dB)$.
- Low distortion: $THD = 0.002\%$ typ. $(f = 20\text{-}20\ 000\ Hz,\ V_o = 10\ V_{rms},\ RIAA$ equalization).
- Supply ripple rejection: $SVR(+V_{cc}) = 56\ dB;\ SVR(-V_{cc}) = 45\ dB$ (typical values at $f = 100\ Hz$ and $R_g = 43\ k\Omega$).
- Maximum operating voltage: $\pm 26\ V$.
- Maximum power dissipation: 500 mW at $T_a = 75°C$.

Note: $R_g = R_4$ in this design.

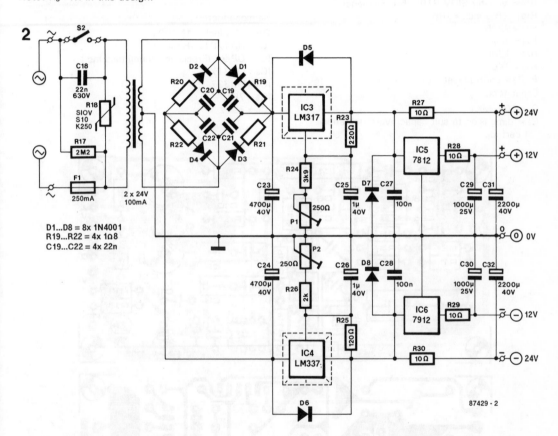

put voltage on the ± 24 V rails.

The printed-circuit boards for the preamplifier and the power supply are shown in Figs. 3 and 4 respectively. The correct values for R_{11}, C_4 and C_5 are achieved by parallel and series connection. All four voltage regulators can be fitted onto a common heatsink if electrical insulation is provided. The accompanying photograph shows a suggested construction of the preamplifier.

It is strongly recommended to use good quality components for the volume adjustment and input source selection--consult the references given below.

References:
1. *Top of the range preamplifier*, Elektor Electronics, January 1987.
2. *Valve preamplifier*, Elektor Electronics, March 1987.
3. *Electronics potentiometers*, Elektor Electronics, April 1987.

33

Parts list

Resistors ($\pm 5\%$):

R1 = 240R
R2;R3 = 100K
R4 = 43K
R5 = 510R
R6 = 47K
R7;R8 = 1M0
R9 = 1K6
R10 = 165RF
R11 = 3K16F + 4K64F
R12 = 95K3F
R13...R16 incl.;R27...R30 incl. = 10R
R17 = 2M2
R18 = varistor SIOV S10K250 (Siemens) *
R19...R22 incl. = 1R8
R23 = 220R
R24 = 3K9
R25 = 120R
R26 = 2K0
P1;P2 = 250R preset

Capacitors:

C1 = 10μ; MKT
C2 = dimension to suit capacitive termination
 of cartridge.

C3 = 100p; polystyrene
C4 = 2n7F//6n8F//150pOF; styroflex
C5 = 1nOF//33nOF; styroflex
C6 = 100p styroflex
C7 = 470p styroflex
C8;C9 = 470n MKT
C10;C12;C14;C16 = 220n MKT
C11;C13;C29;C30 = 1000μ; 25 V; radial
C15;C17 = 100μ; 25 V; radial
C18 = 22n; 630 V
C19...C22 incl. = 22n
C23;C24 = 4700μ; 40 V; radial
C25;C26 = 1μ; 40 V; radial
C27;C28 = 100n
C31;C32 = 2200μ; 40 V; radial

Semiconductors:

D1...D8 incl. = 1N4001
IC1 = HA12017 (Hitachi) [+]
IC2 = OP-77 (Precision Monolithics Inc.)
IC3 = LM317
IC4 = LM337
IC5 = 7812
IC6 = 7912

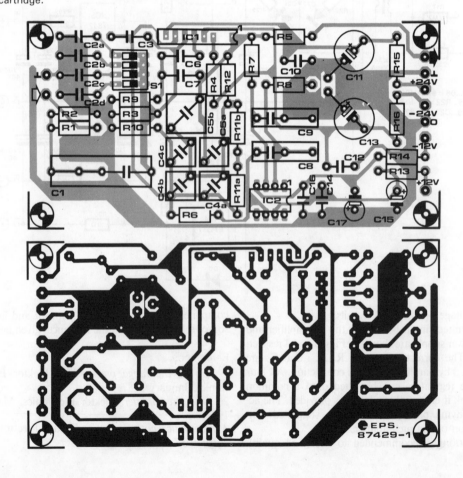

EPS.
87429-1

Miscellaneous:

S1 = 4-way DIP switch block.
S2 = SPST mains switch.
F1 = 250 mA delayed action fuse with PCB mount holder.
TR1 = 2x24 V;100 mA mains transformer for PCB mounting.
Heat-sink for IC3 . . . IC6 incl.
Insulating washers for IC3 . . . IC6 incl.
PCB Type 87429-1 and 87429-2

* Available from ElectroValue Ltd ■ 28 St Judes Road ■ Englefield Green ■ Egham ■ Surrey TW20 0HB. Telephone: (0784) 33603 ■ Telex: 264475.

+ Available from Cirkit PLC ■ Park Lane ■ Broxbourne ■ Hertfordshire EN10 7NQ. Telephone: (0992) 444111 ■ Telex: 22478. Stock number: 61-170-12017.

General note: many special AF components for this project are available from Audiokits Precision Components ■ 6 Mill Close ■ Borrowash ■ Derby DE7 3GU. Telephone: (0332) 674929.

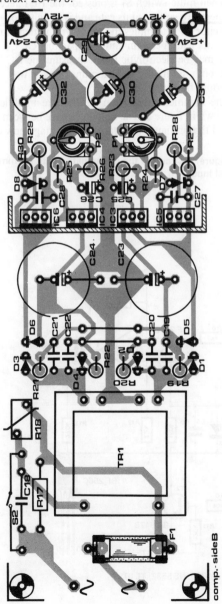

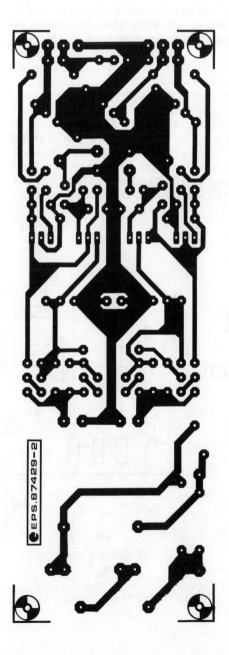

35

MICROPHONE AMPLIFIER WITH MUTE SWITCH

Microphones, unfortunately, produce only a small signal and they, therefore, require a special pre-amplifier to boost their output. Because small signals are involved, the signal-to-noise ratio of the pre-amplifier is a very important parameter.

In this article, we present two circuits for a pre-amplifier suitable for virtually all occasions: a symmetrical and an asymmetrical version. We have incorporated a mute switch, which speakers can use when they want to clear their throat. As there is an number of low-noise operational amplifiers available nowadays, the cost of these pre-amplifiers is relatively low.

The asymmetrical version is shown in figure 1. Switching between high and low impedance matching is possible with switch S_2. Opamp A_1 is arranged as an AC amplifier with a gain of around 27 dB. This stage may also be used as a DC amplifier: R_3 and C_1 are then omitted, and the value of R_2 is lowered to 22 k. Capacitor C_2 limits the bandwidth of the amplifier to ensure stable operation.

Irrespective of whether A_1 functions as a DC or an AC amplifier, the DC component in its output is blocked by C_3. The amplified AC signal is applied to muting stage T_1. This field-effect transistor (FET) normally conducts and the output of A_1 is then further amplified in A_2 by about 5. Finally, the signal is taken to the output terminal via high-pass filter R_{13}-C_6. The load must be greater than 10 kΩ. When mute switch S_1 is pressed, the FET receives a negative voltage at its gate and is switched off. Capacitor C_5 determines the speed with which muting occurs within certain limits. Capacitors C_1, C_3, and C_6 may be electrolytic types: measure the DC level at both terminals to determine which way they should be connected!

The symmetrical version of the pre-amplifier is shown in figure 2. The only difference between this and that in figure 1 is that the input stage now con-

Figure 1. Circuit of the pre-amplifier with asymmetrical input.

1

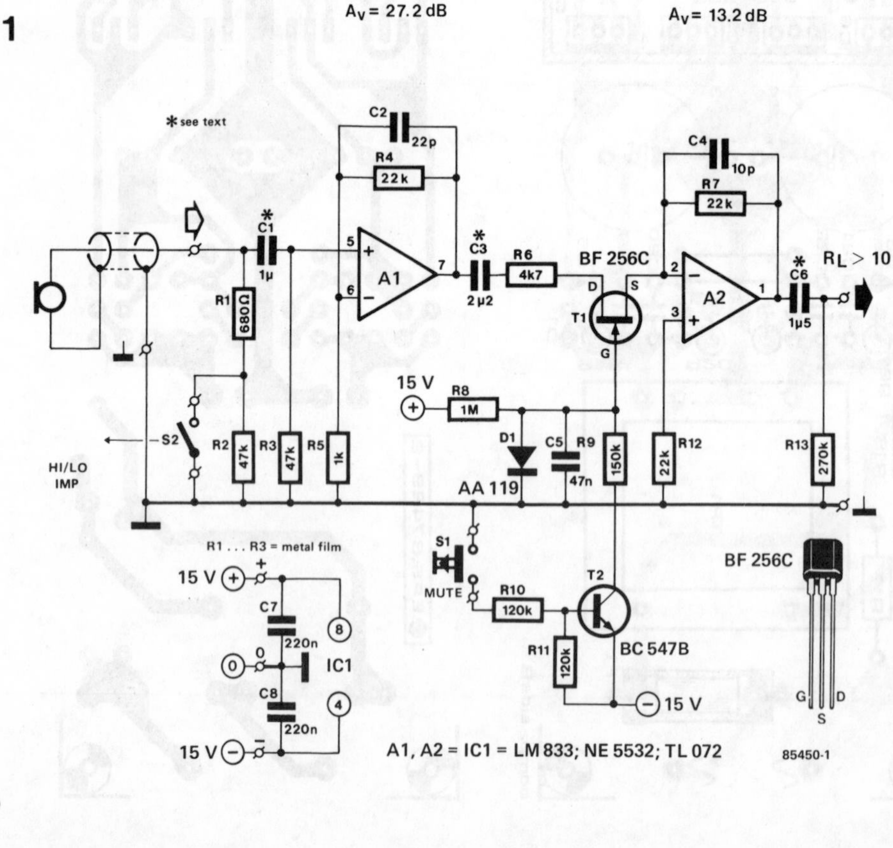

A1, A2 = IC1 = LM 833; NE 5532; TL 072

2

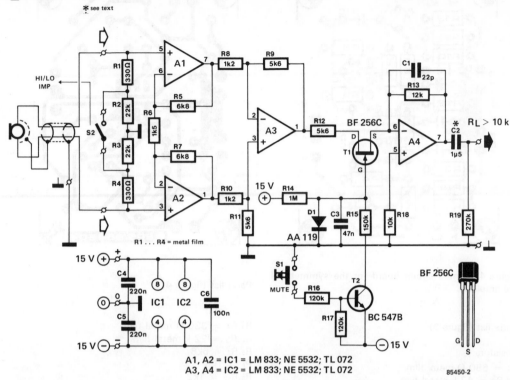

$A_V = 20 dB$ $A_V = 13,3 dB$ $A_V = 6,7 dB$

A1, A2 = IC1 = LM 833; NE 5532; TL 072
A3, A4 = IC2 = LM 833; NE 5532; TL 072

85450-2

Figure 2. Circuit of the pre-amplifier with symmetrical input.

Figure 3. Printed circuit board for the asymmetrical pre-amplifier.

sists of A_1, A_2, and A_3 to obtain symmetry. Opamps A_1 and A_2 provide a total gain of about 20 dB. Opamp A_3 functions as a differential amplifier to ensure that common-mode noise and interference is effectively suppressed.

3

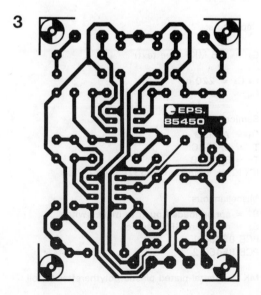

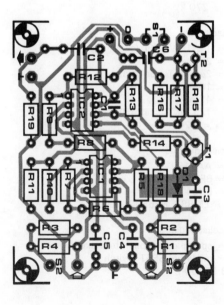

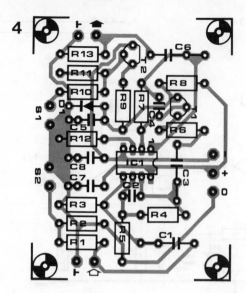

4

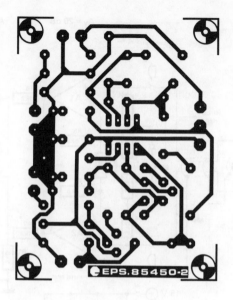

EPS.85450-2

Figure 4. Printed circuit board for the symmetrical pre-amplifier.

Parts list (figure 3)

Resistors:
R1 = 680 Ω metal film
R2,R3 = 47 k metal film
R4,R7,R12 = 22 k
R5 = 1 k
R6 = 4k7
R8 = 1 M
R9 = 150 k
R10,R11 = 120 k
R13 = 270 k

Capacitors:
C1 = 1 μ/16 V MKT (see text)
C2 = 22 p
C3 = 2μ2 MKT (see text)
C4 = 10 p
C5 = 47 n
C6 = 1μ5 MKT (see text)
C7,C8 = 220 n

Semiconductors:
D1 = AA119
T1 = BF256C
T2 = BC547B
IC1 = LM883; NE5532; TL072

Miscellaneous:
S1 = spring-loaded push to make switch
S2 = miniature SPST switch
PCB 85450-2

Parts list (figure 4)

Resistors:
R1,R4 = 330 Ω metal film
R2,R3 = 22 k metal film
R5,R7 = 6k8
R6 = 1k5
R8,R10 = 1k2
R9,R11,R12 = 5k6
R13 = 12 k
R14 = 1 M
R15 = 150 k
R16,R17 = 120 k
R18 = 10 k
R19 = 270 k

Capacitors:
C1 = 22 p
C2 = 1μ5 MKT (see text)
C3 = 47 n
C4,C5 = 220 n
C6 = 100 n

Semiconductors:
D1 = AA119
T1 = BF256C
T2 = BC547B
IC1,IC2 = LM833; NE5532; TL072

Miscellaneous:
S1 = spring-loaded push to make switch
S2 = miniature SPST switch
PCB 85450-1
PCB 85450-2

MKT = metal-plated plastic polythereftalate foil

In broadcasting systems, intercoms, and mobile radio telephones it is necessary to amplify the microphone signal over a restricted range only. This may be achieved with the aid of a compressor or a clipper. The former provides low distortion, but its design is rather complex, whereas a clipper is of simple construction, but suffers from appreciable harmonic and intermodulation distortion. Of these two, intermodulation distortion is far and away the most troublesome; in fact, the acceptability of a clipper in an audio signal processor would be far greater if clipping would not cause such severe intermodulation distortion.

duced, which causes the cross-over point to shift upwards. The lower amplification of the frequencies is then smaller, and this enhances intelligibility. In fact, intelligibility of a signal processed in this manner is much better than a conventionally clipped signal.

3

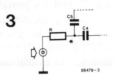

86479-3

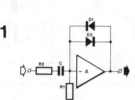

1

86479-1

The diagram in Fig. 2 shows the detailed realization of the principle. Transistor T_1 is a microphone low-noise microphone preamplifier. The clipping circuit is based on A_1: the limiting level is set by P_1. The values of certain components depend on the application: guide lines are given in the table.

Application	C4	C6	C8
Hi-fi	—	47 nF	470 pF
Communications or intercom	100-220 pF	0-4.7 nF	4.7 nF

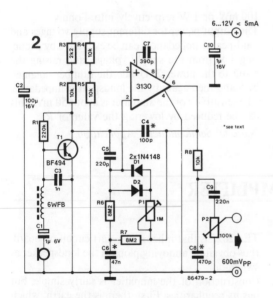

2

86479-2

For input signals above about 100 mV, the microphone preamplifier may be omitted. The input signal is then applied to the junction C_4-C_5 via a resistor (R in Fig. 3). The value of R should be such that the sum of it and the microphone used is about 10 kilo-ohms.

In the accompanying diagram, intermodulation distortion is reduced by signal-control of the cross-over point. The principle of operation is shown in Fig. 1. The amplifier has a very high impedance input (value of R_1). When the signal level is so low that the diodes do not conduct, the cross-over point is determined by R_1-C. As soon as the diodes conduct, the input impedance of the amplifier is re-

This little amplifier, operating from 3...9 V, and providing 1 W output into a 4 Ω loudspeaker, is one of those circuits of which you never have enough. The amplifier is based on one 8-pin DIL IC type LM1895N. Electrolytic capacitors C_2 and C_6 decouple the supply lines; C_7 prevents d.c. reaching the loudspeaker; and C_3 and C_5 provide a low-impedance path to earth for audio frequencies.

The input signal is applied to pin 4 of the LM1895N via P_1 and C_4. Resistor R_4 and capacitor C_8 suppress any tendency to oscillation, i.e., improve the stability.

The amplification is determined by R_1 and R_3: it is of the order of 50. Capacitor C_1, in parallel with R_1, ensures that the amplification drops off for frequencies above about 20 kHz. If the amplifier is intended for use with a small AM receiver, it is desirable that the amplification starts falling off at a lower frequency. This is brought about by enlarging C_1; for instance, if its value is doubled, the amplification starts dropping at $20/2 = 10$ kHz.

On the printed circuit board shown in figure 2 (which is not available ready made), P_1 may be replaced by a wire link; the volume control is then carried out by an external logarithmic potentiometer connected to the PCB via a short length of screened audio cable.

Current consumption is 2.5 mA at 3 V or 7.5 mA at 9 V under no-signal conditions, and 80 mA at 3 V or 270 mA at 9 V under fully driven conditions: in the latter condition, the output power is

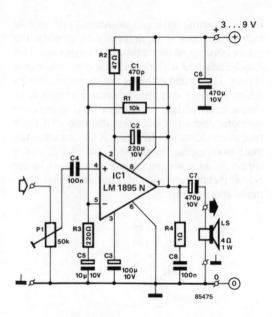

100 mW or 1 W respectively into 4 ohms.

The output power for different supply voltages and loudspeaker impedances can be estimated by deducting 1 V from the supply voltage, and raising the result to the power 2. Divide the number obtained by 8 and then again by the loudspeaker impedance. The sensitivity of the amplifier is about 50 mV. This can be reduced by lowering the value of R_1.

National Semiconductor Application.

021   MINI STEREO AMPLIFIER

This mini amplifier is based on the Thomson Type TEA2025. In this 16-pin DIL device hides a stereo amplifier that with a supply voltage of 9 V will provide 1 watt output per channel into a 4-ohm loudspeaker. At full output, the input sensitivity is about 25 mV$_{pp}$. If this is too sensitive, a resistor R may be connected between pin 6 and C_7 and between pin 11 and C_2. The sensitivity then becomes $(25 + ½R)$ mV, provided $R > 1$ kΩ. Furthermore, the supply voltage may lie between 3 V and 12 V. The operation of the IC cannot be discussed here, but for those interested its internal circuit diagram is reproduced in Fig. 1. One useful feature of the

TEA2025 is that it has a soft-start circuit on board, thus obviating annoying plops in the loudspeaker at switch-on.

Construction of the amplifier is fairly simple, but has its peculiarities. First, there is the earth, which in this case should not be of wire, but rather consist of a metal earth plane (if you design your own PCB, this would be of copper). If at all possible, pins 4 and 5 as well as pins 12 and 13, should be connected to a (copper) area of not less than 5 cm². The two areas should be connected in a suitable manner, and in such a way that a heat sink is formed under the IC as shown in Fig. 2. This ensures both good heat

1

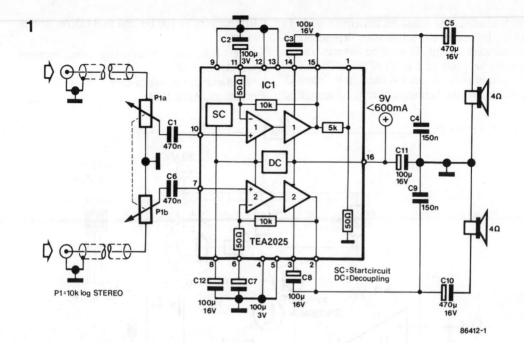

Fig. 1. Circuit diagram of the mini amplifier.

conduction and a good earth. Moreover, all other connections should, of course, be kept as short as possible. This is particularly important in the case of the supply lines, which should be decoupled by C_{11} as close as possible to the IC. The negative terminal of this capacitor should be soldered direct onto the earth plane; the positive terminal is soldered in the normal manner to pin 16.

Finally, the distortion for a power output of about 0.25 W is roughly 0.3 per cent.

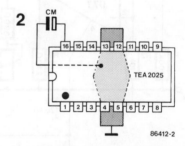

Fig. 2. This construction of earth plane cum heat sink is both practical and saves space.

---

022   MOSFET POWER AMPLIFIER

The output power of an operational amplifier is often increased by a complementary emitter follower. It can also be done with a MOSFET, but it is not a good idea to connect such a device as a complementary source follower because the maximum output voltage of the opamp is then reduced appreciably by the gate-source control voltage of the MOSFET, which can be a couple of volts.

Another approach is to connect two MOSFETs as a complementary drain follower. The (alternating) output current provided by the MOSFETs is limited by the level of the supply voltages and the saturation voltages of T_3 and T_4 Resistor R_8, together

with R_9, provides feedback for both the opamp and the MOSFETs. The open-loop amplification of the opamp is, therefore, increased by $(1+R_8/R_9)$. The closed-loop amplification of the complete amplifier is $(1+R_3/R_2)$, i.e., 11.

The current source formed by T_1 and T_2 is required for arranging the quiescent current of T_3 and T_4 at 50 mA. The values of resistors R_4 and R_5 are such that, without the current source, the voltage drop across the resistors resulting from the direct current through the opamp is not sufficient to switch on T_3 and T_4 With the current source, and depending on the setting of P_1, the voltages across R_4 and R_5 rise,

41

which increases the quiescent current through T_3 and T_4. In view of the temperature dependence of the quiescent current, T_2 must be mounted on the common heat sink (c. 5 K/W) of the MOSFETs. The output power is not less than 20 W into 8 Ω, at which level the harmonic distortion amounts to 0.075 per cent at 100 Hz and to 0.135 per cent at 10 kHz.

Source: *Voice coil drives using complementary power MOSFETS*
by M Alexander in *Motor-Con proceedings*, April 1984

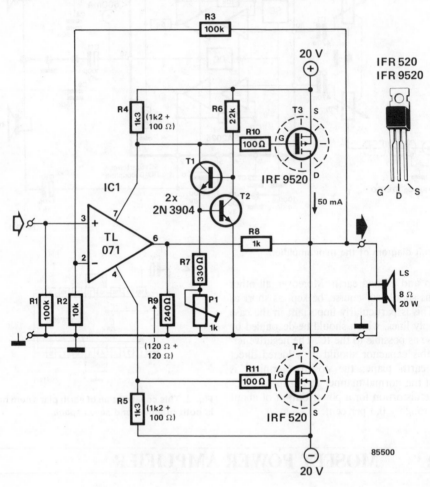

023   NOISE GATE

Noise on an audio signal becomes more troublesome as the signal itself becomes smaller. When a mixer is connected to a number of signal sources, it becomes particularly disturbing when one or more of these sources produce only noise. In these situations, a noise gate is a real help. Such a gate continuously monitors the level of the audio signal and switches it off, after a predetermined period, if the level drops below a preset value.

The circuit consists of two parts: a control section and a regulator section. The control section, based on opamps A_1 to A_4 incl., derives a voltage from the audio signal that is used to drive the regulator. The regulator is a voltage-controlled amplifier, for which one of the two operational transconductance amplifiers contained in a Type LM13600 or LM13700 is used. For a stereo system, one control section and two regulator sections are required. For

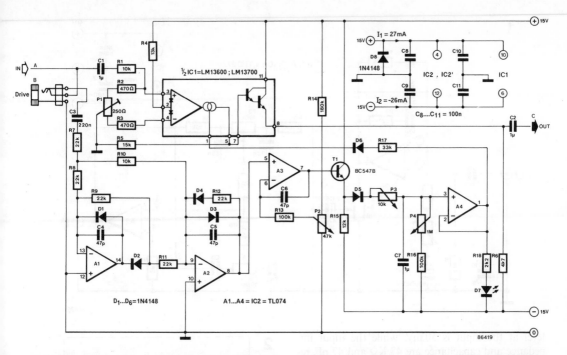

a double mono version, two control sections and two regulators are needed. One LM13600 or LM13700 will thus suffice for all these requirements.

Opamps A1 and A2 form a full-wave rectifying circuit. Opamp A3 compares the peak value of the signal with the direct voltage set by P2. If the peak value is larger, capacitor C7 is charged via T1: the attack time is set by P3. The time lapse after which the audio signal is switched off is determined with P4. The control of the voltage-controlled amplifier (VCA) and the LED indicating whether there is a signal present is effected by A4. Diode D4 ensures that the amplification of the VCA is really zero when the output of A4 is low (i.e. less than —15 V).

The input of the regulator section has an impedance of about 10 kΩ and is designed for audio signals of 1 Vrms. However, even for a 12 dB higher input signal, the distortion is still not greater than 1 per cent. Where higher input voltages are the norm, the value of R1 should be altered according-

ly. Where lower inputs are the norm, a preamplifier should be used.

It is, therefore, seen that the noise gate should preferably be connected between the preamplifier and power amplifier.

The output level is set with R5, while P1 enables the circuit to be adjusted for minimum switching noises. To this end, the drive input is switched on and off by S1, while the audio input remains open-circuit.

It is best to use a 3.5 mm chassis socket with break contact for the drive input: the break contact then replaces S1. As soon as the jack is inserted into the socket, the connection between the audio input and the regulator is broken.

This type of drive input affords a number of special effects, such as the switching in of, say, an echo unit at the command (sufficiently high signal level) of a given instrument (e.g. a snare drum). The command instrument is plugged into the drive input for this purpose, while the regulator is connected into the effects unit.

---

024   SIMPLE PREAMPLIFIER

This design answers the need for an inexpensive, yet good quality, preamplifier equipped with a tone control section.

Fig. 1 shows the circuit diagram. The amplification of the input stage set up around opamp A1 is adjustable between 10 and 20 with preset P1 The 0 dB

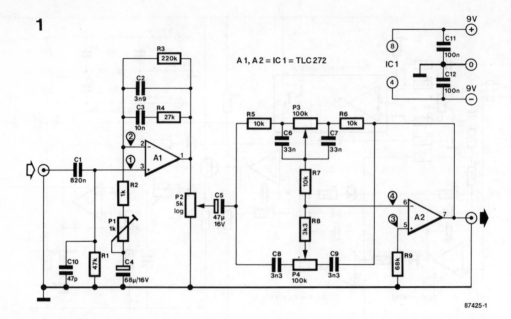

R3
220k

A 1, A 2 = IC 1 = TLC 272

IC 1

9V (+)

C11
100n

0

C12
100n 9V (−)

C2
3n9

C3
10n

R4
27k

2

A1

1

3

C1
820n

R2
1k

P1
1k

R1
47k

C10
47p

C4
68µ/16V

P2
5k
log

C5
47µ
16V

R5
10k

C6
33n

P3
100k

C7
33n

R6
10k

R7
10k

R8
3k3

C8
3n3

P4
100k

C9
3n3

A2

6

5

7

R9
68k

87425-1

level at the input is 50 mV, while the input impedance and capacitance are 47 KΩ and 47 pF, respectively to enable ready connection of most record players and cassette decks. The tone control section is a standard Baxandall type with P_3 and P_4 as the respective bass and treble controls. The gain vs frequency curves for various settings of the tone controls appear in Fig. 2. Here the 0 dB level corresponds to 1 V.

The current consumption of this preamplifier is modest at about 5 mA. When the circuit is correctly balanced, the indicated measuring points should all be very nearly at ground potential. The

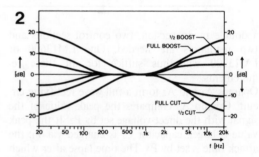

2

circuit shown here must, of course, be duplicated to obtain a stereo preamplifier.

---

025   SINGLE-CHIP 40 W AMPLIFIER

To answer the need for a compact amplifier that is capable of satisfactory operation when driven from a compact disc player, Philips have developed the Type TDA1514 AF amplifier chip, which is remarkable for its excellent specifications, ruggedness and output power. The device is housed in a 9-pin SIL POWER enclosure which has a thermal resistance of less than 1.5 K/W, so that the heatsink required must have a thermal resistance of no more than 3.8 K/W if the chip is operated at its maximum dissipation of 19 W ($U_b = \pm 27.5$ V, $T_a = 50$ °C).

The circuit diagram shows that very few compo-

nents are needed to make this high-performance amplifier. The power supply to feed the chip must be capable of delivering a current of at least 3 A; the quiescent current demand of the amplifier as shown is about 60 mA. The supply voltage should not exceed ± 27.5 V.

Although this project is not supported by a ready-made printed circuit board, you should not experience too much difficulty in constructing the amplifier if it is built on a piece of Veroboard. Make sure, however, that the tracks and connections to the supply and output terminals are as short as possible, and use double tracks where this is necessary. In this context, it is advisable to fit decoupling capacitors C_3 and C_8 as close as possible to the chip supply pins. Resistors R_2 and R_3 determine the amplifier's closed loop voltage gain, which has a range of 20 to 46 dB.

Finally, some measurement data obtained with a prototype of the amplifier:

P_o at $D_{tot} = -60$ dB;
$U_b = \pm 27.5$ V; $R_L = 8\Omega$: 40 W
S/N at $P_o = 50$ mW: 82 dB
Supply ripple rejection
  at f = 100 Hz: 72 dB
Harmonic distortion at
  $P_o = 32$ W: −85 dB
Intermodulation distortion
  at $P_o = 32$ W: −80 dB
3 dB bandwidth at $D_{tot} =$
  −60 dB: 20-25 000 Hz
Slew rate: 15 V/μs

The gain vs frequency curve and the harmonic distortion table show that this amplifier provides very good sound reproduction at a considerable output power level.

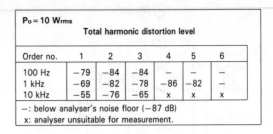

$P_o = 10$ W$_{rms}$

Total harmonic distortion level

Order no.	1	2	3	4	5	6
100 Hz	−79	−84	−84	–	–	–
1 kHz	−69	−82	−78	−86	−82	–
10 kHz	−55	−76	−65	x	x	x

−: below analyser's noise floor (−87 dB)
x: analyser unsuitable for measurement.

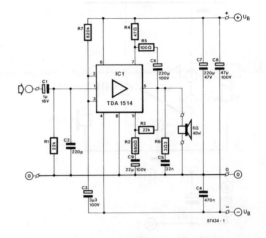

87434 - 1

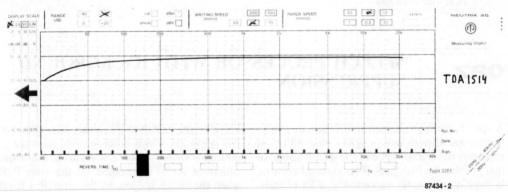

TDA 1514

87434 - 2

026   SMD HEADPHONE AMPLIFIER

Although the use of SMDs (surface mount devices) is not yet widespread among electronics hobbyists, and the availability of these parts is still problematic in certain areas, there appears to be no way of stopping the ever increasing miniaturization of chips and circuits. A good instance of this happening at an accelerating pace is the Type TDA7050 headphone amplifier, which used to be available in a standard DIL enclosure, but is currently only manufactured in SMA technology.

The Type TDA7050 is a complete stereo amplifier with a gain of 26 dB and an output power of 2×75 mW. As seen in the circuit diagram, two electrolytic capacitors are required to block the offset voltage at the amplifier outputs. It is also possible to set up the amplifier in a bridge configuration to obtain an output power of 150 mW: simply omit the capacitors, and connect pins 2 and 4 to ground. Pins 1 and 3 are connected to form the amplifier's input, while the loudspeaker is connected between

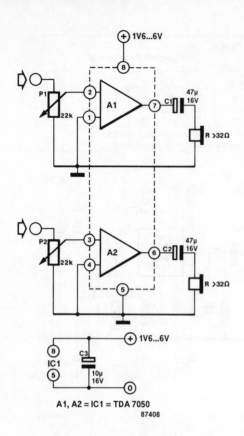

+ 1V6...6V

8

P1
22k

2

A1

1

7 C1 47µ 16V

R >32Ω

P2
22k

3

A2

4

6 C2 47µ 16V

5

R >32Ω

+ 1V6...6V

8

IC1

5

C3
10µ 16V

0

A1, A2 = IC1 = TDA 7050

87408

pins 6 and 7.

The current consumption of the chip at maximum output power is of the order of 100 to 150 mA, while the quiescent current amounts to a mere 5 mA. The amplifiers should be terminated in 32Ω, a common value for modern headphones. The supply voltage is normally 4.5 V, and pins 6 and 7 are at half the supply potential during quiescent operation.

027 SPEECH PROCESSOR WITH BACKGROUND SUPPRESSION

A speech processor is commonly used in public-address installations and in utility transmitters. It augments the average value of the speech signal, so that in spite of a high level of background noise or, in the case of a radio transmission, a lot of interference, speech recognition remains possible. In many cases it is, however, undesirable that this background noise or interference is enhanced together with the wanted signal. A possible remedy, as outlined here, is to provide an adjustable threshold at which the speech processor becomes active.

With reference to the diagram, the signal from the microphone is amplified in T_1 (a low-noise amplifier) and in A_1. Limiting (or clipping) of the signal takes place in A_3.

The signal (taken from the output of A_1) is also amplified in A_2. When the output of this opamp reaches a certain level, electronic switch ES_1 is actuated. Consequently, the monostable formed by

ES_2 changes state, and this closes ES_3, whereupon ES_4 is opened, which in its turn increases the amplification of A_3. When ES_4 is closed, the amplification of A_3 is determined by the ratio $P_1{:}R_5$; when the switch is open, by the ratio $(P_2+R_8){:}R_5$. The mono-time, determined by the time-constant $R_{20}{-}C_{19}$, has been chosen such that speech is not clipped. The low-pass filter between A_3 and A_4 ensures that frequencies above 3 kHz are severely attenuated. The required output level is set by P_3.

Calibration is somewhat unorthodox: a signal source with a continuous output of speech by trained speakers is used. The microphone is positioned in front of the loudspeaker at normal speaking distance and the sound level adjusted to roughly the level of the user. Next, connect a pair of headphones to the output of the processor and make sure that only the output of these phones can be heard. Adjust P_4 for maximum resistance, and then set the clipping level with P_2 (which is a matter of personal taste). At maximum clipping level, intelligibility of the speech will remain good in the presence of interference, but it will have a somewhat harsh, metallic character. Then, adjust P_1 for maximum resistance, and P_4 till all background noise disappears. Finally, set the ratio

signal: background noise with P_1; this is best done by making a recording of the user's speech via the microphone and the processor. When the processor is active, i.e. clips, D_4 lights.

L_1 to L_4 incl. are 6 turns 36 SWG CuL through 3 mm ferrite beads.

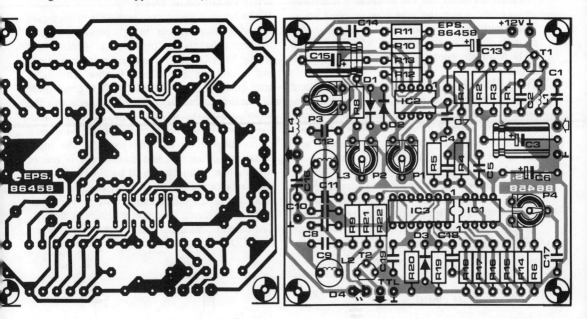

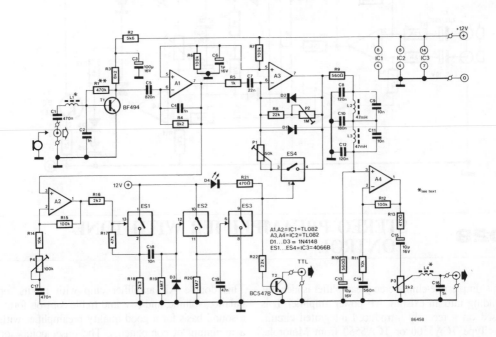

On most FM tuners, the stereo indicator lights upon detection of the 19 kHz pilot tone. However, this need not mean that the programme is actually stereophonic, since the pilot tone is often transmitted with mono programmes also. A similar situation exists on stereo amplifiers, where the stereo LED is simply controlled from the mono-stereo switch.

The LED-based stereo indicator described here lights only when a true stereo signal is fed to the inputs. Differential amplifier A_1 raises the difference between the L and R input signals. When these are equal, the output of A_1 remains at the same potential as the output of A_2, which forms a virtual ground rail at half the supply voltage. When A_1 detects a difference between the L and R input signals, it supplies a positive or negative voltage with respect to the virtual ground rail, and so causes C_3 to be charged via D_1, or C_4 via D_2. The resistors connected in parallel to these capacitors ensure slow

discharging to bridge brief silent periods in the programme. Comparator A_3-A_4 switches on the LED driver via OR circuit D_3-D_4.

When building the circuit into an amplifier, care should be taken to select the right point from which the input signals are obtained. In general, this should be before the volume and balance controls, but behind the mono/stereo selector. The signal level should not be less than 100 mV to compensate for the drop across D_1 or D_2. Also observe that the impedance at the selected "tap" location is relatively low. Should the stereo light come on when a mono programme is being received, the input signals are different, and the sensitivity of one of the amplifier channels should be altered. If this is impossible or undesirable, R_3 may be replaced by a series connected preset and a resistor. The sensitivity of the stereo indicator is adjustable with P_1. The current consumption is less than 7 mA when the LED is off, and about 20 mA when it is on.

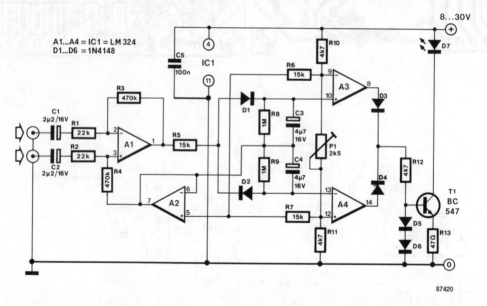

87420

029   STEREO PREAMPLIFIER WITH TONE CONTROL

This simple, one-chip, stereo preamplifier is ideal for building into an existing AF power amplifier. It is based on a recently introduced integrated circuit, the Type TCA5500 or TCA5550 from Motorola.

This double AF amplifier chip with inputs for balance, volume, and bass and treble controls forms a sound basis for a good quality preamplifier with a minimum of components. The onset points for

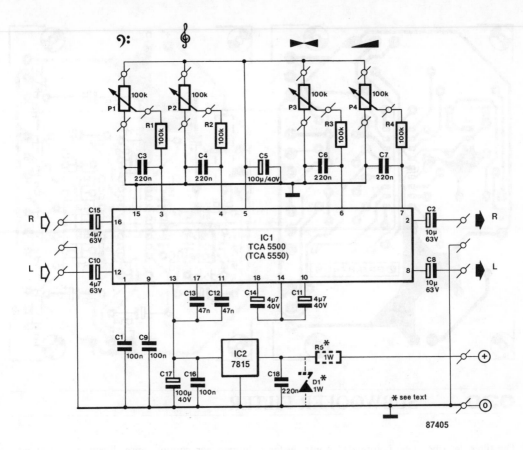

87405

the bass and treble controls are defined with C_3 and C_4 respectively. All (mono) potentiometers are best fitted direct onto the circuit board to make for simple mounting into a cabinet, and also to prevent hum and noise being picked up in the wiring that would otherwise be required.

The preamplifier has a current consumption of 35 mA, of which 5 mA is drawn by voltage regulator IC_2. Zenerdiode D_1 and power resistor R_5 should be added if the positive supply voltage available in the power amplifier is more than about 30 V.

Specifications of the preamplifier:

Distortion: $\leq 0.1\%$ at nominal output level.
Channel separation: ≥ 45 dB.
Supply voltage: 8.8-18 V.
Tone control range: 14 dB.
Volume control range: ≥ 75 dB.
Maximum input voltage: 100 mV.
Amplification: 10.
Low output impedance.

Parts list

Resistors ($\pm 5\%$):
$R_1 \ldots R_4$ incl. = 100K
R_5 = see text
$P_1 \ldots P_4$ incl. = 100K linear potentiometer

Capacitors:
$C_1; C_9; C_{16}$ = 100n
$C_2; C_8$ = 10μ; 63 V; radial
$C_3; C_4; C_6; C_7; C_{18}$ = 220n
$C_5; C_{17}$ = 100μ; 40 V; radial
$C_{10}; C_{15}$ = 4μ7; 63 V; radial
$C_{11}; C_{14}$ = 4μ7; 40 V; radial
$C_{12}; C_{13}$ = 47n

Semiconductors:
D_1 = zenerdiode 27 V; 1 W (see text)
IC_1 = TCA5500 or TCA5550 (Motorola)
IC_2 = 7815

Miscellaneous:
PCB Type 87405

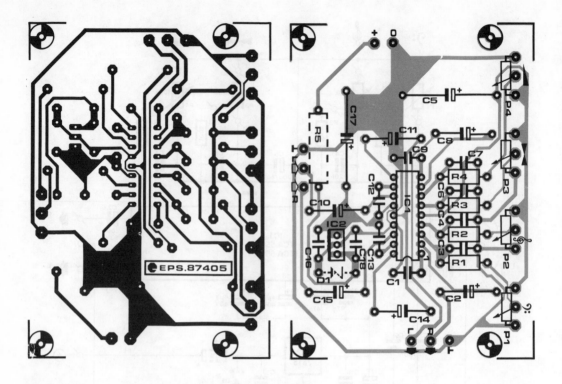

030   SUBWOOFER FILTER

The filter described here is intended primarily for experimenting with a (central) subwoofer (see *Active Subwoofer, EE* March 1986, p. 28). As the human ear cannot sense direction in a standing wave, directional sensitivity is generally poor at low frequencies, so that it would seem superfluous to

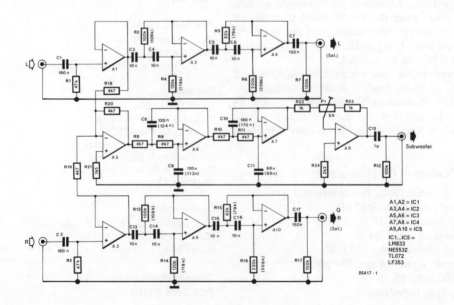

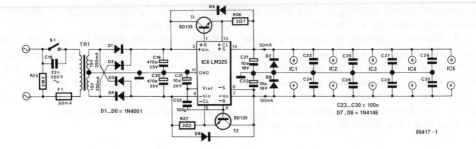

86417 - 1

use a stereo set-up below about 200 Hz. Therefore, the low frequencies can be concentrated on one good bass enclosure, which, of course, keeps the cost of the overall system down. The satellite loudspeakers (see *EE*, April 1986, p. 22) will then have to cope with the higher frequencies only.

The requisite cross-over network described here is based on 24 dB/octave Bessel filters: the cross-over frequency lies around 200 Hz. With reference to the circuit diagram, A_1 and A_2 buffer the left-hand and right-hand signals respectively. The high-pass filters for the two channels are formed by A_3-A_4 and A_9-A_{10} respectively.

At the same time, the two channels are combined in A_5, and the resulting signal is passed through low-pass filter A_6-A_7. The amplification of A_8 can be varied with P_1, so that the level of the low-frequency signal can be matched to that of the high-frequency signals. Note that the component values given in parentheses are the calculated values, wich perfectionists may try to approach.

The power supply is a symmetrical design with short-circuit protection, which also prevents annoying "plops" at on and off switching.

If a different cross-over frequency is required, refer to *Active Cross-over Network* in the September 1984 (p. 28) issue of *Elektor Electronics*.

In the design stages, stability problems were encountered when opamps with JFET inputs (TL074; LF353, for instance) were used, whereas types with bipolar inputs, such as the NE5534 and the LM833, worked perfectly. The reason for the instability in the JFET types is not known.

031   TRUE CLASS B AMPLIFIER

The quiescent current in this amplifier is always nought, so there is no need for zero setting or for a circuit to prevent thermal run-away. Complexity is further reduced by the use of a single supply voltage,

Voltage divider R_1-R_2-R_3 fixes the voltage level at the base of T_1 at just above half that of the supply voltage. Since a current source, consisting of T_3, R_7, D_1, and D_2, has been included in the collector circuit of T_2, this stage provides a very high voltage amplification. The return line of the current source is connected to the output, so that the voltage necessary to stabilize the source does not limit the dynamic push-pull characteristic. The current source has, therefore, a high-impedance character. The complementary power amplifiers, T_4 and T_5, are darlington transistors, which, of course, enable the collector current in the driver stage to be kept relatively low.

The feedback to the emitter of T_1 via R_5 and R_6

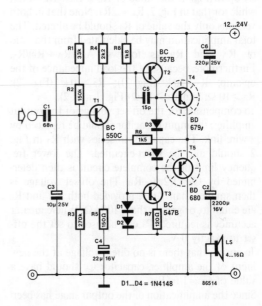

51

determines the overall voltage gain, here 20 dB, and irons out any non-linear components.

Class B operation is normally obtained by direct interconnection of the bases of the power transistors. In practice, this gave an overall distortion of not more than 0.16 per cent (at a drive power of 0.25 W at 1 kHz). The simple addition of diodes D_1 and D_2 improved the distortion to not more than 0.1 per cent. Note that these diodes do not alter the oper-

ation, because the darlingtons have a relatively high base-emitter potential.

With a supply voltage of 12 V, the amplifier delivers some 2 W into 4 ohms (input sensitivity 200 mV), or rather more than 1 W into 8 ohms. A higher supply voltage will increase the output power (to a maximum of 10 W into 4 ohms at 24 V), but the power transistors then need cooling.

032   TUNING AF POWER STAGES

Simple, economically priced audio output stages, such as, for instance, those using the hybrid ICs in the STK series, may be improved in a simple manner as regards distortion, noise, and off-set voltage. To this end, the output amplifier is included in the feedback loop of an op-amp. Fig. 1 shows the set-up for inverting output amplifiers, and Fig. 2 that for non-inverting ones (the normal situation).

In the calculations to arrive at the new gain of the output amplifier, determined by R_1 and R_2, it is assumed that the LF356 provides an undistorted signal of 5 V$_{rms}$; note also that this type of op-amp must work into a load of not less than 5 kilo-ohms to prevent distortion.

For an output power of 50 W into 4 ohms, the output stage must provide a voltage, $U = PR = 14.2$ V$_{rms}$. If the amplification of the stage is 3, the op-amp should deliver 4.73 V. For the set-up in Fig. 1, the value of R_2 is then $R_2 = 3R_1$, while for that in Fig. 2, $R_2 = 2R_1$. Note that in both versions only the value of R_1 should be altered. The total amplification may be calculated from the ratio of R_A and R_B as follows: $A = (R_A + R_B)/R_B$. Furthermore, because of the load impedance of the op-amp, $R_1 > 10$ k (Fig. 1); $R_2 > 10$ k (Fig. 2); $R_A > 10$ Ω; and $R_C > 10$ Ω (Fig. 1 and 2).

To compensate for the off-set voltage of the output amplifier, the input capacitor should be replaced by a wire link. The capacitor in series with R_1 in Fig. 2 should also be short-circuited. The lower frequency limit of the complete circuit is then determined by $C_B = 1/2\pi f_{lim} R_B$. The off-set voltage is then smaller than 3 mV, provided both R_A and R_c are equal to, or greater than, 100 kΩ. Where greater accuracy is required, P_1 can be used to set the off-set to exactly 0 V.

To ensure that there is no direct voltage at the new input of the amplifier, capacitor C_C should have a value of $C_C = 1/f_{lim} R_C$.

Since the amplification of the output stage has been

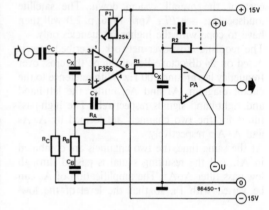

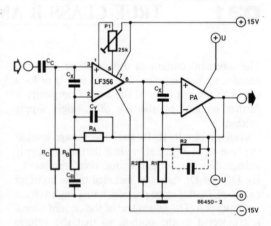

reduced to 3, its feedback factor has gone up, and the distortion has gone down. The additional feedback of the LF356 reduces the distortion even further. An overall reduction in the distortion from 1 per cent to 0.1 per cent is fairly typical. The altered feedback unfortunately results in a change in stability. If there is a tendency to oscillate, the first thing to do is to bring the upper frequency limit back to its previous value with the aid of $C_Y = 1/2\pi f_{lim}R_A$. If the tendency persists, capacitors C_X must be used: their value lies between 100 pF and 1 nF. Our prototype (using STK ICs) worked satisfactorily without either C_X or C_Y.

033   AUTOMATIC CAR ALARM

Even the best car alarm is useless if you forget to set it upon leaving your car, whence this circuit.

The relay has a make and a break contact: the former is necessary to delay the switching in of the alarm after you have got out of your car, and the latter serves to switch on the car alarm proper.

Immediately on re-entering your car, you must press the hidden switch, S₁. This causes silicon-controlled rectifier Th₁ to conduct so that the relay is energized. At the same time, the green LED lights to indicate that the alarm is switched off.

As soon as the ignition is switched off, T₁ is off, T₂ is on, and the buzzer sounds. At the same time, monostable IC₁ is triggered, which causes T₃ to conduct and the red LED to light. The silicon-controlled rectifier is then off, and D₄ is reverse biased, but the relay remains energized via its make contact for a short time, preset by P₁ As soon as this time has lapsed, the relay returns to its quiescent state, and the alarm is set via the break contact. The delay time can be set to a maximum of about 1 minute.

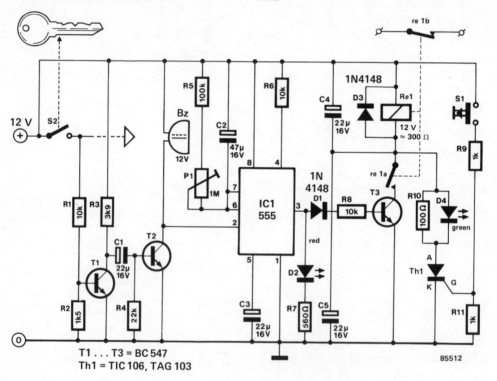

T1 . . . T3 = BC 547
Th1 = TIC 106, TAG 103

85512

034   BICYCLE LIGHTS AND ALARM

A bicycle or tricycle should, as everyone knows, be fitted with front and rear lights. The noteworthy aspect of the lights circuit described here is that it also provides a visible alarm, which is primarily intended for invalid road users. When such handicapped people are in need of assistance during the day, this is quickly spotted by passers-by. At night, this is, unfortunately, not so, whence the present circuit.

The usual dynamo or battery is replaced by a 6 V rechargeable lead-acid battery, which ensures that the bicycle lights are operational even when the bicycle is not moving. When the rider is in need of assistance, the alarm can be switched on: in addition to the normal lights, a small display with the word "HELP" will then flash. Such a signal for help is not easily overlooked!

The circuit is based on an astable multivibrator,

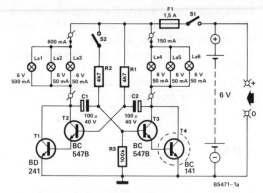

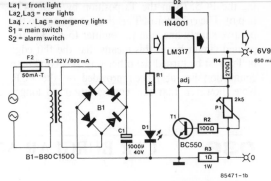

La1 = front light
La2, La3 = rear lights
La4 ... La6 = emergency lights
S1 = main switch
S2 = alarm switch

85471-1a

85471-1b

which does not operate when alarm switch S_2 is open. Provided S_1 is closed, the front and rear lights are on, however.

When the alarm switch, S_2, is closed, the multivibrator operates, which causes the normal lights and the HELP lights to flash alternately.

The circuit is powered by a 6 V 1.8 Ah lead-acid battery which, when properly charged, is sufficient to keep the lights on for about three hours.

The circuit can be fitted in a small, preferably water-proof, case. Lamps La4 ... La6 light the letters "HELP" that have been cut out in the lid. The

BC141 should be fitted onto a small heat sink. Because of the need of regularly charging the battery, the case should be fitted to the vehicle in a manner which allows easy removal and attachment. A circuit for a suitable charger is given in figure 1b. This provides a constant charging voltage of 6.9 V (preset with P_1), while the charging current is limited to about 650 mA. This enables the battery to be fully charged in around 3 hours. The charging voltage should be set carefully, otherwise the battery will not be charged correctly.

035   BRAKE LIGHTS MONITOR

The circuit described below monitors your car's brake lights, and indicates by a light-emiting diode whether they both function correctly. In that sense, it can save you money by preventing your being fined for driving with defective brake lights, and it also leads to increasing road safety.

The monitor depends inevitably on the voltage drop across the supply lines to the two lamps. For the circuit to work correctly, that drop needs to be greater than 0.6 V. If this is not so, the drop must be increased by adding a 5 V diode in series with each lamp. Transistor T_1 and T_2 in figure 1 form a Schmitt trigger, which reacts to the voltage drop across the supply lines to the two brake lights. This reaction manifests itself in D_1 lighting via T_3. If one of the brake lights is faulty, the switch-on current drawn by the other lamp will cause D_1 to light briefly when the brake pedal is pressed. If both brake lights are defective, D_1 will not light at all. All three possible states of the brake lights are thus indicated.

The hysteresis of the trigger, and, therefore, the sen-

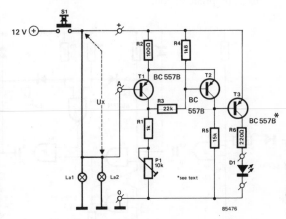

85476

sitivity of the circuit, can be adjusted within narrow limits with P_1. The preset is best adjusted with one lamp out of action in a manner which makes D_1 light briefly as described above.

If you find it disturbing that D_1 lights every time you brake, the operation can be reversed by replacing the BC557B in the T_3 position by a BC547B (n-p-n). The collector of T_3 is then connected to the positive supply line, and the emitter to R_6. On the printed circuit board this means that the flat edge of T_3 must be turned the other way. A second base connection has also been provided on the PCB. Note, however, that this configuration no longer makes it possible to ascertain whether one or both brake lights are faulty, i.e., when the LED lights, one or both lamps need replacing.

The printed circuit board is not available ready made.

In figure 1, S_1 is the brake pedal switch, and La_1 and La_2 are the brake lights.

036   CAR BURGLAR ALARM

This versatile and yet easy to build circuit may be used as an effective deterrent against criminals attempting to steal what you are bound to consider a highly valued and indispensable piece of property: your car.

Extremely simple to control, the circuit leaves the car owner 15 seconds to get out of the vehicle after he has set the alarm. Upon return, he deactivates it again by pressing a hidden reset switch within 7 seconds after having opened the car door(s). Criminals who (hopefully) have not been able to locate the reset switch within the 7 second delay will regale themselves and their accomplices, if any, with a 100 seconds long, intermittend car horn concert which, ideally, should stop them from pursuing their nefarious activities and, in short, scare them off. Also, the lawful owner of the vehicle is alerted by the horn sound that something is amiss, requiring appropriate action.

The present circuit offers the possibility to connect several types of alarm activating devices, such as a vibration and/or ultrasonic detector, a window breakage sensor, etc., provided these supply an active low output level when an alarm condition exists. However, it is also possible to use the courtesy light switches for this purpose, since these usually connect to the car body when a door is opened. To understand the operation of the alarm, refer to the circuit diagram and assume that the circuit is in the non-activated mode. On leaving the car, the user presses the 'set alarm' button, which leaves him some 15 seconds to actually get out and lock the door(s); the 15 second interval is determined by network R_2-C_1; the N_2-N_3 bistable will toggle after this delay and activate the alarm proper (watch function). Note that this condition may be signalled by a suitable LED driver circuit instead of RE_2 as shown in the circuit. Only when on of the alarm in-

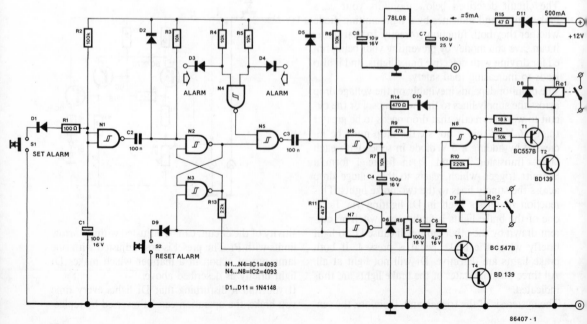

puts goes low (i.e. active) will monostable N_6-N_7 toggle and start a 100 second interval, as determined by network R_8-C_4. However, the horn will not sound immediately, since network R_9-C_5 provides a 7 second delay to reset (deactivate) the alarm before oscillator gate N_8 intermittently switches the horn relay transistors T_1 and T_2. Note that the horn will stop sounding after 100 seconds, but the alarm will remain in its activated state, i.e. any alarm condition signalled by the sensor devices or the door contacts will set it off anew and cause another round of horn sounding. As already stated, T_3, T_4, and R_{13} may be connected to the N_2-N_3 bistable to provide a LED indication of the activated state of the alarm. Instead of the LED, a relay may be connected to break the ignition coil primary connection. It should be noted,

however, that this relay can not be used in cars with electronic ignition; in this case, another means for disabling the car ignition system should be arranged with the alarm in its activated state. The relays employed in this circuit are standard types as available from motorists' shops. The contacts of RE_1 are simply connected in parallel with the existing horn relay contacts.

Finally, note that it is of utmost importance to mount the entire circuit and the relay wiring in an out of the way position; the reset switch may be a coded or key operated type and must be fitted well hidden. Current consumption of the circuit in the non-alarm condition is so low as to hardly load the car battery. A voltage regulator section has been added to prevent the alarm from being triggered in error when the car is started.

037   CAR FUSE MONITOR

This extremely simple to construct contrivance offers motorists a visible indication as to the nature of malfunctions occurring in the car electric system, which, as we all know or come to find out sooner or later, is protected by means of fuses which have a tendency to melting at times and places most inconvenient to driver and his passengers, if any.

This circuit, if constructed with a little mechanical skill, may be plugged across all fuses in the fuse compartment to quickly locate the defective one without having to remove the whole set for visual inspection.

Given the very low cost of the undertaking, it may be worthwile to fit all fuseholders with indicators of the type described; in case a malfunction occurs,

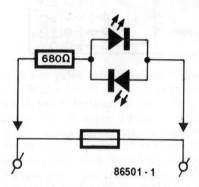

you are immediately notified which fuse had best be replaced (after the necessary repairs have been made, of course).

038   CAR LIGHTS MONITOR

Many traffic accidents are caused by failing car lights. Often, the driver is not aware of such a malfunction, because the warning lights provided on the dashboard do not, strictly speaking, monitor the relevant lights, but rather the switch position since they are almost invariably connected in parallel with the relevant car lights.

The proposed circuit is intended to indicate the failure of one light in a pair: sidelights; headlights (up to 55 W); rear lights; brake lights; or fog lights. The two lamps must have the same rating.

Counter-wound coils, L_1 and L_2, carry the same current when both lamps are working correctly, so that the magnetic fields created by these currents cancel one another. When one of the lamps fails, the magnetic field caused by the current through the other induces a voltage in L_3. This pulse causes the TIC106D to switch on, and this in turn makes D_5 light. If both lamps fail simultaneously (the probability of which is, however, minute), the circuit does, of course, not function.

Because in practice the two lamps do not come on

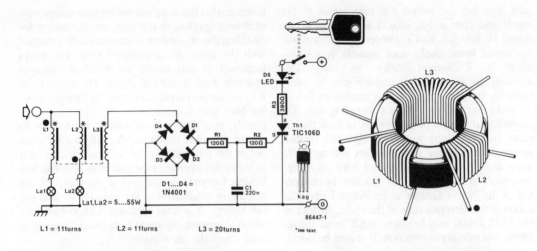

L1 = 11turns L2 = 11turns L3 = 20turns

D1....D4 = 1N4001

La1,La2 = 5....55W

86447-1

*see text

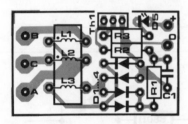

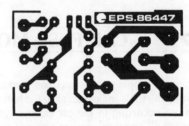

or go out simultaneously, R1-C2-R2 provide a delay to enable the magnetic field to stabilize. Note, however, that C1 must be matched to the particular lamps being monitored: increasing its value makes the circuit less sensitive (longer delay).

The coil is easily made from an old (or new) core of a choke or dimmer switch. First, wind two times 11 turns SWG22 enamelled copper wire around the core as shown in the drawing. Inductor L3 consists of twenty turns SWG40 enamelled copper wire (this coil does not carry a large current). Note that the black spots in the drawing are the same as those in the circuit diagram. If the circuit does not work, it almost certainly means that the connections of either L1 or L2 have to be interchanged.

To monitor all the lights of car, the circuit will have to be built as many times as there are pairs of lamps. The indicator diodes are best fitted in the dashboard. It is, however, possible to use only one LED for a number of circuits: when this lights, it is then, of course, necessary to walk around the car to see which lamp has failed. Once the LED lights, it remains on until either the thyristor or the ignition has been switched off.

039　CAR RADIO ALARM I

It is an unfortunate as well as a generally acknowledged fact that the car radio (plus cassette recorder) ranges among the most desirable and often surprisingly easy to steal objects on many a burglar's "shopping list".

This circuit may help to prematurely end the criminal practice by sounding the horn if it is attempted to remove the radio set; cutting or unplugging an additional ground wire, which has been hidden in the cable for connection to the battery and loudspeaker(s), causes the alarm to be set off, since the connection to the car chassis (ground) is interrupted.

The circuit for the car radio alarm is composed of a single timer, the well-known Type 555, surrounded by a few additional odds and ends to make an astable multivibrator, whose on-time is determined with C1. Horn relay Re should have a coil resistance to enable the timer chip to energize it direct by means of the voltage at output pin 3.

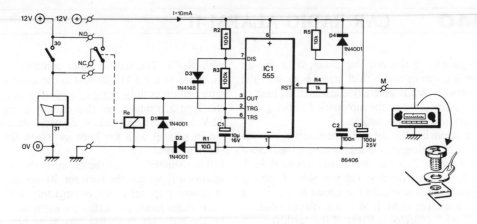

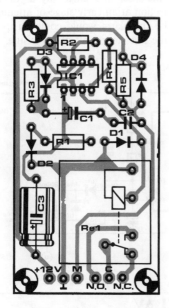

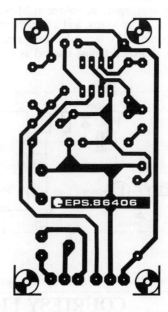

It is seen that the multivibrator is in the reset state as long as point M is connected to earth, i.e. when the set is in the place where it should be. Removing the car radio inevitably causes the voltage at M to rise to nearly 12 V, ending the reset state of IC1, which responds with activating Re, i.e. the car horn, since this is energized via the relay contacts in parallel with the horn switch in the steering wheel.

Note that Re is any small changeover relay having a 12 V coil, provided the 555 is capable of handling the coil current; many motorists' and car repair shops can, no doubt, supply you with a suitable relay for the alarm circuit.

The sense wire to point M should be hidden in the multi-wire cable to the radio set, while the circuit itself must be fitted in an out of the way position, somewhere behind the dashboard.

In order that not even an attempt is made to break into your car, it is, as will be readily understood, prudent to stick adhesives to the car side windows, warning of the presence of the radio alarm.

The purpose of this one-chip circuit is to give an audible alarm in case a thief attempts to steal the car radio, which is generally considered an item of prime importance to the motorist's well-being during any trip with his vehicle.

Since removing the car radio necessarily involves cutting or unplugging the supply cables, the present circuit detects disconnection of an extra earth lead, which has been fitted to the rear side of the car radio (metal) housing. In the circuit diagram, this point is marked as M. If M is at earth potential, T_1 is off (high collector voltage); if the earth connection is cut or unplugged, the voltage at M rises to a positive level, T_1 conducts, and a negative-going pulse triggers timer IC_1, which has been arranged to provide a 30-second timing interval as defined

with R_6-C_3. The second timer contained in IC_1 functions as a 0.5 Hz (R_7-R_8-C_4) oscillator section with an output duty factor of 50% (D_3). Note that the Type 556 dual timer chip directly energizes a 12 V, low-power relay, whose contacts are connected in parallel with the horn switch in the car's steering wheel.

If it is attempted to steal the car radio, the alarm intermittently sounds the horn for 30 seconds. It is, of course, imperative that constructors of this car radio alarm locate the additional earth connection on the radio set in such a way as to necessitate disconnection at an early stage of attempted theft, otherwise the alarm would come on too late, enabling the thief to get off at his leisure.

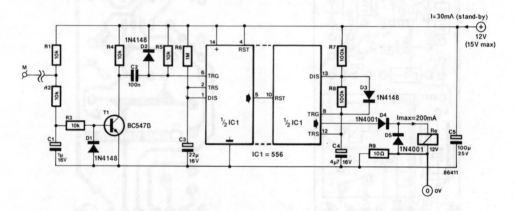

041   COURTESY LIGHT DELAY

Ever been groping about for the safety belt, ignition slot, choke control or a map while in utter darkness and happy to have closed the car door(s) because of the cold, or foul weather? Wouldn't it be convenient to have the courtesy light on for a few more instants in order to get the vehicle started and ready to move off?

Figure 1 shows a courtesy light delay circuit for easy incorporation in almost any type of car. The courtesy light is switched by power MOSFET T_2, which is a Type BUZ72A ensuring a low voltage drop (0.2 V typ.) across drain and source and therefore the lowest possible power loss. The door contact, connected to terminals B and C, is normally a push to break type. T_1 is therefore off and

C_1 discharged when the door is closed; MOSFET T_2 does not conduct, sothat the courtesy light remains quenched. Opening the door, however, causes T_1 to charge C_1, and the courtesy bulb will therefore light in a gradual manner. Although closing the door turns T_1 off again, C_1 continues to supply gate drive to T_2 for a few more seconds; the courtesy light will be dimmed slowly. The suggested MOSFET type should not switch more than about 10 W, which is the usual power rating for the courtesy light.

Figure 2 shows how the circuit may be modified to enable the courtesy light to go out immediately after the ignition key is turned. The terminal numbers refer to the wiring code convention as rel-

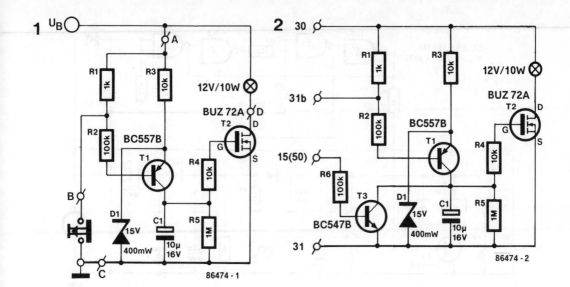

86474 - 1

86474 - 2

evant to most types of European car:

15 = +V_{batt} - ignition on.
30 = +V_{batt} - unswitched.
31 = ground.
31b = door contact (connects to ground).
50 = +V_{batt} - starter motor on.

Figure 3 clearly shows the circuit connections in accordance with the foregoing convention.
In case the suggested MOSFET Type BUZ72A (Siemens) is a difficult to obtain item, any equivalent n-channel power MOSFET to the following specifications will also do adequately: $V_{ds} \geq 100$ V; $I_d \geq 9$ A; $P_d \geq 40$ W; $R_{ds(on)} \leq 0.25$ Ω.

Source: *Siemens Components XX (1985) No. 6.*

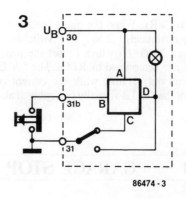

86474 - 3

042   FLASHING REAR LIGHT

This rear light for bicycles is fed from a battery charged with current from the dynamo, and starts to flash when the cyclist halts. To preserve battery power, the unit automatically switches off 4 minutes after halting.
The circuit is essentially composed of a battery charger and a logic switching section. The NiCd battery is charged from a voltage doubler C_1-C_2-D_1-D_2-C_3 to ensure a charge current of about 20 mA when riding at a reasonable speed. This makes it possible for a charge of 3 mAh to be available after a 10 minute ride, i.e., enough for the

light to flash for about 4 minutes after the bicycle is halted. A relay is used to switch between operation while riding and while standing still. When the bicycle is in motion, the voltage from the dynamo, G, ensures that N_4 is enabled, so that T_1 actuates Re, and the small 6 V bulb is illuminated. Since C_3 is only slowly discharged via R_1, N_4 remains enabled for about 4 minutes after halting. Push-button S_1 enables immediately switching off the rear light, because R_2 then discharges C_3 in a few seconds.
Gate N_1 monitors the dynamo voltage, which is rec-

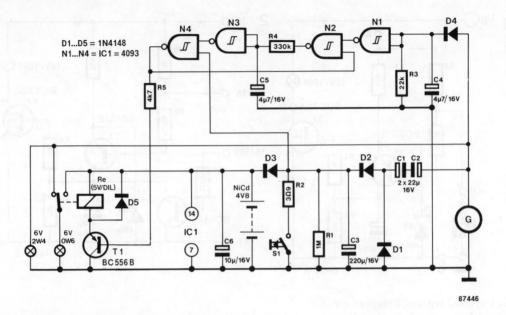

87446

tified by D_4-C_4-R_3. When the direct voltage drops below approximately 2 V, N_1 switches on multivibrator N_2-N_3-N_4 which causes the relay to toggle at a rate determined by R_4-C_5. The 5 V DIL relay requires only 11 mA, while the current consumption of the 4093 is virtually negligible at about 1 μA.

It should be possible to fit the circuit and the battery in a somewhat larger than normal bicycle headlight, equipped with terminals for connecting the dynamo and the rear light. Of course, due care must be taken to avoid the battery contacts touching the metal inside of the light.

043   GARAGE STOP LIGHT

A novel use of solar cells makes positioning your car in the garage rather easier than old tyres, a mirror, or a chalk mark.

The six solar cells in figure 1 serve as power supply and as proximity sensor. They are commercially available at relative low cost. The voltage developed

across potentiometer P_1 is mainly dependent on the intensity of the light falling onto the cells. The circuit is only actuated when the main beam of one of the car's headlights shines direct onto the cells from a distance of about 200 mm (8 inches). The distance can be varied somewhat with P_1

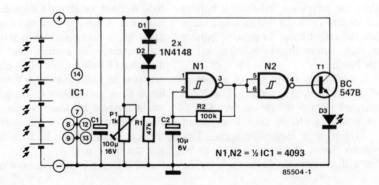

85504-1

Under those conditions, the voltage developed across C_1 is about 3 V, which is sufficient to trigger relaxation oscillator N_1. The BC547B is then switched on via buffer N_2 so that D_3 begins to flash. Diodes D_1 and D_2 provide an additional increase in the threshold of the circuit. The total voltage drop of 1.2 V across them ensures that the potential at pin 1 of the 4093 is always 1.2 V below the voltage developed by the solar cells. As the trip level of N_1 lies at about 50 per cent of the supply voltage, the oscillator will only start when the supply voltage is higher than 2.4 V.

The circuit, including the solar cells, is best con-structed on a small veroboard as shown in figure 3, and then fitted in a translucent or transparent man-made fibre case. The case is fitted onto the garage wall in a position where one of the car's headlights shines direct onto it. The LED is fitted onto the same wall, but a little higher so that it is in easy view of the driver of the car. When you drive into the garage, you must, of course, remember to switch on the main beam of your headlights!

A descriptive article on the operation and use of solar cells appeared in the June 1985 issue of *Electronics: solar battery* — p. 6-65.

044   HALOGEN LAMP PROTECTOR

Halogen lamps are, unfortunately, rather prone to burn out when they are switched on, and this is mainly owing to the high current consumption of these devices during the initial stage of heating up to the normal operating temperature of the filament in haloid gas.

A typical value for the cold resistance of a 6 V - 4 W halogen lamp is about 0.3 ohm, demanding a turn-on current of 20 A. In view of the relatively low internal resistance of car and motor-cycle bat-teries, such a current surge is not at all to be dismiss-ed as purely theoretical, and it is easily seen that the ensuing rapid heating inside the lamp is a prime cause for the thin filament to melt at the sudden temperature effect. What is required, therefore, is a series regulator system to limit the current during the heat-up phase; in other words, a soft turn-on fa-cility.

The circuit diagram shows that C_1 is charged to the battery voltage by means of R_1 and R_2, causing FET T_1 to become slowly conductive after S_1 has been closed. The Type BUZ10(A) power FET is used in view of its low drain-source resistance in the fully conductive state; a typical value for $R_{ds(on)}$ is 0.19 ohm, which ensures a low voltage drop across the FET, and, therefore, a sufficiently high operating voltage for the halogen lamp. Parts D_1

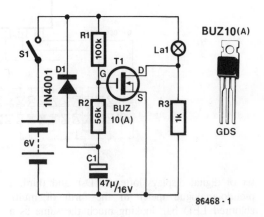

and R_3 discharge C_1 after opening S_1, so that the power-on delay functions correctly any time the lamp is turned on.

Lamp voltages other then 6 V require R_2 to be modified according to $R_2 = 200,000/(V_{batt} - 2)$ [Ω]. In case the BUZ10(A) proves hard to obtain, other types of n-channel power MOSFET may be used in the circuit. The minimum requirements are: drain-source voltage $V_{ds} = 50$ V, drain current $I_d = 19$ A, and drain-source on resistance $R_{ds(on)} = 0.2\ \Omega$.

045   LED REVOLUTION COUNTER

A close look at the dashboards of a number of cars may reveal the use of three basic types of rev counter: first, the still most commonly found needle and round scale, analogue combination; second, a

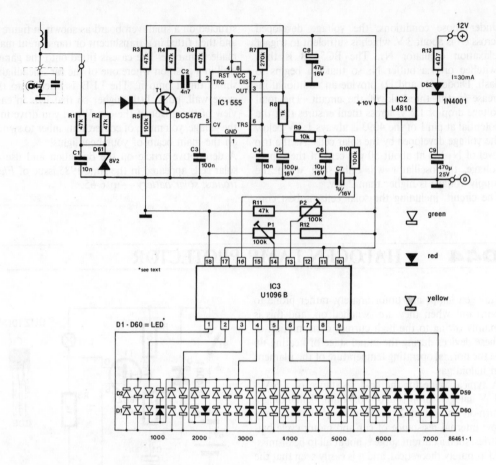

set of digital displays (often LCDs); and third, a pseudo-analogue meter in the form of multi-coloured LED bar, looking much the same as a LED-based VU meter on modern recording equipment.

The circuit presented here belongs to the third category. However, contrary to the straight LED bar indication, this design features a round scale with a coloured LED needle imitation, just as the good old mechanical rev counter.

The circuit is based on the Telefunken Type U1096B analogue input LED driver which can light one of 30 LEDs on the rpm scale, whose lower and upper indication limits may be set to individual requirements; e.g. the 30 LEDs may merely indicate a limited rpm range to attain a higher resolution.

The circuit diagram shows IC_1 to receive the contact breaker pulses and to reshape them for conversion to an analogue voltage in an R-C filter, which passes the signal to the input of the LED driver.

The detailed operation of the circuit is as follows. Zener diode D_{61} and parallel capacitor C_1 safeguard the base of inverter transistor T_1 against

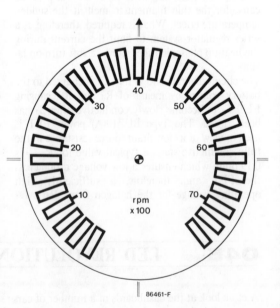

86461-F

Parts list

Resistors:
$R_1 \ldots R_4; R_6; R_{11} = 47$ k
$R_5; R_{10} = 100$ k
$R_7 = 270$ k
$R_8 = 1$ k
$R_9 = 10$ k
$R_{12} = 220$ k
$R_{13} = 4.7\ \Omega$
$P_1; P_2 = 100$ k preset

Capacitors:
$C_1; C_4 = 10$ n
$C_2 = 4n7$
$C_3 = 100$ n
$C_5 = 100\ \mu; 16$ V
$C_6 = 10\ \mu; 16$ V
$C_7 = 1\ \mu; 16$ V
$C_8 = 47\ \mu; 16$ V
$C_9 = 470\ \mu; 25$ V

Semiconductors:
$IC_1 = 555$
$IC_2 = L4810$
$IC_3 = U1096B$ (Telefunken)
$D_1 \ldots D_{60} = LED$
 (see text)
$D_{61} =$ zenerdiode 8V2;   400 mW
$D_{62} = 1N4001$
$T_1 = BC547B$

Miscellaneous:
PCB Type 86461

receiving high voltage pulses induced in the ignition coil secondary winding. The Type NE555 timer has been configured to function as a monostable with an output pulse period time of 3 ms, during which time R_3 causes T_1 to conduct so as to prevent erroneous triggering of the monostable. The analogue voltage, proportional to the engine rpm rate, is established by means of smoothing network R_8-C_5, R_9-C_6 and R_{10}-C_7. The indication range for the LEDs may be set with P_1 and P_2, the presets for the lower and upper limit, corresponding to LEDs D_1-D_2 and D_{59}-D_{60} respectively. Note the relative simplicity of the LED array connection to IC_3; only nine IC output lines suffice to drive any one

65

of 30 pairs of LEDs, whose colour may be chosen to individual taste, while it is also possible to use series-connected LEDs to achieve a brightly as well as functionally lit rpm scale.

The circuit diagram shows two rows of LEDs; the upper one is the normal rpm indication scale, for which the following coloured subdivision may be used: 0 to 5000 rmp are green LEDs; from 5000 to 6000 rpm yellow or orange types; 6000 rpm and up are bright red types. This range and subdivision may, of course, be adapted for the specific type of engine.

The lower row of LEDs may be used to indicate a number of fixed rpm rates on the scale, for instance at 1000 rpm intervals.

The PCB track layout and component overlay with this design should enable anyone to readily construct the LED scale revolution counter, but note that the LEDs are mounted at the PCB track side to get the correct indication in clockwise direction with increasing the rpm rate. Also note the use of the low voltage-drop regulator IC_2 which supplies IC_1 and IC_3 with a stable, noisefree 10 V rail.

046   MOTOR-CYCLE GEAR INDICATOR

This circuit provides motor-cycle riders with a gear indication to the foot-operated lever at one side of the engine block. The proposed indication unit will be appreciated by those riders in the habit of forgetting which gear they have selected when attempting to drive off at traffic lights or crossroads and finding that the engine stalls because it had been switched to second gear.

The circuit as shown is based on the use of two gear-lever operated, plunger or roller type microswitches, along with the neutral gear indication lamp, which is a standard item on most types of modern motor-cycle.

Bistables N_1-N_2 and N_3-N_3 serve as debouncer circuits for micro-switches S_1 (lever down) and S_2 (lever up). If either one switch is actuated, N_{14} or N_{15} will cause bistable N_{12}-N_{13} to be set or reset; counter IC_5 counts up (U/D = 1) or down (U/D = 0) as a result of actuating S_2 or S_1 respectively. On release of the relevant microswitch, AND simulator

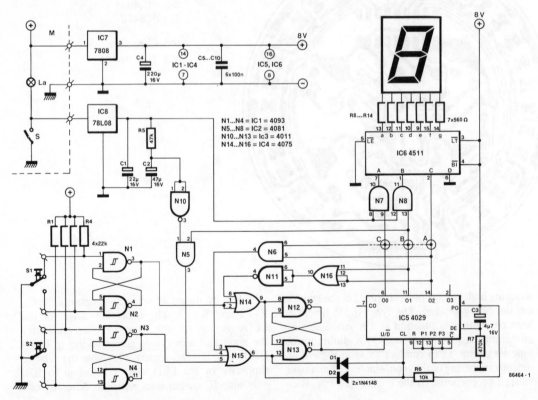

D_1-D_2-R_6 supplies IC_5 with a clock pulse, incrementing or decrementing the gear readout composed of IC_6 and the indication-panel mounted 7-segment LED display.

Input pin 5 of gate N_6 may be wired to point A, B, or C to suit 4-, 6-, or 5-gear types of motor-cycle respectively. N_6 inhibits OR gate N_{15} from supplying further clock pulses if S_2 is operated when driving in top gear. N_{16} and N_{11} have the same function for the bottom gear, preventing the counter from decrementing the display reading at gearing up from neutral to 1.

If the neutral switch — S — is closed, IC_8 supplies the A and B inputs of IC_6 with logic low levels; the level at the C input need not be forced low, since the neutral gear is in between first and second, both of which positions cause the most significant bit — C — to be low anyhow.

Parts R_5-C_2-N_{10}-N_5 have been included to prevent an erroneous display reading at gearing down from 2 to neutral and up again; for two seconds, N_{15} is disabled from clocking IC_5, so that the lever-up pulse is not detected.

At power-on, R_7 and C_3 preset counter IC_5 to state 1.

In conclusion, it goes without saying that S_1 and S_2 should be good quality microswitches, sealed against moisture and dirt.

047 4-WAY DAC EXTENSION

This extension circuit makes it possible to use a single DAC (digital-analogue converter) for generating four analogue voltages. Evidently, the cost of the extension described here is only a fraction of that of four DAC chips.

The operation of the 4-way DAC is fairly simple. Assuming that inputs A, B and E of multiplexer/demultiplexer IC_1 are driven low, the output of A_1 is fed to the + input of A_2, while the output of this opamp is connected to the − input of A_1 via the demultiplexer and R_1. Capacitor C_2 functions as a storage device. The output voltage available at

terminal 1 equals U_{DAC} because A_1 is dimensioned for unity gain. When the $\overline{E}$ input is driven high, or when a new code is applied to inputs A-B, the input voltage for A_2 is derived from C_2, so that the programmed voltage remains available at the output. The function of the other output buffers and capacitors is, of course, similar to that of A_2-C_2.

For optimum performance, C_2-C_5 should be low leakage capacitors, e.g. multilayer MKT, and the input current to A_2-A_5 should remain low. The latter condition is satisfied by using opamps with FET inputs (typical bias current:

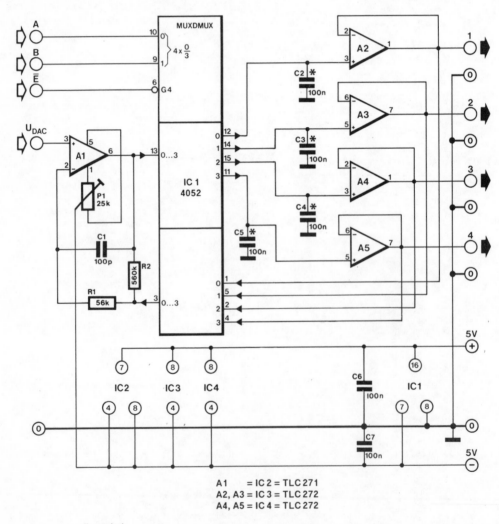

A1   = IC 2 = TLC 271
A2, A3 = IC 3 = TLC 272
A4, A5 = IC 4 = TLC 272

* see text

1 pA). Only A_1 requires an offset compensation since feedback is provided via the lower multiplexer in IC_1. The $\overline{E}$ (enable) input serves to disable IC_1 during switchover to another channel. R_2 then gives A_1 unity gain to prevent the — input being left open.

When a Type HCT4052 is used in the IC_1 position, standard TTL levels can be used to drive inputs A, B and $\overline{E}$.

A "normal" CMOS 4052 requires 5K6 pull-up resistors to be fitted on these inputs, but only if TTL signals are used to drive the extension. The current consumption of the circuit is less than 10 mA. U_{DAC} should be between −3.5 V and +3.5 V.

048   8-BIT ADC

Before any analogue voltage can be measured and subsequently processed by a computer, a converter device with the necessary precision is required to provide the computer with the digital n-bit equivalent of the voltage as applied to the DAC circuit. Obviously, the higher n, the more steps involved in the conversion process, but also the higher the accuracy that can be obtained.

This 8-bit ADC circuit works with very few parts;

yet it is versatile, fast, and sufficiently accurate for most purposes. The maximum input voltage to the circuit is arranged at 5V, as determined by the resistor network connected to the A_{in} terminal of the Type ZN427 ADC chip. Given this upper limit for V_{in}, the conversion accuracy equals $5V/(2^8-1) = 19.6mV/step$. Other input voltage levels may be accommodated by appropriate redimensioning of the input voltage divider.

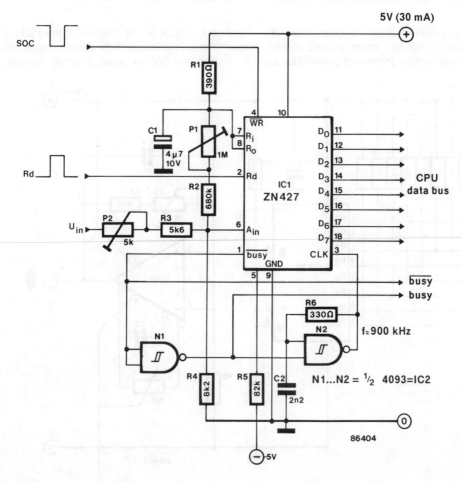

Since the proposed ADC chip features an analogue-to-digital conversion time of only 10μs (typical value), alternating voltages may be measured (digitalized) and processed under machine language control; just as with the above DAC circuit, BASIC is usually not very suitable for this purpose, and its use is restricted to applications where timing requirements are less stringent. It will be understood that fast and therefore smooth computer response to, say, joystick movement is only feasible if the ADC reading subroutine is written in machine code.

A low SOC (start of conversion) pulse at the $\overline{WR}$ input of the chip triggers the internal voltage conversion process and the $\overline{BUSY}$ output is activated (i.e. pulled low); this, in turn, enables Schmitt trigger gate N_1 to generate the ADC clock frequency of about 900kHz. On completion of the clock-controlled conversion, BUSY goes high, and the CPU may read the 8-bit value contained in the ADC latch by activating the read line. Note that the SOC and read signals must be decoded with suitable circuitry as required by the type of computer or CPU. Provision has been made in the ADC circuit to select either the BUSY or $\overline{BUSY}$ signal in order to flag the conversion condition to the host computer CPU.

Calibration of the present circuit is straightforward, since this merely involves setting two presets. First, a simple test loop may be written in machine language; next, adjust P_1 (offset) for a computer reading of 0 with no input voltage applied to the circuit; P_2 is set to give a reading of 255 (FFhex) with the maximum input voltage at V_{in}, i.e. 5V. Finally, test the ADC linearity by applying 2.5V from a sufficiently accurate source; the computer should read 128 (80hex).

049   8-BIT DAC

This simple circuit enables computer users to generate analogue voltages under software control, which, no doubt, offers interesting possibilities for intelligent control of, for example, volume adjustment of audio equipment, light dimmer circuits, etc. It is also possible to write machine language

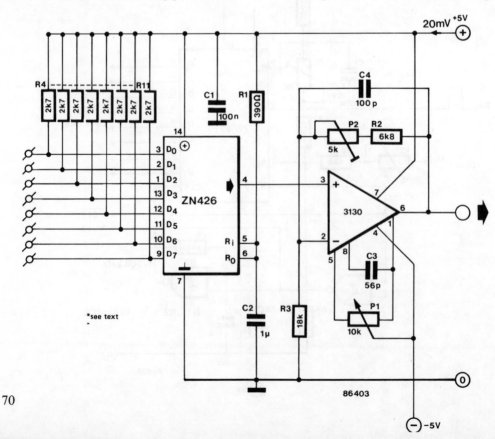

algorithms for the generation of several different, complex periodic output voltages, in short, to construct a computer-controlled function generator using a minimum amount of hardware.

The circuit is based on the Type ZN426 digital-to-analogue converter (DAC), which is an 8-bit resolution (255-step), high conversion speed (1 µs) device for direct microprocessor interfacing. The circuit may be connected to an 8-bit output port which provides TTL or CMOS compatible digital levels; most computers currently on the market have such a port, or the manufacturer has made provision to add one or more of these in the form of an expansion. The conversion time of the DAC chip allows the use of machine code for high frequency output voltages; BASIC is usually too slow for this purpose. The DAC output voltage is buffered with an BIFET opamp, which can be adjusted for a step response of

15mV/step, which means that the maximum output voltage of the present circuit is 3.825V, since 8 bits represent 255 steps (2^8-1).

Adjustment of the circuit is straightforward: connect a DVM to the output and adjust P_1 for an indication of 0.00V with nought ($\emptyset$) written to the DAC; next, write 255 (FF_{hex}) and adjust P_2 for the maximum voltage indication of 3.825V.

The circuit is also very suitable as an D-to-A converter driven by 8-bit I/O port (EE, December 1985) as part of the universal I/O bus. It should be noted, however, that writing FF_{hex} to this port gives an analogue output voltage of $\emptyset$V, since the ULN2003 buffer IC in the 8-bit output port is an inverting device: moreover, the eight data lines to the DAC chip should be fitted with pull-up resistors as shown in the circuit diagram.

050   16-KEY INPUT FOR MSX MICROS

This simple circuit is an unusual, but interesting, application of the joystick port available on an MSX microcomputer. With some modifications, it should also work with other types of computer equipped with a similar "game" input. The use of the joystick port for reading 16 switches is advan-

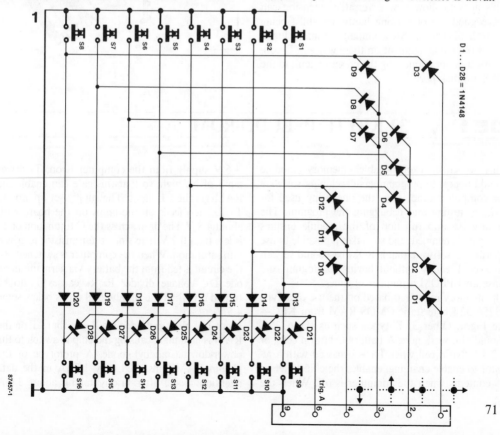

tageous because very little additional hardware is required, and programmers can avail themselves of standard BASIC instructions relating to the joystick.

On MSX computers, the position of the joystick handle is read with the aid of instruction STICK(n), where n is 1 or 2, i.e., the number of the relevant joystick. The instruction returns an integer between 1 and 8, from which the handle position is deduced as shown in Fig. 1. Instruction STRIG(n) enables determining the state of the trigger (fire) button on joystick n, and returns —1 when this is actuated.

A diode matrix is used here to enable connecting eight pushbuttons S_1-S_8 to the four direction inputs on the joystick port. When actuated, either one of these buttons forces a logic low level upon one or two of the input lines, enabling the computer to identify the key number. Eight additional diodes, D_{21}-D_{28}, make it possible to double the number of keys (S_9-S_{16}). These can be kept distinct from the former 8 by connecting them to the trig. A input. The 16 keys are identified in BASIC with the aid of instructions

X = STICK (1) (or X = STICK (2)) and
Y = STRIG (1) (or Y = STRIG (2))
so that the key number is simply
Z = X—(Y*8)+1.

This goes to show how a versatile extension can make good use of existing hardware whilst being controllable with BASIC commands. Finally, Fig. 3 shows the pin assignment on the 9-way sub D connector used for connecting the present circuit to the MSX joystick port.

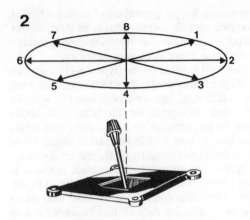

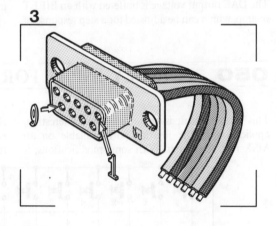

O51   32 KBYTE PSEUDO-ROM

This versatile, exchangeable, memory module should appeal to programmers developing software for computers other than the one being used for writing, testing and debugging the program. The battery back-up function of the module ensures that data is retained, and so makes it possible to use "portable", software that is ROM-based and yet can be altered readily without having to program and erase an EPROM a number of times.

The memory module is based on the use of a Type 43256 32 Kbyte static CMOS RAM from NEC—see Fig. 1. Other 32 K types, such as the 62256, should also work here. A battery (2 button cells, or a 2.4 V NiCd cell when D_1 is bypassed with a resistor to enable charging) enables the chip to retain its contents when the computer is off. When the

+5 V supply from the computer is on, T_1 drives pin 1 of N_5 high, so that this gate can enable the RAM via the $\overline{CE}$ input. The supply set up around T_3-T_2 then feeds all the chips on the board with about 4.8 V. The drop across the C-E junction of T_2 is less than 0.2 V here since the transistor is driven into saturation. When the computer is switched off, the circuit is fed from the battery via germanium diode D_1. Voltage divider R_5-R_6 causes T_1 to be turned off when the supply level drops below some 4.5 V.

Input 1 of N_5 is grounded via R_7, so that $\overline{CE}$ on the RAM is held high, causing the chip to switch to the power-down (standby) mode. A prototype of the plug-in RAM consumed only 1.5 μA in the data retention mode, after briefly taking about 3 mA

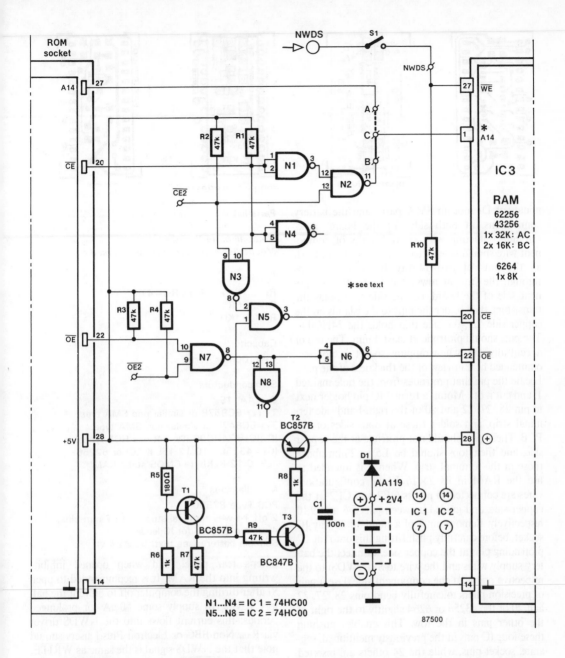

N1...N4 = IC 1 = 74HC00
N5...N8 = IC 2 = 74HC00

87500

when the input voltage dropped from 1.5 to 1 V. This effect is normal, however, and is due to the inputs of the HC gates briefly being in an undefined state. The ICs fitted were Types 74HC00 (SMD) and a 43256C-12L (120 ns).

The module is configured as a 32 Kbyte RAM block by fitting wire jumper A-C, while jumper B-C selects 2 × 16 Kbyte. The latter configuration is required when the socket that receives the module is intended for a maximum memory capacity of 16 Kbyte (ROM or RAM), as on the BBC sideway extension board. A Type 6264 RAM can be used in the IC3 position when only 8 Kbytes are required. Neither jumper need then be fitted.

Successfully constructing the RAM module requires great care in soldering the SMA parts onto the board shown in Fig. 2. It is absolutely necessary to first fit all the SMA parts at both sides of the board, then the three wire links and jumper B-C or A-C as required. Do not forget to solder the ter-

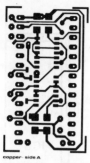
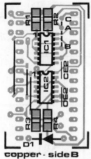
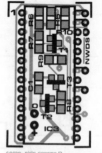

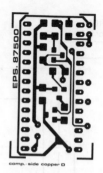

copper- side A   copper- side B   comp.- side copper E   comp.- side copper D

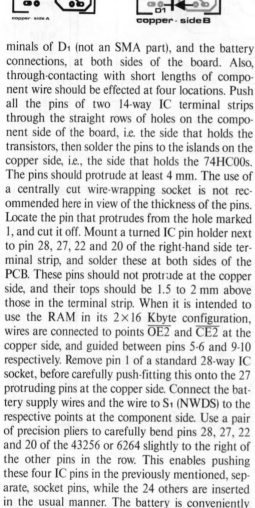

minals of D_1 (not an SMA part), and the battery connections, at both sides of the board. Also, through-contacting with short lengths of component wire should be effected at four locations. Push all the pins of two 14-way IC terminal strips through the straight rows of holes on the component side of the board, i.e. the side that holds the transistors, then solder the pins to the islands on the copper side, i.e., the side that holds the 74HC00s. The pins should protrude at least 4 mm. The use of a centrally cut wire-wrapping socket is not recommended here in view of the thickness of the pins. Locate the pin that protrudes from the hole marked 1, and cut it off. Mount a turned IC pin holder next to pin 28, 27, 22 and 20 of the right-hand side terminal strip, and solder these at both sides of the PCB. These pins should not protrude at the copper side, and their tops should be 1.5 to 2 mm above those in the terminal strip. When it is intended to use the RAM in its 2×16 Kbyte configuration, wires are connected to points $\overline{OE2}$ and $\overline{CE2}$ at the copper side, and guided between pins 5-6 and 9-10 respectively. Remove pin 1 of a standard 28-way IC socket, before carefully push-fitting this onto the 27 protruding pins at the copper side. Connect the battery supply wires and the wire to S_1 (NWDS) to the respective points at the component side. Use a pair of precision pliers to carefully bend pins 28, 27, 22 and 20 of the 43256 or 6264 slightly to the right of the other pins in the row. This enables pushing these four IC pins in the previously mentioned, separate, socket pins, while the 24 others are inserted in the usual manner. The battery is conveniently mounted at some distance from the module. When a miniature battery is available, this can be fitted underneath the RAM chip. For BBC users: wires $\overline{OE2}$ and $\overline{CE2}$ are conveniently connected to pins 22 and 20 respectively of a 28-way IC socket for plugging into the adjacent ROM/RAM socket on the BBC's sideway extension board; the NWDS signal is available at pin 8 of IC_{77}. Switch S_1 is mounted at a convenient location on the com-

Parts list

Note: all parts Surface
Mount Assembly types unless marked +.

Resistors:
$R_1 \ldots R_4$ incl.;R_7;R_9;$R_{10} = 47K$
$R_5 = 180R$
R_6;$R_8 = 1K0$

Capacitor:
$C_1 = 100n$ or $47n$

Semiconductors:
$D_1 = AA119$ +
T_1;$T_2 = BC857B$ or similar pnp SMA type.
$T_3 = BC847B$ or similar npn SMA type.
IC_1;$IC_2 = 74HC00$ (Do **not** use HCT types).
$IC_3 = 43256C-10/12/15L$ (NEC) or 62256
  LP10/12 32Kbyte CMOS static RAM +.

Miscellaneous +:
PCB Type 87500
2 off 14-way terminal strips with 7 mm pins.
4 off turned pins for IC leads.
Suitable battery (see text, $V_b \geqq 2.4$ V)

puter's rear panel, and when opened inhibits writing into the RAM. It is recommended to open S_1 after turning the computer off to prevent the battery having to supply some $50 \mu A$ for prolonged periods: this current flows into the NWDS driver via R_{10}. Non-BBC or Electron Plus-1 users should note that the NWDS signal is the same as $\overline{WRITE}$, not READ/WRITE.

The MOVE command in the ADT ROM available for the BBC computer enables exchanging data between resident and sideway memory. Programmers should have little difficulty, however, in writing a short routine that selects the relevant sideway socket(s) via the socket latch at $FE3F_H$, and copying one or two 16 Kbyte blocks.

Over the past few years, the cost of 5¼ inch floppy disk drives has gone down to the extent that modern, 80-track, double-sided drives now cost less than a simple, 40-track, single-sided type some three years ago. It is, therefore, not surprising to see many computer owners upgrade their systems with a set of 80-track, slim-line drives to boost the mass storage capacity of their micro.

However, 40-track stored programs are not readily retrievable in the new system, because the distance between tracks in the 40-track drive is twice that in the 80-track model.

This circuit offers a solution to the problem, in that it doubles the step distance for the R/W head in the 80-track disk drive, so as to make it "look like" a 40-track type to the computer which should, of course, be programmed with a 40-track disk operating system (DOS).

It is seen from the circuit diagram that Gate N1 receives the FDC controller STEP pulse, which is used in the circuit as a timing reference for the automatic generation of another STEP pulse to follow the first after 3 ms.

It should be noted that, when incorporating the circuit in an 80-track drive, the track-to-track access time in the 40-track mode is double that as given in the drive specifications, which refer to 80-track use.

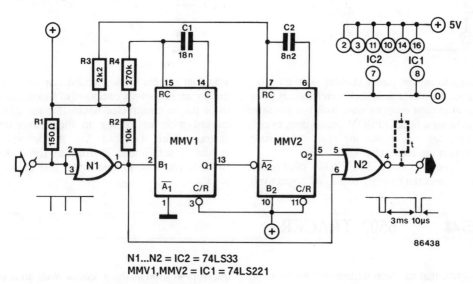

N1...N2 = IC2 = 74LS33
MMV1,MMV2 = IC1 = 74LS221

Thanks to the development of an ever expanding range of capacious EPROMs in the 27xxx and 25xxx series, the Type 2708 has become completely obsolete. Not only is this forerunner in EPROM technology relatively hard to program, it is also expensive in view of its modest 1 Kbyte holding capacity.

It stands to reason that replacement of the 2708 with either the 2716 (2 Kbytes) or the 2732 (4 Kbytes) is most readily accomplished if the differences in pin functions are first taken into consideration.

The pinning overview and associated table go to show quite conclusively that the replacement is no daunting task, since the former positive and negative supply pins to the 2708, 19 and 21 respectively, may be hard wired as suggested for either the 2716 or 2732.

It should be noted that pin 18 ($\overline{CE}$ for the 2716 as well as the 2732) is tied to ground, while pin 20 ($\overline{OE}$) is driven by the computer $\overline{CS}$ signal. This new arrangement is of no consequence for neither EPROM nor computer, since $\overline{OE}$ may function as $\overline{CE}$ if it is realized that the EPROM can not be

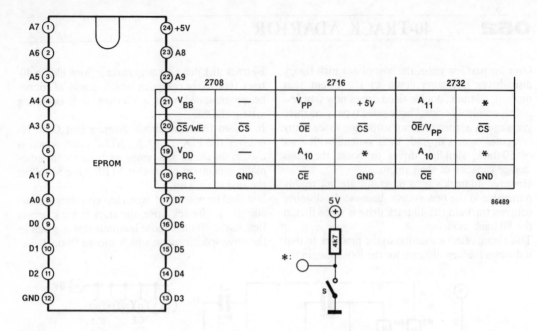

switched to its low power standby state anymore. However, this minor drawback merely causes an increase in current consumption, whilst at the same time offering a faster EPROM access time, as only the three-state bus drivers are enabled internally, rather than the entire chip logic.

As the Type 2716 and 2732 EPROMs offer double and four times the capacity of a 2708, respectively, a manual address block selection may be added to the circuit; this set-up, composed of a switch and resistor (to be constructed double for the 2732) is marked with an asterisk in the accompanying diagram. Wire A_{10} (and A_{11}, if applicable) to ground if you intend to stick to the 1 Kbyte EPROM contents, located in the first 1024 bytes block.

054   6502 TRACER

A program that has been written into an assembler will rarely run error free on the first run. It often exhibits blurbs and other ramblings: in bad cases, there is a complete hang up and it is then necessary to start the computer afresh with a RESET.

To find such faults in a relatively easy manner, the tracer described here will be found very useful.

The circuit layout of the tracer is shown in figure 1. Gate N_1 is an address decoder, whose output in the address range $F000 \ldots $FFFF$ is logic 0. NAND gate N_2 is fed with the SYNC signal from the computer and the 0 signal; it is disabled by either the address decoder, N_1, or bistable FF_2 The address decoder disables N_2 when the EPROM is addressed from the CPU. This prevents the SYNC line of the 6502 processor generating an MI (maskable interrupt). If the processor passes through a machine program somewhere in the RAM, N_2 generates an interrupt as soon as the processor reads an opcode, which makes the SYNC line logic 1. This non-maskable interrupt directs the processor to an interrupt program in the monitor program. All CPU registers are safeguarded by this interrupt program and subsequently displayed on the monitor screen. At the same time, the processor disassembles the next command.

The programmer can, therefore, see beforehand under what conditions the processor starts with the execution of the next opcode. Since the status register and all its flags are also displayed on the screen, the programmer can easily ascertain whether a flag in the status register has been set incorrectly.

Bistable FF_1 serves as a debounce stage; FF_2 toggles on receipt of a leading edge from FF_1: that is, every time S_1 is pressed. When the tracer is

1

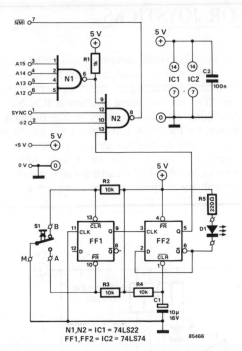

N1,N2 = IC1 = 74LS22
FF1,FF2 = IC2 = 74LS74

85466

Parts list

Resistors:
R_1 = 1 k
$R_2 \ldots R_4$ = 10 k
R_5 = 220 Ω

Capacitors:
C_1 = 10 μ/16 V
C_2 = 100 n

Semiconductors:
D_1 = LED (red)
IC_1 = 74LS22
IC_2 = 74LS74

Miscellaneous:
S_1 = miniature spring-loaded press-to-make switch
S_2 = miniature spring-loaded press-to-make switch (see text)
PCB 85466

2

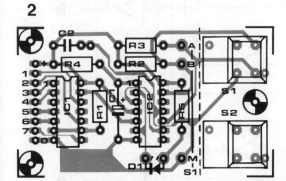
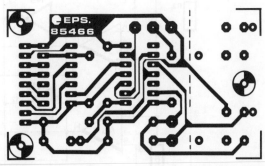

switched on, D_1 lights. Resistor R_4 and capacitor C_1 form a power-on reset network that automatically switches the tracer off when the computer is switched on.

The printed circuit board for the tracer is shown in figure 2. If you want to build the tracer into the computer case, the PCB can be cut along the dashed line, so that the section containing S_1 and S_2 may be fitted in the most convenient position. Switch S_1 must be connected to the tracer via a suitable cable, but S_2 may be connected to the manual RESET of the system.

Although joysticks come in an astounding variety of versions, their internal organization is virtually always a standard concept, based on either a set of relatively fragile, springy, membrane contacts, or two potentiometers. Many computer enthusiasts will agree that the latter, analogue, type offers better reliability and quality. Unfortunately, however, these can not be used in conjunction with a popular home micro such as the Commodore C64, and that is where the present circuit comes in. The four comparators in IC1 function as switches to translate the handle movement into digital signals. The outputs of the comparators are buffered in IC2 to enable interfacing to the computer's joystick port. The two remaining inverters in IC2, N5 and N6, along with two inverters in IC3, function as drivers for the LEDs that indicate the handle position. Gates N9-N12 are set up as a wired NOR function to enable LED D5 to light when the joystick handle is in the centre position. Finally, the current consumption of the converter is about 25 mA.

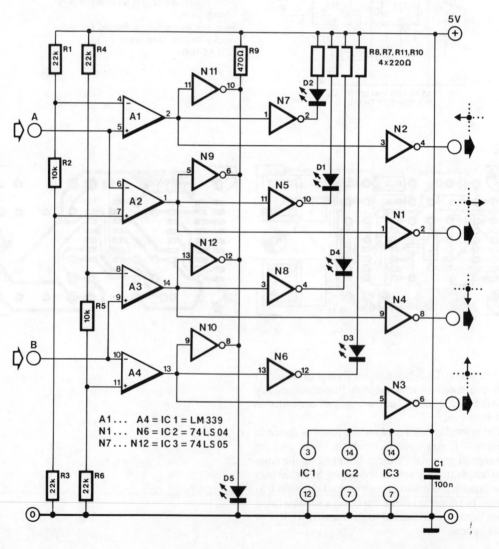

A1 ... A4 = IC1 = LM339
N1 ... N6 = IC2 = 74LS04
N7 ... N12 = IC3 = 74LS05

87417

056 BIDIRECTIONAL PARALLEL INTERFACE FOR C64

The so-called User Port on the Commodore C64 home micro is intended for connecting peripherals such as a modems, RS232 interfaces, and control circuits. In some applications, it is also used for communication with other C64s. This circuit makes it possible to use port lines PB0-PB7 as inputs *and* outputs. Software enables the computer to select between input and output by means of the PA2 line (terminal M). Examples:

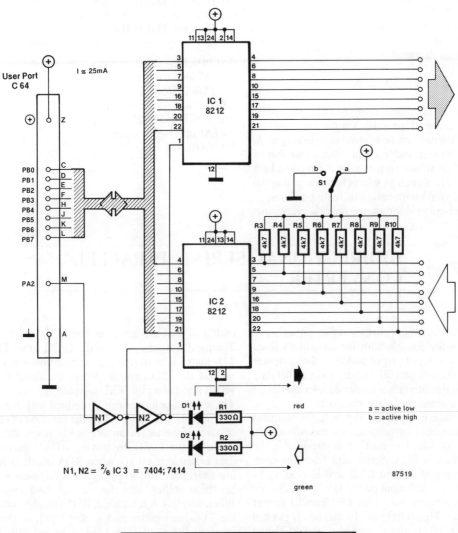

a = active low
b = active high

N1, N2 = ²⁄₆ IC 3 = 7404; 7414

87519

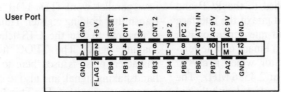

Data input:
```
10 POKE 56579,0
 :REM user port is input.
20 POKE 56576,255
 :REM interface is input.
30 A = PEEK(56577)
 :REM read variable A.
```

Data output:
```
10 POKE 56579,255
 :REM user port is output.
20 POKE 56576,251
 :REM interface is output.
30 INPUT B
 :REM read dataword.
40 POKE 56577,B
 :REM and send to interface.
```

The circuit is essentially composed of 2 three-state octal bus drivers Type 8212. Via the logic level on PA2, each driver can be enabled individually so as to select between the input or output function of the interface, whose current state is indicated by a pair of LEDs. Switch S_1 selects between pull-up (a) or pull-down (b) termination of the input lines.

Finally, an example for interactive data processing:

```
10 POKE 56567,255
 :REM interface is input.
20 POKE 56579,0
 :REM user port is input.
30 A = 255-PEEK(56577)
 :REM read variable A.
100
 :REM example of logic control:

110 IF A = 1 THEN B = 64
111 IF A = 2 THEN B = 128
112 IF A = 4 THEN B = 192
113 IF A = 1 THEN B = 32


300 POKE 56577,B
 :REM load data register
310 POKE 56579,255
 :REM user port is output
320 POKE 56576,251
 :REM interface is output
330 GOTO 10
```

057 BIDIRECTIONAL SERIAL- PARALLEL CONVERTER

This interface circuit enables doing rather more than normally possible with the computer's serial (RS232) port. Serial output data from the computer is converted into parallel format, and parallel data applied to the interface is converted into a serial bit stream for reception by the computer.

The interface is based on the industry standard UART (universal asynchronous receiver/transmitter) Type AY-5-1013, or the CMOS version of it, the CDP1854 from RCA. Serial data from the computer is received at input RXD, and inverted in T_1 for driving the RSI input on the UART, which converts the received word into 8-bit parallel format (RD_0-RD_7). The shifting in of serial bits is clocked by the 19,200 Hz signal applied to the RCP and TCP input. This fixes the baud rate of the interface at 1200 (19,200/16). The baud rate generator is a conventional design based on a binary counter/divider with built-in clock oscillator, which is crystal controlled here and operates at 2.4576 MHz. The parallel output of the UART is buffered with the aid of IC_2 to enable controlling 8 relay drivers B_1-B_8. The parallel word applied to the UART at its TD_0-TD_7 inputs is converted into serial format and output via the TSO terminal, where the signal is inverted and fed to the TXD output.

The serial data format can be defined with the aid of wire links B-F: Table 1 lists the function of each of these. Inverter T_4 automatically resets the receiver in the UART by driving $\overline{RDAR}$ (received data available reset) low when RDA (received data available) goes high to signal that a complete word has been shifted into the receiver hold register. When wire link A is installed, RDA can also control the $\overline{TDS}$ (transmitter data strobe) input, so that a new parallel word (TD_0-TD_7) is loaded into the transmitter holding register. Thus, jumper A makes it possible to use the CTS (clear to send) handshaking signal. The TEOC (transmitter end of character) pulse is used here to generate the RTS handshaking signal, and also to control the $\overline{TDS}$ input, together with CTS. This handshaking input, when active, prompts the UART to output a new serial word. Set-reset bistable N1-N2 precludes conflicts arising between the signals in question. Power-on network C1-R1 ensures that the UART is properly reset and initiated. TSO and TEOC then go high, while RDA is forced low. When link A is not fitted, the presence of the inverted TEOC pulse at input $\overline{TDS}$ causes the transmission process to commence.

The author has developed this circuit mainly to enable two IBM PCs to communicate with the aid of the Turbo Pascal program listed in Table 2. Before this can be run, the status of serial port COM1: (AUX:) should be defined by typing DOS command

MODE COM1:1200,n,8,2 <CR>

(1200 baud, no parity, 8 data bits and 2 stop bits). Pins 6 (DSR) and 20 (DTR) on the 25-way D socket should be interconnected, and the same goes for

pins 4 (RTS) and 5 (CTS) when no handshaking is being used. When it is intended to use the handshaking facility on the bidirectional interface, link A should be removed, and socket pins 4 and 5 connected to interface terminals CTS and RTS respectively.

Table 1		
link	fitted	not fitted
A	no RTS & CTS	RTS & CTS
B	no parity bit	parity bit
C	2 stop bits	1 stop bit
D/E	----- see below-----	
F	even parity	odd parity

D	E	data word
0	0	5 bits
0	1	6 bits
1	0	7 bits
1	1	8 bits

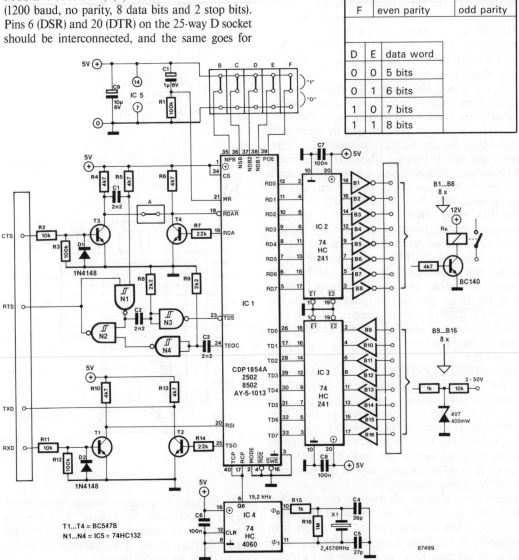

The majority of MSX computers do not require a $\overline{\text{BUSDIR}}$ (bus direction) signal from add-on circuits plugged into slots. A problem arises, however, if the extension circuits published in *Elektor Electronics* are used in conjunction with, for example, a Sanyo MSX machine, which has a few peculiarities in its external I/O concept. In general, the more slots on an MSX computer, the higher the probability that either one of, or both, these circuits are required to be able to use the home-made extensions.

Two solutions are offered to provide for the $\overline{\text{BUSDIR}}$ signal. One is usable for the *Universal I/O Bus* and the *I/O & Timer Cartridge*, the other for the *Cartridge Busboard*. Each of these circuits consists of one IC only.

Circuit A is used with the two I/O extensions, and is readily incorporated in the computer, at a suitable location near the slot that receives the extension. If necessary, all slots on the computer are fitted with this circuit, but this makes it impossible to utilize cartridges that do supply a $\overline{\text{BUSDIR}}$ pulse, unless S_1 is included to disconnect the output of N_4 from slot pin 10. Note, however, that this switch must not be operated when the computer is on.

As I/O range 40_h-FF_h is reserved for the computer-resident hardware, address lines A_6 and A_7 must be low for the selection of external I/O circuitry. Moreover, $\overline{\text{IOREQ}}$ and $\overline{\text{RD}}$ must be low to ensure that BUSDIR is only active when the CPU *reads* data from an I/O device. Interrupts from an external device can only be processed correctly when $\overline{\text{BUSDIR}}$ is low in response to $\overline{\text{M1}}$ and $\overline{\text{IOREQ}}$ being low also. This requires an OR function for logic low levels:

$$\overline{\text{BUSDIR}} = \overline{\text{M1}} \cdot \overline{\text{IOREQ}} + \overline{\text{IOREQ}} \cdot \overline{\text{RD}} \cdot \overline{A7} \cdot \overline{A6}$$

If you are hesitant about opening the computer to install circuit A, you may consider the use of a part of the EPROM cartridge board to hold the 74HCT32 as shown in the accompanying photograph. Note that the 50-way track connector plugs straight into a computer slot, and that a slot connector is fitted at the other side of the "adaptor-PCB" to receive cartridges.

Circuit B is intended for use on the *Cartridge Busboard*. Its function is to pass $\overline{\text{BUSDIR}}$ pulses from cartridges to the computer. To this end, it is necessary to first break the interconnecting tracks between slot pins 10 so as to make all cartridge

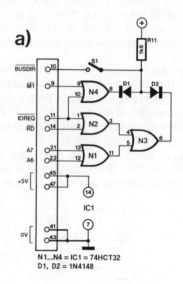

a)

N1...N4 = IC1 = 74HCT32
D1, D2 = 1N4148

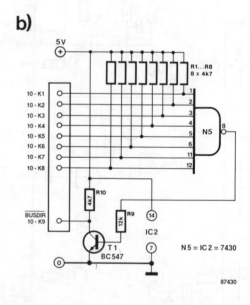

b)

N5 = IC2 = 7430

87430

$\overline{\text{BUSDIR}}$ outputs separately available for wiring to 8-input NAND gate N5. Inverter T_1 turns this simple add-on unit into an 8-input OR gate for logic low levels. The collector of this transistor is wired to pin 10 of K_9 on the busboard.

It may well happen that both circuit A and B are required for a specific I/O arrangement. In that case, it is suggested to fit circuit A on one slot of the *Cartridge Busboard*, and consequently use only that slot for external I/O. Pin 8 of N_4 is then connected direct to the relevant input of N_5.

Note: articles in the series *MSX Extensions* were published in the following issues of *Elektor Electronics*:
January 1986, February 1986,
March 1986, January 1987,
March 1987, April 1987.

059 COMMUNICATION PROGRAM FOR C64

This program enables users of the popular Commodore C64 home computer to exchange messages between two machines.

No hardware whatsoever is needed to accomplish:
- communication over several tens of metres using a three-wire connection—see Fig. 1. Longer distances, or communication over the telephone, of course require the use of a modem.
- split screen operation: the upper half of the screen displays the operator's input (LOCAL), the lower half displays the received messages (REMOTE).
- full duplex communication, i.e. transmission and reception are quasi-simultaneous processes.

The flowcharts in Fig. 2 illustrate the structure of the proposed program. TX is short for transmitter, RX for receiver. Note that screen pointer updating routines are not apparent from these diagrams.

Unfortunately, since the C64 BASIC interpreter does not allow structured programming to be car-

ried out, the constructs shown in the flowcharts are not readily detected in the practical BASIC program listed in Fig. 3.

Keyed-in text is transmitted to the far computer after pressing the RETURN key. The BORDER colour changes to warn the user when the screen is full. Typing errors can be corrected in the usual way with the aid of the INST/DEL key. A short beep is sounded to signal the receipt of a message from the REMOTE computer.

Testing the program is straightforward, and does not require two computers. Figure 4 shows the connections that can be made temporarily on the computer's user port. This creates a zero modem, and causes LOCAL text to be echoed on the REMOTE screen.

For those computer enthusiasts interested in analysing the BASIC program, and for those who intend to rewrite it for other types of computer, the function of the major lines can be summarized as follows:

I (C 64):   II:

1

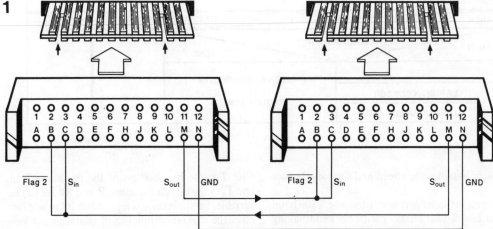

2 ✳ MAIN LOOP

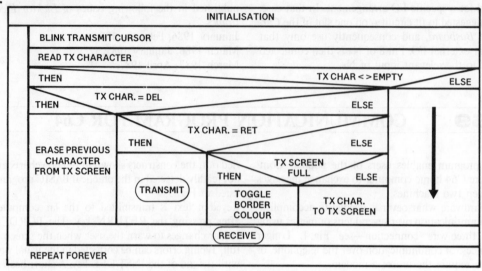

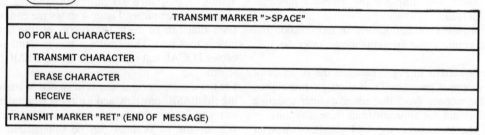

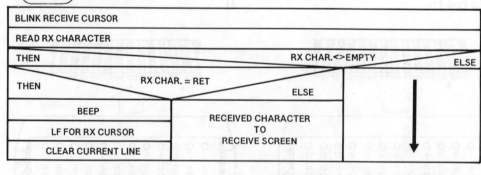

87461-2

100-125: initialize the screen and the sound generator.

130: open the serial port with parameters 300 baud, 8 data bits, 1 stop bit, no parity, no handshaking, full duplex.

140: T is the base address of the transmit screen, and T0 is the associated index. R and R0 are similar variables for the receive screen, while R1 in addition gives the maximum number of character per line.

160: blink the cursor and read the keyboard buffer.

180-200: test for DELETE, and erase the previous character.
210-230: test for RETURN and transmit message.
240-260: toggle the BORDER colour when the screen is full.
270: go to the receive subroutine.
280: repeat the above loop.
710: transmit the "begin of message" marker.
720-750: transmit and erase all characters. Monitor the receive channel for messages, after transmission of every character; reception has the highest priority.
760: transmit the "end of message" marker.
810: blink the cursor and read the receive buffer.
820: buffer empty?
830: end of message.
840: have the sound generator produce a beep.
850-870: advance the cursor to the next line.
880: clear the new line.
900: display received character on REMOTE screen.
910-920: advance cursor to next position.

C64:

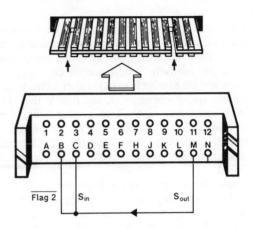

Flag 2   S_in   S_out

3

```
100 POKE53281,12:PRINT"":POKE53280,9:POKE53281,0:PRINT CHR$(152):POKE53272,23
110 SI=54272:POKE 24+SI,15:POKE SI,207:POKE 1+SI,34:POKE 5+SI,10
120 FOR H=1033 TO 1044: READ A: POKE H,A: NEXT H
125 FOR H=1273 TO 1283: READ A: POKE H,A: NEXT H
130 OPEN 2,2,0,CHR$(6)+CHR$(0)
140 T=1104: T0=0: R=1344: R0=0: R1=0
150 REM MAIN
160 POKE T+T0,60: POKE T+T0,32: GET T$
170 IF T$="" THEN GOTO 270
180 IF T$<>CHR$(20) THEN GOTO 210
190 IF T0>0 THEN T0=T0-1
200 POKE T+T0,32: GOTO 270
210 IF T$<>CHR$(13) THEN GOTO 240
220 GOSUB 700
230 GOTO 270
240 IF T+T0>=R-80 THEN GOTO 260
250 POKE T+T0,ASC(T$): T0=T0+1: GOTO 270
260 POKE 53280,1: FOR H=0 TO 15: NEXT H: POKE 53280,9
270 GOSUB 800
280 GOTO 150
700 REM TRANSMIT
710 PRINT#2,CHR$(62);: PRINT#2,CHR$(32);
720 FOR K=T TO T+T0-1
730 PRINT#2,CHR$(PEEK(K));: POKE K,32
740 GOSUB 800
750 NEXT K
760 PRINT#2,CHR$(13);: T0=0
770 RETURN
800 REM RECEIVE
810 POKE R+R0,60: POKE R+R0,32: GET#2,R$
820 IF R$="" THEN GOTO 930
830 IF R$<>CHR$(13) THEN GOTO 900
840 POKE 54276,0: POKE 54276,33
850 IF R1=40 OR R1=0 THEN GOTO 870
860 POKE R+R0,32: R1=R1+1: R0=R0+1: GOTO 850
870 R1=0: IF R+R0=2024 THEN R0=0
880 FOR H=R+R0 TO R+R0+39: POKE H,32: NEXT H
890 GOTO 930
900 POKE R+R0,ASC(R$): R0=R0+1: R1=R1+1
910 IF R1=40 THEN R1=0
920 IF R+R0=2024 THEN R0=0
930 RETURN
950 DATA 42,32,84,82,65,78,83,77,73,84,32,42
960 DATA 42,32,82,69,67,69,73,86,69,32,42
970 END

READY.
```

While many computer enthusiasts are keen on getting their system to run at the highest possible clock speed, there are often quite awkward constraints posed by relatively slow, bus-connected support chips, and the ensuing frustration after failing to get reliable system operation at, say, double the 'old' clock speed may readily lead to abandoning the speed-up project altogether, for lack of precise information regarding the necessary clock-based synchronization between CPU and peripheral chip(s).

A noteworthy example of this happening in practice is the go at incorporation of the Type 9367 CRT controller in a 6502-based computer system running at 2 MHz; the specific application concerns the high-resolution graphics card published in *Elektor Electronics*, November 1985 ff.

This circuit ensures a correctly timed, synchronized slow-down of the system clock speed, when appropriate for CPU access to a memory-mapped (E150-E15F) device. Following the reception of a high level on the relevant $\overline{I/O}$ line, the proposed circuit arranges for the clock signal frequency to be divided by two, while a low $\overline{I/O}$ causes division by four.

It is important to point out why the commonly used method of using $\Phi2$ to enable the address decoder chip is to no avail when it comes to synchronous

and glitch-free clock speed switching under software control; the following paragraphs therefore aim at offering an insight into the basic operation of the gear-box circuit and its incorporation in a 6502-plus-graphics card system.

Figure 1 shows the hardware to the gear-box. A logic level at the $\overline{I/O}$ input is passed to the D (data)input of bistable FF3, as well as to the $\overline{R}$ (reset) input of FF4. FF3 toggles and activates its Q output; this causes the 4 MHz clock signal, divided by two in FF4, to be output as 2 MHz towards the CPU Φ_{in} terminal. Division by four (1 MHz clock output) should take place in a synchronous timing arrangement as soon as $\overline{I/O}$ goes low; just prior to this pulse transition, Φ_{in} has already gone low, so that the level change at the FF4 reset input is of no consequence to the CPU operation at that time, however the bistable can not change state anymore. Thus, FF3 will have to supply the output clock signal; the D input follows the $\overline{I/O}$ signal transitions, since Q of FF2 was forced to go low in consequence of $\overline{S}$ (set) being activated. The first leading edge coming from the FF1 $\overline{Q}$ output will cause Q of FF3 to go logic high, ending the set condition of FF2. Given an input clock frequency of 4 MHz, the outlined timing sequence results in $\overline{Q}$ of FF2 going high after 250 ns, followed by a low

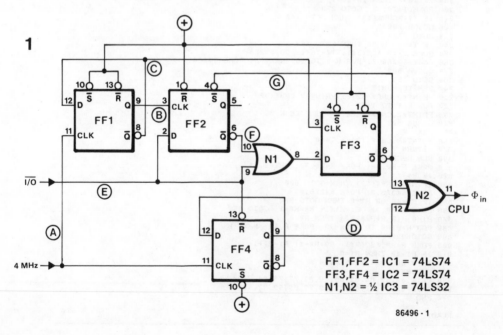

1

FF1,FF2 = IC1 = 74LS74
FF3,FF4 = IC2 = 74LS74
N1,N2 = ½ IC3 = 74LS32

86496 - 1

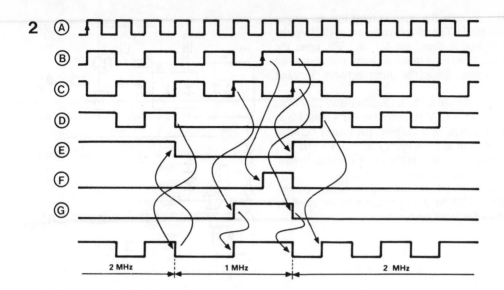

2

Ⓐ
Ⓑ
Ⓒ
Ⓓ
Ⓔ
Ⓕ
Ⓖ

2 MHz   1 MHz   2 MHz

level at $\overline{Q}$ of FF₃ after another 250 ns. The timing diagram shown in Fig. 2 clarifies this, admittedly rather complicated, timing arrangement in the gearbox circuit. It is noted that a complete 1 MHz period has lapsed, provided FF₁ is properly synchronized during the CPU initialisation cycle. Theoretical research into this matter, however, has shown that this is not always the case; the result is an asymmetrical output clock period with a logic low and high level duration of 250 and 500 ns respectively. The remedy for this undesirable effect is simple, since it merely involves interchanging the clock signal connections to FF₂ and FF₃.

It is seen that Φ2-based $\overline{I/O}$ decoding is less desirable, since it involves too long a delay; what remains is to indicate the method of obtaining $\overline{I/O}$

from the graphics card system (EE, November 1985, p. 71).

$\overline{XX5X}$ is dismissed for now obvious reasons, but $\overline{P=Q}$ at pin 19 of IC₁ can be used for our purpose, while the possible objections to the resultant, rather coarse address decoding are readily rendered devoid of relevance by the incorporation of a single 3-to-8 decoder Type 74LS138, mounted piggy-back onto IC₂ and connected direct to pins 1...5, 16 and 8. The remaining pins of the additional IC are either cut off or bent to preclude wrong contacts from being made in the circuit. However leave pins 6 and 10 in function, since the former should be tied permanently to +5V (small wire to pin 16), while the latter can now be used to supply the correct $\overline{I/O}$ pulse for the CPU gear-box.

061   CURRENT LOOP FOR MODEM

A modem, such as the *direct-coupled modem* featured in the October 1984 issue of *Elektor Electronics*, opens a whole new world to the computer user by making possible communication between two computers anywhere in the world (provided, of course, they can be coupled to a telephone line). Ironically, although the distance between the computers may be very large, that between computer and modem is strictly limited. This is because the RS 232 input is voltage driven and is, therefore, very susceptible to noise. This is not a new problem: it existed many years ago when, for instance, two

telex machines had to be interconnected. The solution then found, and still in use today, is the current loop. Such a current loop can also be used when the distance between the modem and the computer is relatively large: up to 1 km.

A current loop so used converts RS 232 compatible voltages into RS 232 compatible currents. The standard in the RS 232 protocol is a current loop of 20 mA.

In view of the arrangement of the circuit it is possible for the current loop to be used as a voltage driven input and output. In the receiver, the opto-isolator converts the input current into an output voltage via T_1. The output voltage is ± 12 V. As the current loop is closed via V^+ and V^-, mind the polarity. If you want to use an input voltage instead of a current, apply the input between V^- and earth.

The input voltage to the transmitter may vary from TTL level to ± 12 V. Its output signal is available as either a voltage or a current: the former between V^+ and earth and the latter between V^+ and V^-. Current consumption in the quiescent state is zero; with full load, it amounts to 20 mA.

The maximum bit rate at which the circuit operates reliably is 1200 baud, but this can be increased by the use of a faster opto-isolator.

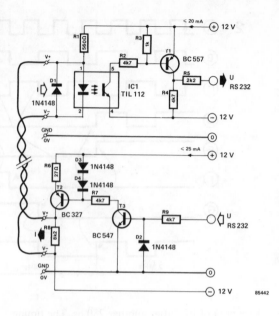

---

062   DIRECT READING DIGITIZER

The computer to which this digitizer is coupled reads a 3-digit number that is a direct representation of the measured voltage in millivolts.

The analogue-to-digital converter is an RCA type CA3162, which was designed for use in a 3-digit digital voltmeter. The input range of the IC stretches from —99 mV to 999 mV: the resolving power is, therefore, 1098 units. In other words, this converter offers a resolving power that is better than that of a standard 10-bit device for the price of an 8-bit device.

The 3-digit information at the output of the 3162 is multiplexed. The data can, for instance, be written into the micro via seven PIA (peripheral interface adapter) input lines. That means, however, that some machine language is required to be loaded into the RAM every time the converter is to be used. The present circuit uses hardware to obviate this difficulty.

The 3-digit information, which is emitted every 20 ms, is automatically loaded into three 4-bit buffers, IC_8, IC_9, and $\frac{1}{2}IC_{10}$, whose outputs are connected direct to the data bus. Each of these buffers has its own address. Writing the converted value into the computer has become simply a matter of reading the three memory locations, which can be carried out by PEEKs in BASIC.

The address decoder consists of $IC_3 \ldots IC_5$ and IC_7. The present circuit occupies a block of eight ad-

dresses of which only the first four are used. When the first address is read, monostable IC_{11} is started, which causes IC_1 to commence the conversion process. When the monostable returns to its stable state, IC_1 goes to the HOLD mode, and the measured voltage can be read.

An interval of not less than 50 ms is required between the start of the conversion process and the reading of the buffers.

The eight successive memory locations required for the digitizer may be placed anywhere in the memory range by means of the open inputs of gates $N_5 \ldots N_{16}$. If any of these inputs is connected to +5 V, the relevant address line becomes logic 1; if the input is linked to 0 V, the address line goes logic low.

Assuming that the decoding has been set to address $E300, the first address is read with a PEEK, which starts the conversion.

Wait for 50 ms.

Write the data from address $E301, which is the least significant bit (LSB), i.e., the extreme right-hand digit of the 3-digit number. Then write $E302 and finally $E303. At each of these transfers, an AND action must by carried out with 00001111 (binary) or 15 (decimal), because only the four lowest data bits are of import.

If the converted voltage during the further processing of the three written digits is negative, this is indi-

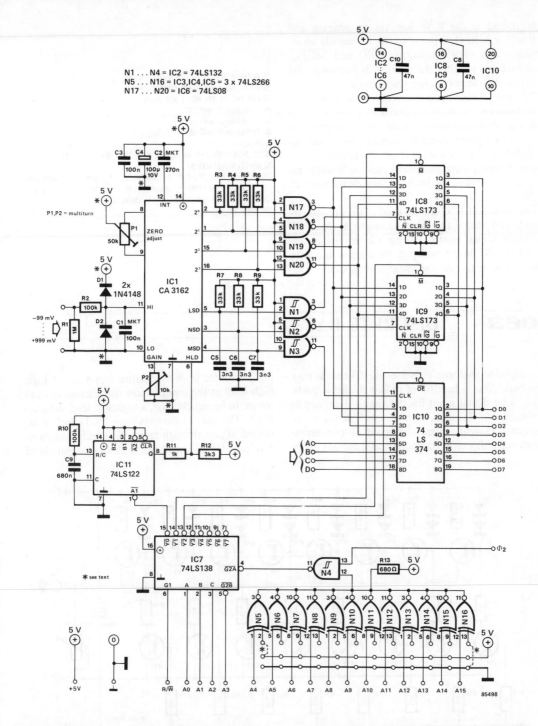

N1 ... N4 = IC2 = 74LS132
N5 ... N16 = IC3,IC4,IC5 = 3 x 74LS266
N17 ... N20 = IC6 = 74LS08

cated by the data at address $E303, which is 10. Overflow is also easily recognized: if the value read from address $E301 is 11, the voltage is greater than 999 mV; if the value is 10, there is a negative overflow.

The small BASIC program given here is an example of a possible conversion routine for the Junior computer.

The circuit as shown can be used with a 6502 μP; if it is required to be used with a Z80, $\overline{RD}$ must be

89

connected to the R/W̄ line via an inverter, and IORQ or MREQ is put onto the Ø2 line via an inverter. The choice between IORQ and MREQ depends on whether the digitizer is located in the I/O or the memory range respectively.

Take care during the construction to keep the connections marked with an asterisk (0 V and +5 V to IC₁) as short as possible. These lines go together to C₃ and C₄, from where the connection is made to the 0 V and +5 V lines of the digital part of the circuit. Keeping these lines short prevents possible interaction between the analogue and digital parts of the circuit.

Four inputs of IC₁₀ are not used in the present circuit, and they can, therefore, serve as four additional digital inputs. During the reading of address $E303 (in the example), the highest four data bits indicate the state of these four inputs.

```
10 A=14%16^3+3%16^2: REM ADDRESS $E300
20 B=PEEK(A): REM START CONVERSION
30 FOR T=1 TO 15: NEXT: REM DELAY
40 X=PEEK(A+1) AND 15
50 Y=PEEK(A+2) AND 15
60 Z=PEEK(A+3) AND 15
70 S=1
80 IF Z=10 THEN Z=0: S=-S: REM SIGN IS NEGATIV IF Z=10
90 AD=S%(100%Z+10%Y+X)
100 IF X=11 THEN PRINT " POS.OVERFLOW "; CHR$(13);: GOTO 130
110 IF X=10 THEN PRINT " NEG.OVERFLOW "; CHR$(13);: GOTO 130
120 PRINT "   U=";AD;" mV       "; CHR$(13);
130 GOTO 10
```

063 DISCRETE DAC

A digital-to-analogue converter (DAC) that is easy to build from a handful of readily available parts. The 8-bit digital input for the circuit is applied to resistors R₁₇-R₂₄ incl., each of which drives an associated current source composed of two series-connected diodes, a transistor and a current defin-

ing resistor fed from the positive supply rail. A logic high level at the input causes the relevant current source to be switched on, a logic low level switches it off. The sum of currents from T₁-T₈ incl. is arranged to pass through preset P₁, which thus drops a voltage U₀ in accordance with the magnitude of

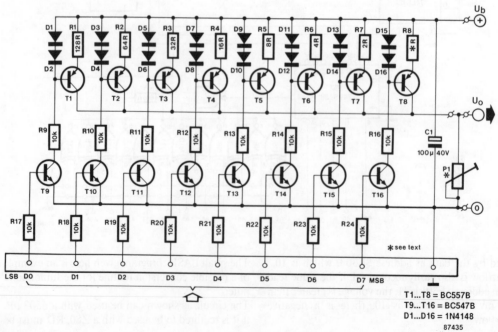

T1...T8 = BC557B
T9...T16 = BC547B
D1...D16 = 1N4148
87435

the 8-bit word written to the circuit.

The current supplied by each current source is about $700/R_x$ [mA], where R_x is the value of the associated resistor between the emitter and the $+V$ rail. In order to ensure satisfactory linearity of the analogue output voltage, resistors R_1-R_8 incl. must be dimensioned to obtain a current ratio of 1:2 between any two adjacent sources. In practice, it is wise to first apply a logic high voltage to the MSB (most significant bit) input of the circuit, leaving the remaining inputs low, and measure U_o with the aid of a good-quality voltmeter. Next, drive D_6 high and all other inputs low, and make sure that U_o drops to half the previously obtained level by dimensioning R_7 as required. The other current determining resistors are similarly established; the value of R_1-R_8 incl. that gives the correct level of U_o is obtained by making suitable combinations of series and/or parallel connected high stability resistors. Alternatively, it is possible to use multi-turn presets. As all resistors R_1-R_7 incl. must be dimensioned starting from a particular value of R_8, this resistor must first be calculated considering that the output linearity of the circuit is affected unless

$$1.4P_1/R_8 < |U_{bl}| - 2$$

In practice, the maximum feasible level of U_o is about $\frac{1}{2}U_b - 1$ [V] with only MSB high, and this level should be observed in the dimensioning of R_8 and the setting of P_1

Although this 8-bit DAC should be sufficiently accurate for most practical applications, it is of course possible to opt for a greater or smaller number of current sources with a corresponding increase or decrease in the available resolution of U_o.

064   DRIVE SELECTOR

This circuit makes it possible to use double-sided disk drives with a computer that supports only single-sided units. Many of the older generation of computers were designed to operate in conjunction with Shugart-compatible, single-sided disk drives. These have rapidly been superseded, however, by the more economical double-sided drive, which has a greater storage capacity.

The Shugart standard supports the use of four disk drives, which are selected with drive select lines $\overline{DS0}$-$\overline{DS3}$. Two further lines, $\overline{HS0}$ and $\overline{HS1}$, control the head selection on each of these drives. When this circuit is installed between the computer's disk controller output and two double-sided drives, the disk operating system (DOS) can recognize four logical drives. When the computer selects drive A or B, the situation is similar to before the conversion. Selection of drive C or D, however, causes the second head in the relevant drive A or B to be ac-

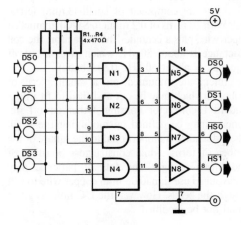

N1...N4 =   IC1 = 74LS08, 74HCT08
N5...N8 = ⅔ IC2 = 7407

87445

Table 1

logical drive		DS3 DS2 DS1 DS0			DS0 DS1 HS0 HS1		physical drive
A (1)	=	1 1 1 0	→	0 1 0 1	=	A side 0
B (2)	=	1 1 0 1	→	1 0 0 1	=	B side 0
C (3)	=	1 0 1 1	→	0 1 1 0	=	A side 1
D (4)	=	0 1 1 1	→	1 0 1 0	=	B side 1

tivated. In this way, the total storage capacity of the double-sided drives is available even under "primitive" circumstances.

Note that the use of drive denotations A-B-C-D or 0-1-2-3 is particular to the type of computer, or the DOS version. Finally, Table 1 provides information about the combination of the original four $\overline{DS}$ lines into two $\overline{HS}$ and two $\overline{DS}$ lines.

065   FILTERED CONNECTOR

Computers and computer-driven peripherals are notorious sources of RF interference, and receiver jamming may occur at frequencies well above 100 MHz, even though the computer is said to run at a mere 16 MHz or so. The cause of this problem lies in the very fast pulse rise time of the switching and timing signals internal and/or external to the computer system and its peripherals, which are often located well away from one another (printer, modem, mass storage).

Much of the interference originating from long peripheral wiring systems may be suppressed quite effectively by inserting simple low-pass filters in the signal lines for data and handshaking. The proposed L-C filters are composed of small (3 mm) ferrite beads with 10 turns of 0.2 mm (36 SWG) enamelled copper wire, plus a ceramic 1 nF capacitor; the coil inductance is about 80 μH, which gives a cut-off frequency of about 60 kHz (120 Kbaud).

The filters are mounted on a small piece of veroboard which may be cut and filed to fit into a standard D-connector housing. Other cut-off frequencies may be defined by modifying the small coils; inductance is proportional to the square of the number of turns, while constructors boasting of good (near) eyesight and lots of patience may endeavour to use thin (0.05 mm) copper wire to run through the beads. However, the L-C ratio as given should not be modified.

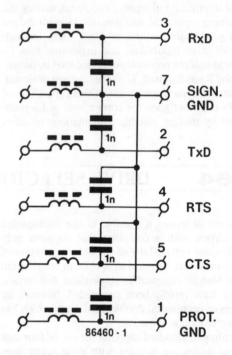

In conclusion, it should be noted that a filtered connector dimensioned for, says 10 kHz, should not be connected to a high frequency (20 MHz) computer output, since the excessively high capacitive load may cause damage to the line driver IC.

066   FLOPPY CENTRING UNIT

In modern disk drive mechanisms, as, for instance, the TEAC FD55x, the motor starts automatically when a disk is inserted into the drive. When the lid is closed, the motor stops again. This arrangement ensures better centring of the disk. Better centring means less wear on the centre fixing hole, the life of the disk is extended, and read/write errors owing to eccentricity off the disk are prevented.

Owners of older drive mechanisms, such as the BASF 6106, can incorporate that facility with the circuit proposed here. The signal from the write protect phototransistor is used to determine when a disk is being inserted (this signal is normally gated when the drive is closed), and to start the motor for the total period of monostable MMV1. The SPEED signal is not absolutely necessary: it stops the motor direct when the lid is closed. If it is not used, pin 3 must be connected to the +5 V line.

The motor will then run for the duration of the period of MMV1, i.e., about 10 s. The monostable period can be reduced by lowering the value of the capacitor.

The points where to connect the circuit in the 6106 are easy to find. Looking at the pcb from the front, you will see a cut-out in the front centre of the board. Immediately to the left of this are three ICs (see photograph). The one at the front is a 7474, the one in the middle a 7432, and the one at the back a 7404. The signal SPEED is taken from pin 6 of the 7474, and the signal DI from pin 2 of the 7404. The signal MOTOR ON is applied to pin 3 of the 7404. As all existing connections remain, the connecting wires of the auxiliary circuit can be soldered direct to the relevant IC sockets. In the same way, it is possible to derive the supply voltage for the auxiliary circuit: for instance, + 5 V from pin 14 of the 7404, and 0 V from pin 7 of this IC.

It is important to note that there are two types of pcb used in 6106 drives: the ICs and the IC function are the same in both versions, but the construction may look different.

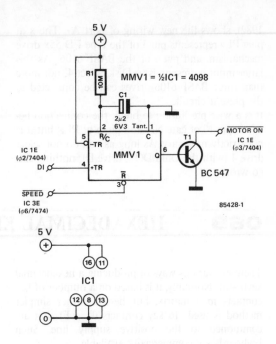

067   FLOPPY DISK DRIVE

This is a much simplified version of the circuit published in the April 1984 issue of *Elektor Electronics*, but it is, unfortunately, not usable with all disk drive motors.

First, a recap of the operation. The drive motors are switched on when one of the drives is accessed by a DISK SELECT signal. There is a delay of a few index pulses before access proper to give the motor speed time to stabilize. A few seconds after all the drives have been deselected, the motor is switched off. This arrangement reduces operation of the drive mechanisms, the heads, and the disks to a minimum, which ensures a longer life of these devices.

In contrast to the earlier published article, the READY output of the drive mechanism is used, wherein lies the reason that the older circuit cannot be as compact and simple as the present one: it has to take into consideration that not all drive mechanisms have this output. However, as far as we can find out, most drive mechanisms do have it, but there must be some, of course, that do not.

Figure 1, which is part of the circuit of the *floppy controller board (Elektor Electronics*, November

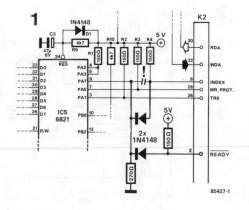

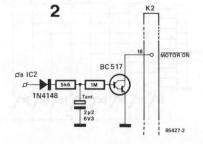

93

1982), shows the new wiring of port A7. The x at plug PL2 represents pin 3 of the type FD-55x drive mechanism, and pin 6 of the BASF 6106. As this latter input corresponds to Disk Select 4, not more than three BASF 6106 drives can be connected to the present circuit.

It is a wise precaution to break the connection between pin 10 of gate N25 and pin 6 of PL2, but it is not strictly necessary. As long as you do not select drive 4 (with the Ohio DOS, drive D), nothing can go wrong.

One connection that must be broken is that between pin 16 of PL2 and earth. Instead, pin 16 must be connected to pin 8 of IC2 as shown in figure 2. If you are really a dab hand at soldering, you may be able to make the changes, with the appropriate lengths of wire, on the relevant printed circuit board. Most of you will, however, find it much easier to use a 15x20 mm piece of veroboard, which after completion can be glued or screwed on short spacers underneath C16 on the floppy controller board.

068   HEXADECIMAL KEYBOARD

There are various ways of producing a hexadecimal keyboard. Normally, it is based on a number of key contacts in a matrix, but here a rather simpler method is used: 16 key contacts (0...F) that are commoned to the positive supply line. Such keyboards are commercially available.

Code conversion is carried out by two priority encoders, IC3 and IC4. If one of the inputs I0...I7 of these ICs is connected to the positive supply line via

one of the contacts S1...S16, i.e., made logic high, the relevant binary code appears at the associated output, Q0...Q2, of which Q0 is the least significant bit (LSB). As the encoders are cascaded, there is a total of 16 inputs.

Corresponding outputs of the encoders are combined in OR gates N6...N8 to form the lowest three output bits D0...D2. the fourth data bit is taken from the GS (group select) output of IC4. This

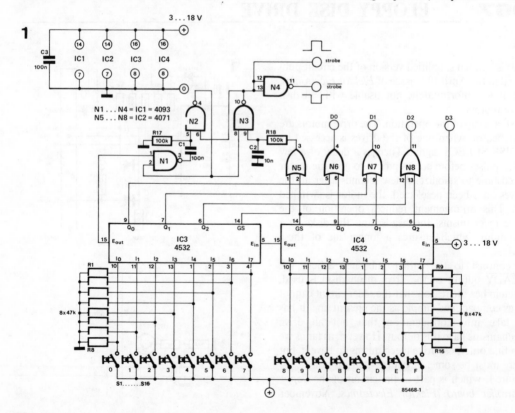

output is logic high when one of key contacts S9...S16 (8...F) is closed.

As the GS outputs of the two ICs are combined in OR gate N5, D3 is active high when a key is pressed. The signal at pin 9 of N3 is delayed by R_{18}-C_2. At the same time, the signal at pin 15 of IC3 triggers monostable N1-N2. During the pulse period of about 10 ms, pin 8 of N3 is logic low so that, independent of the delayed signal at pin 9, the output of N3 remains logic high. If pin 9 of N3 is still high when the pulse begins to decay, the output of N3 goes low and remains so until pin 9 becomes logic 0 again. During this time, pin 6 of N2 remains low, so that the monostable cannot be triggered erroneously. The timing diagram in figure 2 further clarifies the operation, which results in a debounced strobe or strobe pulse.

If more than one key is pressed, the highest is selec-

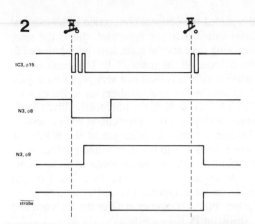

ted, as is to be expected from a priority encoder! The circuit requires a power supply of 3...18 V: current ccnsumption is not greater than 10 mA.

069 IMPROVED SOUND FOR THE BBC MICRO

Despite the many laudable qualities of the BBC microcomputer as to speed and ease of peripheral interfacing, many users are slightly disappointed with the sound quality of the standard version as manufactured by the Acorn company. An investigation into this matter has revealed that Acorn have

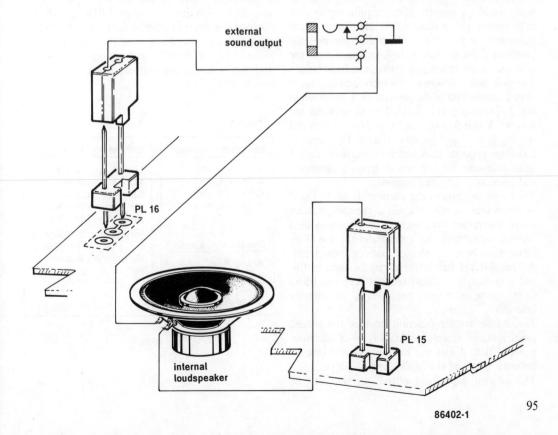

external sound output

PL 16

internal loudspeaker

PL 15

disregarded the optional connection of an external audio amplifier to the computer; this is the more surprising since special holes have been provided to this purpose on the main PCB. The result of this omission manifests itself in a very poor sound quality, caused by the small loudspeaker in the cabinet, the high noise level of the improperly driven audio amplifier chip, and the rather coarse volume setting. However, a minor modification to the BBC computer is sufficient to boost its sound production by means of an external, more powerful audio amplifier which may be connected to a sound output socket on the computer. Proceed as follows:

1. Open up the computer, remove the keyboard and the main PCB.
2. Locate the PCB holes for plug 16, to the left of IC7, the Type LM386 audio amplifier chip.
3. Use desoldering braid to open up the holes for plug 16, if these are filled with solder.
4. Cut off the centre pin of a three-pin, 0.1 inch pitch single row PCB header, and solder it in the holes provided for plug 16.
5. Mount a 3.5 mm jack-type audio socket with a breakcontact at the rear side of the computer, and wire P$_{16}$, P$_{15}$, and the internal loudspeaker as shown in Fig. 1.
6. Reassemble the computer and test the new audio output by connecting an external amplifier set to the jack socket. Insertion of the jack plug should silence the internal loudspeaker.

Now that we are on the subject of the BBC computer, it is just as well to give a few hints concerning reduction of the total power consumption of the computer. The Type 6522 VIA chips may be replaced with their new CMOS equivalents 65C22 to reduce the total current consumption by some 240mA. The 6850 chip may also be replaced with a 6350, but this is a riskier matter since the former chip is soldered direct onto the PCB.

O70   JOYSTICK ADAPTOR

Some popular computer games require the joystick to be turned 45° in order to get the correct cursor movement on the screen. Obviously, this presents problems if the joystick is desk mounted or of the type that is ergonomically styled and hand-held.

The electronic solution to this inconvenience starts from a redefinition of the joystick axes, as shown in Fig. 2. Direction A is defined as in between the positive X and Y axes; direction D as in between the negative X and positive Y axes. Directions C and B are opposite to A and B respectively. Table 1 summarizes the old and new direction assignments and associated activated outputs.

The circuit diagram of the adaptor circuit — Fig. 2 — shows that the output levels to the computer are active low rather than high as in the unmodified joystick connection; this necessitates the use of inverter gates between adaptor and computer input. A Type 74LS04 hex inverter may be used to this end, and the trigger (fire) function(s) can also be inverted at the same time, since this IC contains six inverters.

The double trigger function enables the turned joystick to be connected to MSX types of computer as well. Table 2 lists the relevant connections for both the C64 and the MSX computer type.

The adaptor input and output signals may be visualized with red and green LEDs, clearly indicating the electronic signal turn over 45°. When the joystick is moved into direction A, for instance, input LED $+Y$ lights, as well as output LEDs $+Y$ and $+X$. Current consumption of the adaptor circuit is about 75 mA.

Table 1

Direction	Contact
A →	+X and +Y
B →	+X and −Y
C →	−X and −Y
D →	−X and +Y

Direction	Contact
A and B →	+X
B and C →	−Y
C and D →	−X
D and A →	+Y

Table 2

CBM64	MSX
(1) +Y	(1) +Y
(2) −Y	(2) −Y
(3) −X	(3) −X
(4) +X	(4) +X
(5) −	(5) +5V
(6) trigger	(6) trigger 1
(7) +5V	(7) trigger 2
(8) ground	(8) output
(9) −	(9) ground

1

D1 ... D4 — 220Ω each, green LEDs
N15, N16, N17, N18

D5 ... D8 — 220Ω each, red LEDs

A
B
C
D

N1, N2, N3, N4
N5, N6, N7, N8
N11, N12, N13, N14

+Ȳ
+X̄
−Ȳ
−X̄

E — N9
F — N10

Ē
F̄

1k2 1k2 1k2 1k2 3k9 3k9

86445 · 1

N1...N4 = 74LS02
N5...N10 = 74LS04
N11...N14 = 74LS38
N15...N18 = 74LS05

2

+5 V

+y
D   A
−x   +x
C   B
−y

1 2 3 4 5
6 7 8 9

---

071   LEVEL ADAPTOR FOR ANALOGUE JOYSTICK

An analogue joystick usually contains two potentiometers, whose wipers are controlled from the central handle on the unit. Unfortunately, the angle covered by the handle is generally only about 90°, whereas the potentiometer's spindle and wiper can be rotated over 270°. The voltage range provided by a potentiometer in a joystick is, therefore, relatively small. Two of the circuits described here make it possible to enlarge the output voltage range of both potentiometers in the joystick. The circuit is readily doubled, thanks to the use of dual CMOS operational amplifier Type TLC272.

Each of the two wiper voltages from the joystick is processed separately, which enables interesting effects to be achieved. The amplification of the circuit is determined by P3. This preset enables the enlarging of the potentiometer's "range" to individual requirements. Preset P2 serves to shift the operative range of the potentiometer within the limits of the supply voltage, which may lie between 3 and 16 V. Setting up this circuit is straightforward. Commence with setting P3 for minimal resistance, i.e., A1 should give unity gain. Set the joystick handle to its centre position, so that the wiper of P1 is at mid-travel. Adjust P2 to make the output voltage of the circuit equal to ½Vdd. Move the joystick

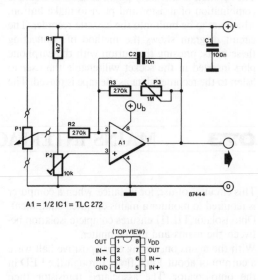

A1 = 1/2 IC1 = TLC 272

(TOP VIEW)

OUT	1	8	VDD
IN−	2	7	OUT
IN+	3	6	IN−
GND	4	5	IN+

87444

handle to the outer positions in the relevant plane, and note the corresponding output voltages from the circuit. Adjust P3 such that the circuit outputs the required voltage span. The adjustment of P2 enables changing the toggle point of the circuit, that is, the voltage it outputs when the joystick handle is set to its centre (rest) position.

The current consumption of the circuit depends on the supply voltage level, and also on the value of P_1. When $V_{dd} = 5$ V, and $P_1 = 4K7$, the current drain is less than 10 mA. The Type TLC272 was chosen because it works fine from a single supply voltage, and also because it has an extensive input voltage range, 0 to $V_{dd} - 1.5$ V.

072   LISTEN-IN KEY FOR DATA RECORDERS

The pros and cons of using data (cassette) recorders for mass memory storage in a computer system are likely to be so well-known that any further discussion as to the relative cost efficiency of the cassette tape would seem to be superfluous.

There is, however, one distinct disadvantage to the data recorder that is relatively easy to get rid of, viz. the trouble many users experience in positioning the tape to the leader note of the desired program or file to load into the computer. Many datarecorders, while offering the highest possible save and load speed, fail to produce the sound on tape when the computer audio cable is plugged into the earphone socket, forcing the user to plug and unplug this cable in a desperate search for the program.

The solution to this sorry plight consists of a simple combination of resistor and push to make button, which are to be built into the cassette recorder. The circuit diagram shows the method of connecting these parts; pressing the button with the earphone plug inserted in the socket will enable the user to listen to the recorded data as the tape is played. The

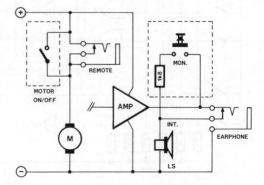

value of the resistor may have to be adapted to suit the specific output power of the data recorder, given the optimum playback level for the computer.

Now that you have opened the recorder for the outlined modification, it is just as well to mount a second button enabling tapes to be wound and played while the remote control plug rests inserted in the associated socket; this simple modification may also be of appreciable interest for the improved efficiency in locating files on tape.

073   MAINS INTERFACE

This circuit is of use, for instance, when a computer is required to monitor a mains-operated equipment. Opto-isolator TIL111 ensures complete isolation between the mains and the computer.

With the mains on, during every positive half-wave a current of about 1 mA flows through the LED in the opto-isolator. The associated transistor then conducts and its collector current of about 100 μA is sufficient to drive T_1. Remember, however, that this is a pulsating current: capacitor C_1 ensures that T_1 conducts continuously as long as the mains is on. If a 50 Hz square wave is required at the collector of T_1, C_1 should, of course, be omitted.

The two 100 k resistors in series with the LED

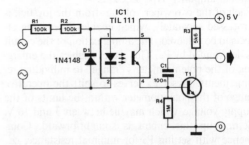

should not be replaced by one 220 k resistor, because the maximum permissible voltage drop across a standard ¼ W resistor should not exceed 150 V_{rms}.

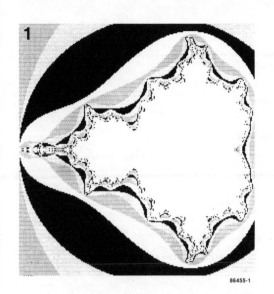

86455-1

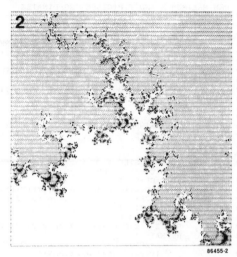

86455-2

The computer-based implementation of certain iterative types of calculation may offer highly attractive graphics screen representations, as we got to know when keying in a program to crunch a few numbers in the Mandelbrot series, and found that doing so with the support of the computer's graphics facilities took us through a regular graphics adventure. On further investigation, it was found that the degree of complexity of the resultant graphics image is in direct proportion with the number of iterative steps the control program is arranged to perform. However, since the necessary calculations to obtain a Mandelbrot series become the more complex, and therefore time consuming, as the computer crunches through its approximations and evaluations, it should not strike the programmer as odd that obtaining a nicely detailed graphics image may take as long as 12 to 24 hours, even with the fastest types of personal or semi-professional types of computer, such as the BBC equipped with a second processor.

The Mandelbrot series of numbers is basically obtained with the use of complex numbers, in a calculation that converges rather than diverges the intermediary results according to the equation $Z=Z^2+C$, where C is the complex number constant having a real part between —2 and 1, while the imaginary part ranges between —1.5i and 1.5i; Z is the result of the preceding calculation.

Stepping through a section of the series is possible by assigning start values and/or differently dimensioned step rates to either the real or the imaginary part of C. It goes without saying that calculation time and image resolution increase with the number of iterations used for obtaining results in accordance with the set requirements; the calculations may be stopped when the result is larger than 2. The colour assigned to any pixel on the screen depends on the number of iterative steps required to satisfy the Mandelbrot equation; if this is not the case, the iteration loop is consequently aborted.

The program shown in Listing 1 has been written for the Electron or BBC computer, and arranges for 15 iterative steps; the screendump of Figure 1 shows the result. Figure 2 illustrates how a section of the graphics image is enlarged by means of relevant redefinition of the equation variables, as outlined above. Obviously, the suggested program allows a good deal of further patching and experimenting to arrive at even more attractively styled graphics designs, but it should be pointed out that producing Fig. 2 took our BBC no less than . . . 2 days!

Listing 1.

```
>L.
    10 REM MANDELBROT
    20 MODE 1
    30 REM MAXIMUM X AND Y PICTURE COORDINATES
    40 MAX%=200:REM MAX%<700
    50 VDU23,1,0;0;0;0;:REM CURSOR OFF
    60 VDU19,2,2,0,0,0: REM GREEN FOR YELLOW
    70 REM DEFINE DISPLAY WINDOW AT CENTRE OF SCREEN
    80 VDU24,640-MAX%/2;512-MAX%/2;640+MAX%/2;512+MAX%/2;
    90 VDU29,640-MAX%/2;512-MAX%/2;
   100 REM DEFINE TEXT DISPLAY AT BOTTOM OF SCREEN
   110 VDU28,0,31,39,28
   120 REM DEFINE ANGLE AT BOTTOM LEFT. ANGLE=AngleR+AngleIi
   130 AngleR=-2: AngleI=-1.25
   140 REM LENGTH OF SIDE IN COMPLEX SURFACE
   150 Side=2.5
   160 REM DISTANCE BETWEEN TWO POINTS IN COMPLEX SURFACE
   170 Distance=Side/MAX%
   180 T=TIME
   190 REM CALCULATION
   200 FOR Y%=0 TO MAX% STEP 4
   210    FOR X%=0 TO MAX% STEP 4
   220       REM C=CR+CIi
   230          CR=X%*Distance+AngleR: CI=Y%*Distance+AngleI
   240       REM Z=ZR+ZIi. Start value for Z equals C
   250          ZR=CR: ZI=CI
   260          Iteration%=0
   270       REM Z=Z^2+C where Z^2=ZR^2-ZI^2+(2*ZR*ZI)i
   280       REPEAT
   290          A=ZR^2: B=ZI^2: Length=SQR(A+B): ZI=2*ZR*ZI+CI: ZR=A-B+CR
   300          Iteration%=Iteration%+1
   310       UNTIL Length>2 OR Iteration%>15
   320       GCOL0, Iteration%MOD4
   330       PLOT69,X%,Y%
   340    NEXT
   350    CLS
   360    PRINT"TIME"(TIME-T)/100"  S"
   370 NEXT
```

075 MORSE TRAINING WITH THE JUNIOR COMPUTER

Here is yet another small program to be added to the large amount of software already available for the Junior Computer. It is intended to teach prospective short wave listeners to read morse code. The program can be used even with the basic version of the JC. The only additional hardware is the amplifier stage shown in the accompanying figure. The input to this is taken from port line PB5.

The number and speed of the morse characters can be predetermined. After the program has started, the JC will generate 1 to 6 morse characters, which the trainee should decode and write down. The letters corresponding to the generated characters appear on the display after a short delay, so that the trainee can check his decoding with the actual text. During this phase, the computer is on stand by until an arbitrary key, other than ST and RST, is pressed. The hex dump given is sufficient to write the program into the JC. Once that has been done, you can prepare the start, but the program needs the following information before it can run.

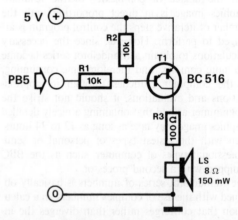

- in address 0010 write data 00...05;
- in address 0011 write data 01...55 (max);
- in address 0014 write data from table 1 for the first character to be generated minus 1;
- in address 0015 write data from table 1 for the last character to be generated.

Table 1.   Table 2.

alphanumeric character	hexadecimal code	alphanumeric character	hexadecimal code
A	01	S	13
B	02	T	14
C	03	U	15
D	04	V	16
E	05	W	17
F	06	X	18
G	07	Y	19
H	08	Z	1A
I	09	1	1B
J	0A	2	1C
K	0B	3	1D
L	0C	4	1E
M	0D	5	1F
N	0E	6	20
O	0F	7	21
P	10	8	22
Q	11	9	23
R	12	0	24

address	function
026F	alphanumeric display routine
028D	tone generation routine
02A8	random number routine
02CB	display code table
02EF	morse code table
0000 to	
0005	display buffer
0010	number of letters
0011	length of dots and dashes (speed)
0014	lower limit of block of characters to be generated
0015	upper limit of block of characters to be generated

```
      0  1  2  3  4  5  6  7  8  9  A  B  C  D  E  F
0200: A9 FF 8D 83 1A 8D 81 1A 85 01 85 02 85 03 85 04
0210: 85 05 18 A5 11 65 11 65 11 85 12 A5 10 AA 20 A8
0220: 02 A8 B9 CB 02 95 00 B9 EF 02 85 21 29 07 85 20
0230: 06 21 B0 07 A5 11 85 13 4C 3F 02 A5 12 85 13 20
0240: 8D 02 C6 20 D0 EA A5 12 85 13 C6 40 D0 FC C6 13
0250: D0 F8 CA 10 C9 20 6F 02 20 AC 1D F0 F8 20 6F 02
0260: 20 AC 1D F0 F0 20 6F 02 C6 40 D0 F9 4C 00 02 8A
0270: 48 A9 FF 8D 81 1A 8D 83 1A A2 08 A5 04 20 E3 1D
0280: CE 7C 02 10 F6 A9 05 8D 7C 02 68 AA 60 A9 FF 8D
0290: 83 1A EE 82 1A D0 FB C6 13 D0 F7 A5 11 85 13 C6
02A0: 40 D0 FC C6 13 D0 F8 60 8A 48 38 A5 E9 65 EC 65
02B0: ED 85 E8 A2 04 B5 E8 95 E9 CA 10 F9 C5 15 B0 EA
02C0: C5 14 30 E6 85 30 68 AA A5 30 60 08 03 27 21 06
02D0: 0E 42 09 7A 72 0A 47 48 2B 23 0C 18 2F 52 07 63
02E0: 41 01 36 11 64 79 24 30 19 12 02 78 00 10 40 42
02F0: 84 A4 83 01 24 C3 04 02 74 A3 44 C2 82 E3 64 D4
0300: 43 03 81 23 14 63 94 B4 C4 7D 3D 1D 0D 05 85 C5
0310: E5 F5 FD
```

Now, the program can be run; it starts in address 0020 when key GO is pressed. Programming example: the JC is to generate morse characters for the letters B to G. Before the start, the following data should be written:

■ in address 0010 — data 05
■ in address 0011 — data 55
■ in address 0014 — data 02
■ in address 0015 — data 07

As soon as these data have been written, the program starts when key GO is pressed.

The hex data for the letters of the alphabet and numbers 0...9 are given in table 1. The most important addresses are given in table 2.

101

Despite its neat design and relatively low cost, the Acorn Electron computer suffers from an unfortunate lack of I/O support, which is remarkable, considering the fact that it is a relatively simple matter to add, say, two I/O ports to enable the computer to drive a printer, plotter, modem, or other peripherals by means of the proposed PIA (peripheral interface adapter).

The circuit diagram of the PIA-based extension shows that address decoding over the full 64 Kbytes is by means of two 8-bit magnitude comparators Type 74LS688. Address selection is manual with switches $S_1 \ldots S_{14}$, which provide a logic low level when closed; observe this when writing out the ones and zeros to arrive at the desired address in the I/O map. The PIA chip is enabled when the preset

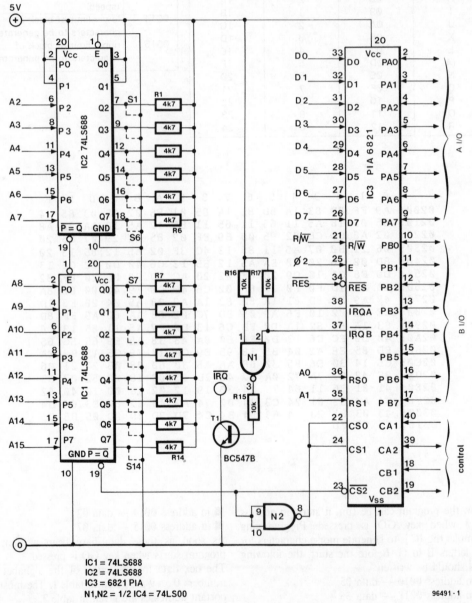

IC1 = 74LS688
IC2 = 74LS688
IC3 = 6821 PIA
N1,N2 = 1/2 IC4 = 74LS00

96491-1

address matches that on the computer's address bus; writing simple I/O drivers is therefore mainly a matter of assigning the relevant address block to control words and PIA I/O data.

T1 has been included to enable the PIA circuit to generate and forward interrupt request pulses by means of the wired-OR arrangement for this control line.

In case it is desirable to switch heavier loads than is normally permissible with the PIA outputs, it is suggested to employ power drivers/inverters such as those in the ULN2000 series.

077   QL RAM EXTENSION

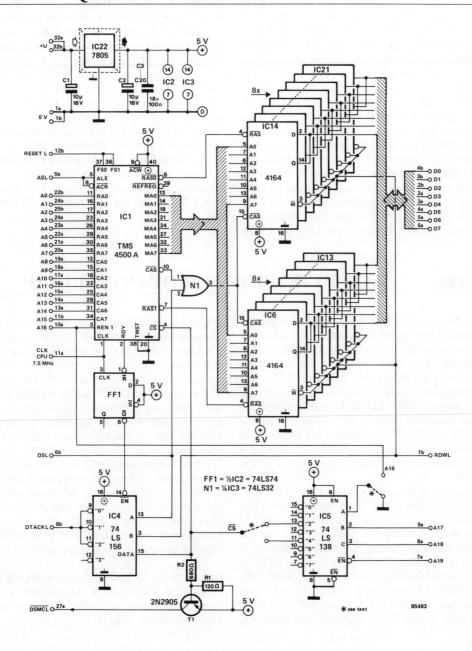

Sinclair's QL has as standard a 128 K RAM, which sounds like a lot in comparison with most 64 K machines. Unfortunately, the software writers, in the knowledge that there is more than enough memory, have been rather wasteful in their work, so that at the end of the day, there is not all that much more in the QL than in the 64 K machines. So, you need more memory...

The accompanying circuit is an application of the TMS4500A as RAM extension for the 68008. This chip can drive a maximum of 128 K dynamic RAM and provides virtually everything: multiplexing of the address lines, $\overline{RAS}$, $\overline{CAS}$, and REFRESH.

The memory ICs are 64 K $\times$ 1 (128 or 256 refresh are both permitted) and have a speed of better than 150 ns. Since the QL uses a clock frequency of 7.5 MHz rather than the normal 8 MHz, such a RAM can run without wait cycles. An 8 MHz CPU that regularly has to carry out a wait cycle is appreciably slower than a 7.5 MHz type!

The 68000 family is provided with a data acknowledge input. As with other processors, the CPU places addresses and data onto the bus and indicates the validity with an address strobe and data strobe respectively. It continues to do so until the memory sends a $\overline{DTACK}$ signal. The present extension generates this signal with the aid of the LS156.

Normally, this acknowledgment is given almost immediately, but it may happen that the 4500 is in the middle of a refresh. In that case, the CPU has to wait, which is arranged via the ready output (pin 2). To prevent the QL waiting forever when an address is read that has no memory, the $\overline{DTACK}$ is generated internally: this must, however, be disabled for addresses where the RAM extension is located, and fortunately this can be done easily via $\overline{DSMC}$. By making this logic high as quickly as possible, the internal $\overline{DTACK}$ is cancelled.

If you cannot get the 2N2905 transistor, you may use a BS250, in which case resistor R_1 can be omitted and R_2 should be replaced by a wire link.

The circuit as shown is for the 128 K version. It is also possible to omit the eight RAMs connected to RAS1 and make a 64 K extension. Input A of the LS138 must then be connected to A_{16} and pin 11 instead of pin 13 must be used as $\overline{CS}$.

There is no 5 V supply available on the connector, but there is a 9 V line. This can be reduced to 5 V by a standard 7805. The current drawn depends on the types of RAM and will be 200...300 mA. It is important to decouple the supply lines properly: each RAM IC and the 4500 require a 100 n capacitor!

078   RAM EXTENSION FOR QUANTUM LEAP

The Sinclair Quantum Leap (QL) computer is eminently suitable for a low-cost introduction into working with Motorola's 68000 true 16-bit microprocessor. Many computer enthusiasts did not fail to note the spectacular price cuts for the QL when its production was discontinued. An excellent support program, TOOLKIT II, became available and is still considered indispensable by many for getting to grips with the QL. The present 512 Kbyte RAM extension should be very welcome for running a RAM disk, and/or programs such as ICE and QIMP.

The circuit is based around the Type THCT4502 RAM controller from Texas Instruments. This dedicated controller takes care of all the DRAM controlling, including the refresh timing, and the addressline multiplexing. The address decoder is made with a single XOR gate, N_7. The DSMCL line is made high within 30 ns with the aid of three-state buffer N_5. Bistable FF_1 delays the ASL signal somewhat, so that DTACL is only activated when the RDY output of IC_1 is stable. The databus is

buffered by bidirectional octal transceiver IC_{23}.

The extension memory is divided in two banks of 256 Kbyte. Note that $\overline{CAS}$, unlike $\overline{RAS}$, is common to both banks. It is possible on the QL to omit the second bank without altering the address decoding. This is thanks to QDOS, which searches for correctly operating continuous, and unique, i.e., non-mirrored, memory. It is interesting to note that machine code in the extension memory runs at almost double the normal speed.

The RAM chips used should have an access time of 150 ns or less. Current consumption of the extension is low at 50 mA or 150 mA in the non-active and active mode respectively. Non-used inputs on gates should be tied to ground.

Finally, note that the Type THCT4502 controller may not be available everywhere yet.

Distributor for TI Semiconductors in the UK is DC Distribution ● Freepost ● Hitchin Road ● Arlesly ● Bedfordshire SG156BR. Telephone: (0462) 834444 or (0454) 273333.

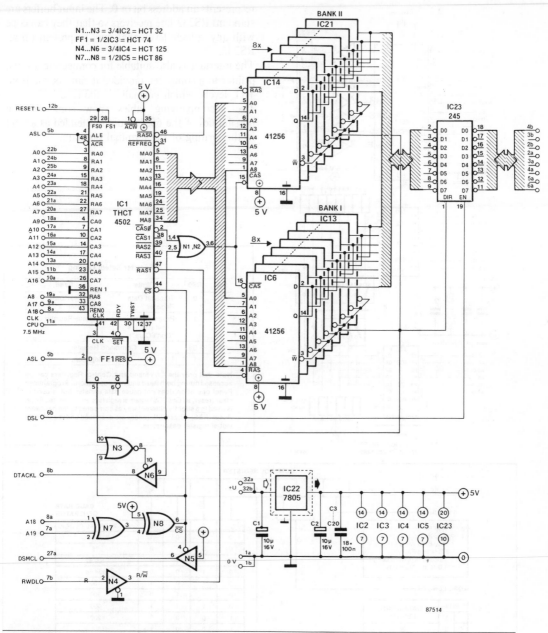

079 RS232 INTERFACE

This circuit is intended as an interface between the Elektor modem (*Elektor Electronics*, October 1984) and a computer. The software for each individual computer must, of course, be written separately. Since the writing of a terminal program can only be carried out in machine language, the interface can be kept quite simple.

Signals at TTL level are sufficient to operate the modem and LS05 buffers are therefore used. Complete address decoding of the 6551 is ensured by IC_2 and IC_3 so that only four locations in the memory are required, and these should be available on virtually any computer. The fourteen common address bits are selected with $S_1 \ldots S_{14}$: a closed switch

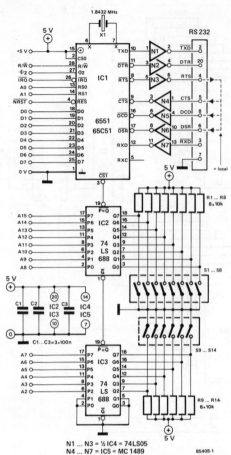

N1 ... N3 = ½ IC4 = 74LS05
N4 ... N7 = IC5 = MC 1489

85408-1

respresents an address bit or 0. The input buffers are standard RS232 line receivers so that they can cope with any voltage levels that may be present on an RS232.

The interface is also suitable for connecting a serial printer to a computer, provided it can operate from TTL levels, which normally is the case.

The accompanying tables show some of the possibilities of the 6551 and are intended as an aid in the writing of the terminal program.

Register Select Coding

RS1	RS0	Write	Read
0	0	Transmit Data Register	Receiver Data Register
0	1	Programmed Reset (Data is "Don't Care")	Status Register
1	0	Command Register	
1	1	Control Register	

Note that only the Command and Control Registers can be accessed during both Read and Write operations. Programmed Reset operation does not cause data transfer, but is used to clear (reset) all G65SC51 internal registers. Programmed Reset is used in a slightly different way as compared to the hardware Reset (RES). These differences are described under each individual register description.

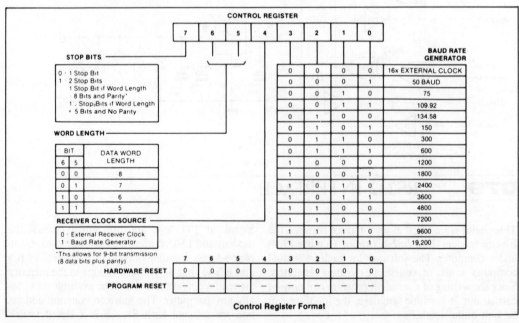

CONTROL REGISTER

7	6	5	4	3	2	1	0

STOP BITS

0 : 1 Stop Bit
1 : 2 Stop Bits
    1 Stop Bit if Word Length
    : 8 Bits and Parity*
    1 : Stop Bits if Word Length
    = 5 Bits and No Parity

WORD LENGTH

BIT		DATA WORD LENGTH
6	5	
0	0	8
0	1	7
1	0	6
1	1	5

RECEIVER CLOCK SOURCE

0 : External Receiver Clock
1 : Baud Rate Generator

*This allows for 9-bit transmission (8 data bits plus parity)

BAUD RATE GENERATOR

3	2	1	0	
0	0	0	0	16x EXTERNAL CLOCK
0	0	0	1	50 BAUD
0	0	1	0	75
0	0	1	1	109.92
0	1	0	0	134.58
0	1	0	1	150
0	1	1	0	300
0	1	1	1	600
1	0	0	0	1200
1	0	0	1	1800
1	0	1	0	2400
1	0	1	1	3600
1	1	0	0	4800
1	1	0	1	7200
1	1	1	0	9600
1	1	1	1	19,200

	7	6	5	4	3	2	1	0
HARDWARE RESET	0	0	0	0	0	0	0	0
PROGRAM RESET	—	—	—	—	—	—	—	—

Control Register Format

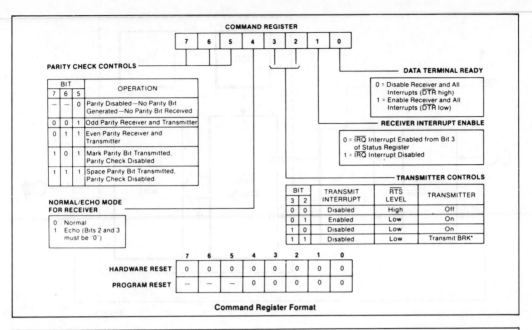

COMMAND REGISTER

| 7 | 6 | 5 | 4 | 3 | 2 | 1 | 0 |

PARITY CHECK CONTROLS

BIT 7	BIT 6	BIT 5	OPERATION
—	—	0	Parity Disabled—No Parity Bit Generated—No Parity Bit Received
0	0	1	Odd Parity Receiver and Transmitter
0	1	1	Even Parity Receiver and Transmitter
1	0	1	Mark Parity Bit Transmitted, Parity Check Disabled
1	1	1	Space Parity Bit Transmitted, Parity Check Disabled

NORMAL/ECHO MODE FOR RECEIVER

0	Normal
1	Echo (Bits 2 and 3 must be "0")

DATA TERMINAL READY

0 = Disable Receiver and All Interrupts ($\overline{\text{DTR}}$ high)
1 = Enable Receiver and All Interrupts ($\overline{\text{DTR}}$ low)

RECEIVER INTERRUPT ENABLE

0 = $\overline{\text{IRQ}}$ Interrupt Enabled from Bit 3 of Status Register
1 = $\overline{\text{IRQ}}$ Interrupt Disabled

TRANSMITTER CONTROLS

BIT 3	BIT 2	TRANSMIT INTERRUPT	$\overline{\text{RTS}}$ LEVEL	TRANSMITTER
0	0	Disabled	High	Off
0	1	Enabled	Low	On
1	0	Disabled	Low	On
1	1	Disabled	Low	Transmit BRK*

	7	6	5	4	3	2	1	0
HARDWARE RESET	0	0	0	0	0	0	0	0
PROGRAM RESET	—	—	—	0	0	0	0	0

Command Register Format

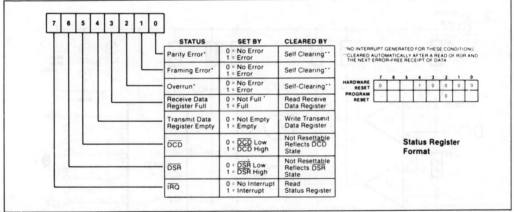

| 7 | 6 | 5 | 4 | 3 | 2 | 1 | 0 |

STATUS	SET BY	CLEARED BY
Parity Error*	0 = No Error / 1 = Error	Self Clearing**
Framing Error*	0 = No Error / 1 = Error	Self Clearing**
Overrun*	0 = No Error / 1 = Error	Self-Clearing**
Receive Data Register Full	0 = Not Full / 1 = Full	Read Receive Data Register
Transmit Data Register Empty	0 = Not Empty / 1 = Empty	Write Transmit Data Register
$\overline{\text{DCD}}$	0 = $\overline{\text{DCD}}$ Low / 1 = $\overline{\text{DCD}}$ High	Not Resettable Reflects DCD State
$\overline{\text{DSR}}$	0 = $\overline{\text{DSR}}$ Low / 1 = $\overline{\text{DSR}}$ High	Not Resettable Reflects DSR State
$\overline{\text{IRQ}}$	0 = No Interrupt / 1 = Interrupt	Read Status Register

*NO INTERRUPT GENERATED FOR THESE CONDITIONS
**CLEARED AUTOMATICALLY AFTER A READ OF RDR AND THE NEXT ERROR-FREE RECEIPT OF DATA

	7	6	5	4	3	2	1	0
HARDWARE RESET	0			1	0	0	0	0
PROGRAM RESET					0			

Status Register Format

080 SAMPLE & HOLD FOR ANALOGUE SIGNALS

Conventional analogue sample and hold circuits are notorious for their tendency to drift, a phenomenon unknown in digital memories. It is, therefore, interesting to study the use of a digital memory element for storing an analogue signal.

The present circuit is based on intermediate storage of digitized analogue information, and therefore requires an analogue-to-digital converter (ADC) at the input, and a digital-to-analogue converter (DAC) at the output. Unfortunately, DACs and ADCs are typically expensive components, and the present circuit is therefore set up with a DAC only, driven by an up/down counter—see Fig. 1. The counter is essentially an ADC, since the output voltage of the R-2R based DAC is continuously compared to the input voltage with the aid of a window comparator. The error signal produced by the comparator arranges for the counter to count up or down, depending on the magnitude of the difference between the input and output voltage. The up/down counter is corrected until the input and output voltage are equal. The digitized result of the A-D conversion is available at the counter outputs.

The extensions for converting the basic set-up into

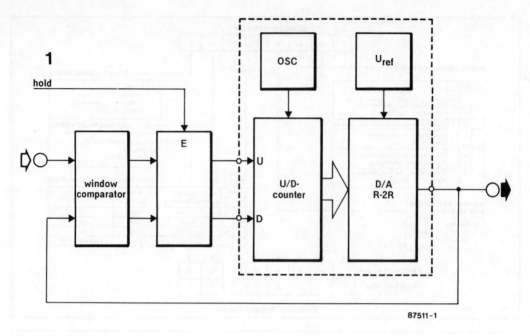

1

hold

window comparator

E

OSC

U_{ref}

U/D-counter

D/A R-2R

U

D

87511-1

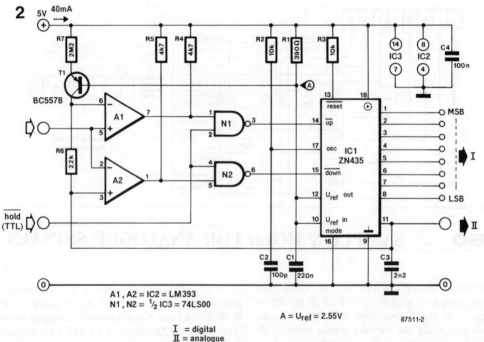

2

5V 40mA

R7 2M2

T1 BC557B

R6 22k

hold (TTL)

R5 4k7 R4 4k7

A1

A2

N1

N2

R2 10k R1 390Ω R3 10k

(A)

IC3 14/7 IC2 8/4 C4 100n

13 reset 18

14 up

17 osc IC1 ZN435

15 down

12 U_{ref} out

10 U_{ref} in mode

16 9

1 MSB
2
3
4
5   I
6
7
8 LSB

11   II

C2 100p C1 220n

C3 2n2

0 0

A1, A2 = IC2 = LM393
N1, N2 = ½ IC3 = 74LS00

A = U_{ref} = 2.55V

I = digital
II = analogue

87511-2

a sample & hold circuit are relatively simple. The current count is retained by activating the HOLD input, which enables halting the U/D counter. Evidently, the counter state is not subject to drift, so that the analogue output signal is available unaffected for as long as the circuit is pow-

ered. The converter used here is the Type ZN435 ADC/DAC from Ferranti. This chip contains everything shown in the dashed box of Fig. 1. With reference to the practical circuit diagram, Fig. 2, the internal voltage reference and the oscillator are adjusted with R_1-C_1 and R_2-C_2 respectively. The latter are dimensioned for 400 kHz, i.e., nearly the maximum oscillator operating frequency. The internal counter is controlled via inputs up, down and mode. The logic level applied to the mode input determines whether the counter continues or halts upon reaching state 0 or the maximum value, 255. In the present application, the counter is halted. Gates N_1 and N_2 are added to enable blocking the U/D counter. Opamps A_1-A_2 form the window comparator. Current source T_1-R_7 and R_6 arrange for the toggle threshold of A_1 to be 20 mV higher than that of A_2. This off-set creates the window, or

inactive span, needed to suppress oscillation of the counter's LS bit, and to prevent unwanted effects arising from the comparators' offset voltages. Decoupling capacitor C_3 is fitted for suppressing spikes that occur during state changes on the counter outputs. The conversion time of this design is about 640 μs, as determined by the oscillator frequency (400 kHz), the resolution (8 bits) and the input voltage change (2.55 V_{pp} max.). This corresponds to a slew rate of 4 mV/μs at the input. Finally, bear in mind that the output impedance (IC_1, pin 11) is relatively high at about 4 kΩ.

081   SERIAL DATA CONVERTER

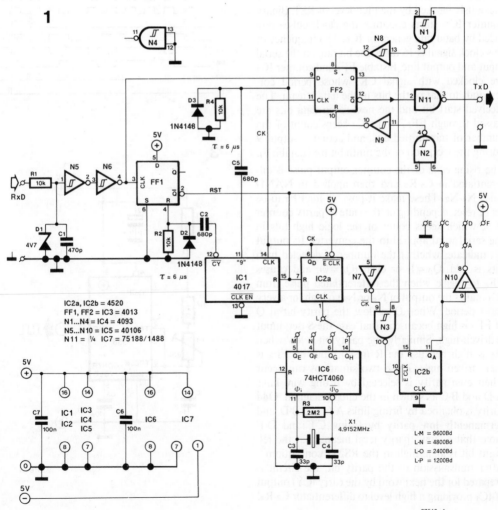

87516 - 1

Some computers and communication programs are unable to output serial data composed of 7 data bits and a parity bit. The present circuit has been designed to output this data format when it is driven with serial data organized as 1 start bit, 8 data bits, no parity bit, and 1 stop bit. This format is widely used for accessing bulletin boards, data banks, and the like with the aid of a modem, and should be available on most computers equipped with an RS232 port. The converter has a built-in clock generator which can be set to the baud rates shown in the circuit diagram, Fig. 1. Both odd and even parity can be generated, and no handshaking is required with the computer or console.

The basic operation of the converter is as follows (also refer to the timing diagram in Fig. 2). The rising edge of the start bit in the incoming 10-bit word clocks bistable FF_1, whose output $\overline{Q}$ goes low and so enables counters IC_1, IC_{2a} and IC_{2b}, which were previously blocked by the high level of RST. Binary counter IC_{2a} starts counting the clock pulses provided by baud rate generator IC_6. The frequency of this clock signal is 16 times the bit rate on the serial input and output line. Bistable FF_2 and counter IC_1 are clocked with signal CK, whose period corresponds to that of the bits in the data stream. The received start bit and the next seven data bits are passed through FF_2, while IC_1 keeps count of the number of transmitted bits, and actuates output 9 during the reception of the ninth bit (i.e., databit 7).

The rising edge of the counter output pulse is differentiated in C_5-R_6 and then applied to NAND gates N_1-N_2. These make it possible for FF_2 to be set or reset, depending on the state of parity counter IC_{2b}, which keeps count of the logic high bits in the serial word applied to the converter. Its output Q_A indicates whether the number of detected high bits is odd ($Q_A = 1$) or even ($Q_A = \emptyset$), and causes FF_2 to toggle when the differentiated pulse from IC_1 makes the output of N_8 or N_9 go high for a very short period. When Q_A is low, the parity bit at Q of FF_2 is high because in that case the S (set) input is driven high. Similarly, the parity bit is low when Q_A is high because the R (reset) input on FF_2 is then driven high. These two situations can occur when **even** parity is selected by fitting wire links A-D and B-C as shown in the circuit diagram. **Odd** parity is obtained by fitting links A-C and B-D, and **permanently low** parity by fitting C-E and D-F (note that a "low" parity level means that the relevant bit is logic high in the RS232 convention). After transmission of the parity bit, the circuit is prepared for the next word by the carry (CY) output of IC_1 providing a high level to differentiator C_2-R_4.

This resets FF_1, which in response drives the RST line high to reset the counters.

The convention adopted for the logic high and low levels of the data bits in the proposed converter requires that this is inserted in an RS232 or RS432 data line. Line driver N_{11} may be omitted, and the serial output signal taken from Q on FF_2, if the driven input can operate with pulse levels of 0 and $+5$ V.

Finally, Fig. 3 shows a suitable alternative for the crystal-operated clock generator, which may be considered too extensive if the circuit is to work at a fixed baudrate of 1200. Multiturn preset P_1 is set for an output frequency of 19,200 Hz.

2

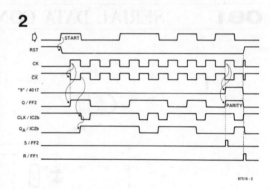

3

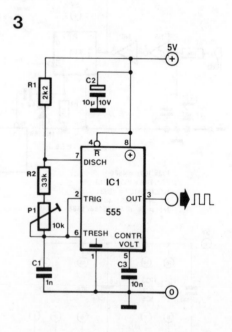

110

This circuit owes its existence to the need for data communication over relatively long distances (up to 100 metres), inexpensively, reliably, and suitable for speeds up to 2400 bauds. At the distances considered, the main expense is normally the cable, so here a readily available 60 Ω coaxial cable is used. Because of its relative immunity to noise, current drive is employed.

In the line driver — figure 1 — transistor T_1, diode D_4, and resistors R_3 and R_4 form a current source that can be fed direct from a non-regulated supply of 8...10 V. The transistor should be mounted on a heat sink. The current level of 40 mA ensures an adequate input signal to the line receiver. Transistor T_2 is a current switch that short-circuits the current source and the cable to earth of the input to the driver is logic high: only when that input is logic low, is the current of 40 mA fed into the cable. Diodes D_2 and D_3 protect the driver against

noise emanating from the cable, while capacitor C_1 decouples the supply line.

The line receiver is based on a type LM 311 comparator. Matching of the input is effected by a wire link at a relevant tap of resistive divider R_5-R_6-R_7/R_8 (in our case: 60 Ω). Resistors R_9 and R_{10}, and diode D_5 protect the LM 311 against noise emanating from the cable. The sensitivity of the receiver is set with P_1 Resistor R_{14} provides some hysteresis. Pull-up resistor R_{15} ensures that IC_1 provides at its pin 7 a TTL output signal that is in phase with the input signal to the line driver.

The circuit is best calibrated with the aid of an oscilloscope once it has been installed in its final position. The level of input to the receiver is then compared with the voltage at the wiper of P_1 The setting of P_1 is optimum when the voltage at its wiper (wave form A in figure 3) is exactly opposing the input voltage (wave form B in figure 3).

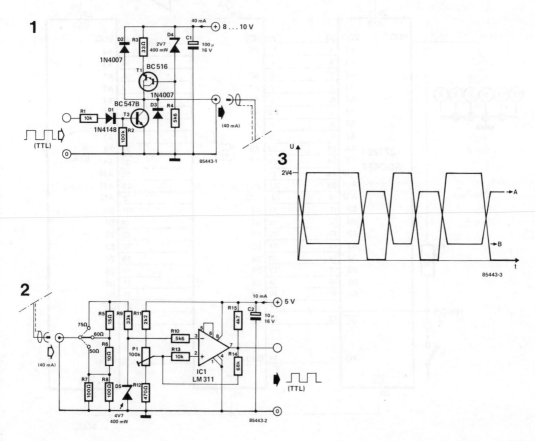

SIDEWAY RAM FOR BBC AND ELECTRON PLUS ONE

As already reported on numerous occasions in *Elektor Electronics*, the BBC micro ranges among the most widely used types of personal computer currently available. To newcomers in the computer field, the amount of commercially available ROM-supplied software is truly staggering, and there seem to be programs to suit almost any requirement and budget.

However, the number of ROMs that may be located in the BBC computer is limited to four in the basic version and sixteen when it is equipped with a sideway ROM expansion card. Users in posession of a good many ROMs and EPROMs are, therefore, often forced to exchange these before a program can be run; a method that is both cumbersome and possibly bad for the ICs and their sockets.

A way of getting round this problem is to install RAM rather than ROM or EPROM chips on the sideway board, so that software may be readily moved about between ROMs, direct access memory, disk and RAM, since many of the originally ROM-based programs may also be run from RAM, it has appeared.

Since it was thought convenient to plug 16 Kbytes of static RAM into any one vacant ROM socket, the circuit was constructed in all-SMD technology on a ready-made PCB of very small size.

The circuit diagram shows two 8 Kbyte, low-power static RAMs Type 6264FP-15 as a replacement for a 16 Kbyte EPROM Type 27128; a single inverter selects the relevant 8 Kbyte block when the (formerly) ROM socket is addressed.

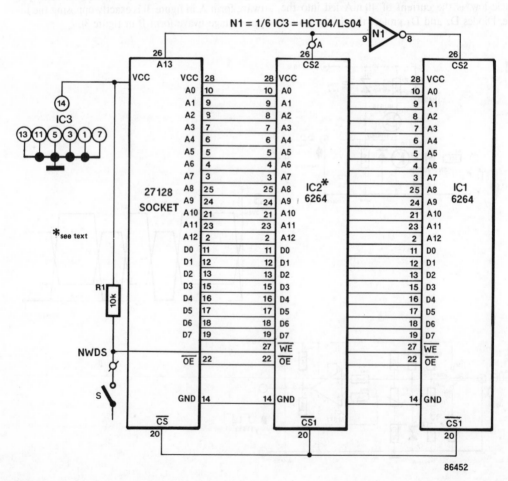

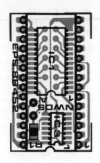 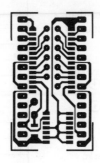 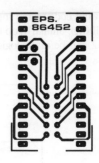

Working with SMD parts to achieve a truly miniature ROM replacement should be based on the necessary skills in soldering and handling these new parts, and the construction of the proposed extension therefore requires to be done as follows.

It should be noted that the through-plated PCB for this project comes together with the SMD die. Fit 28 short (1 cm) pins at the sides of the PCB to enable it to be received in an IC socket.

The SMD RAMs are mounted piggy-back onto the PCB, with the exception of pin 26 of the top mounted RAM; this terminal should be wired to socket pin 28. The SMD parts 74HC04 (IC₃) and R₁ may now be fitted to conclude the PCB construction. Once the unit has been plugged into a ROM socket, a short wire is run from pin 8 of IC₇₇ on the BBC main board to the NWDS input on the SMD board.

Parts list

R₁ = 100 k
IC₁;IC₂ = 6264FP-15
IC₃ = 74HC04
PCB 86425
Miniature switch for write protection, if
   required

Finally, although not mentioned so far, the Electron Plus One computer may also benefit from the proposed sideway RAM circuit which, as will be readily understood, need not necessarily be constructed with SMD parts; a veroboard and normal sized components, along with a bit of wiring, will also do in many cases, although it may be hard to surpass the elegance of the plug-in unit.

084   SIMPLE D-A CONVERTER

Two simple to build 4-bit digital-to-analogue converters are described here. One translates a 4-bit BCD code into 10 analogue voltage levels, the other accepts a 4-bit binary code and outputs 16 voltage levels. Both circuits comprise a digital decoder with open collector outputs for controlling a resistance ladder. The analogue voltage is obtained by controlled connection to ground of a particular section of the ladder, and buffering the drop so obtained with a transistor.

Notwithstanding their relatively low resolution (10 or 16 steps), the circuit should have many possible applications, including driving digitally controlled power supplies, triangular wave and sawtooth generators, and A-D converters.

Table 1 lists the relative values of the resistors in the ladder network, starting from R₁ = 1K0. Three values are given for each resistor: the left-hand column shows the theoretical value, while the nearest equivalent from the E24 and E96 series appears in the centre and right hand column, respectively. Note that the starting value can be changed to individual requirements, provided all other resistors are dimensioned accordingly, i.e., their values should be multiplied with the same factor with respect to 1K0.

It is a relatively simple matter to add an 11th or 17th output level by driving the decoder such that none of its output transistors is enabled. This results in an output voltage which is 0.6 V lower than the supply for the ladder network. In the case of the 74LS145, this condition is obtained by applying a non-valid code to the inputs, i.e., one greater than 9_{10} (1001_2). Similarly, on the 74159, enable input $\overline{G1}$ or $\overline{G2}$ can be made logic high.

Table 1 Resistor values relative to 1 kΩ						
R_n	10-step BCD version			16-step binary version		
R_1	1000	1K0	1K0	1000	1K0	1K0
R_2	111	110	110	66.7	68	66.5
R_3	139	130	140	76.3	75	76.8
R_4	179	180	178	87	91	86.6
R_5	238	240	237	103	100	102
R_6	333	330	332	122	120	121
R_7	500	510	499	145	150	147
R_8	833	820	825	178	180	178
R_9	1667	1K6	1K69	222	220	221
R_{10}	5000	5K1	4K99	286	270	287
R_{11}				381	390	383
R_{12}				533	510	536
R_{13}				800	820	806
R_{14}				1333	1K3	1K33
R_{15}				2667	2K7	2K67
R_{16}				8000	8K2	8K06

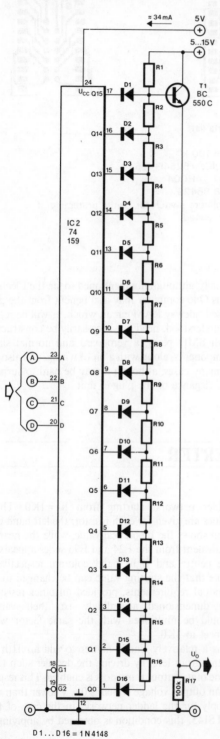

D 1 ... D 16 = 1 N 4148

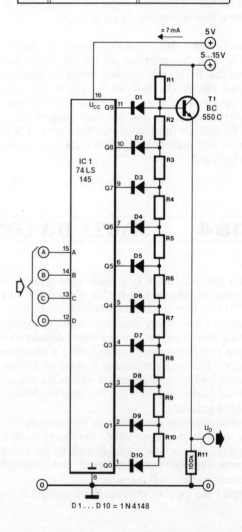

D 1 ... D 10 = 1 N 4148

87418

The inverter must be connected before the TV modulator in the ZX81. Switch S₁ enables bypassing of the inverter when inversion of the picture is not required. The composite video signal is inverted by gate N_1. Gates N_2 and N_3 separate the sync signal from the input: the sync signal is then available at the output of N_3 at a level of 5 V_{pp}. The inverted video signal and amplified sync signal are then added again, resulting in an inverted video signal with the sync signal in the correct position and at the right level. Preset P_1 serves to adjust the contrast.

The circuit can be constructed on a piece of veroboard so small that it can easily be added in the ZX81 case. The power supply can be taken from IC_1 in the ZX81: +5 V at pin 40 and earth (0 V) at pin 34.

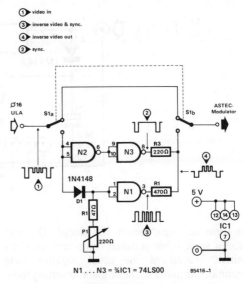

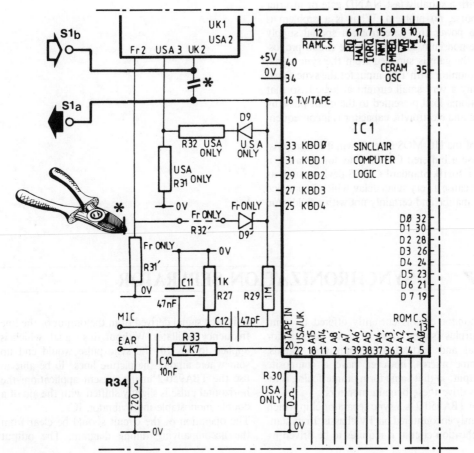

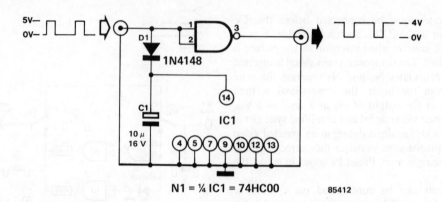

N1 = ¼ IC1 = 74HC00   85412

For some unknown reason, the Sinclair QL (and perhaps some other personal computers) provides positive, instead of the usual negative, field synchronizing pulses to the monitor. Inverting these pulses with a suitably fast NAND gate or inverter is, of course, no problem. What is a problem is where to power this gate from: a special supply would be nonsense. However, in the circuit proposed here, the gate is supplied from the sync signal itself. A monitor with TTL input for the sync signal draws only a very small current at logic 1, so that the additional load presented to the input pulse by the diode and electrolytic capacitor is inconsequential.

Instead of the HC-MOS gate shown, it is also possible to use a buffered CMOS gate, for instance, a type HEF4011B. Standard CMOS devices, such as the 4011, cause a very small delay, which in practice does not matter, and certainly not with a field sync

signal. Note that it is important, as always with CMOS devices, to connect unused pins to earth (pin 7) or to U_b (pin 14).

Many monitor chassis currently offered by computer surplus stores have separate inputs for horizontal and vertical synchronization signals. Most home micros, however, have a composite video output, so that some form of interfacing is required to drive these bargain monitors.

The Type TBA950-2 is a sync separator chip which is frequently encountered on TV chassis. In its standard application circuit, it requires to be driven by

a flyback signal derived from the output of the line frequency oscillator. Without this signal, which is applied to pin 10, the sync pulse would end up somewhere among the picture lines. To be able to use the TBA950-2 in the present application, the horizontal pulse is slightly shifted with the aid of a double monostable multivibrator, IC2.

The operation of the circuit should be clear from the accompanying timing diagram. The output

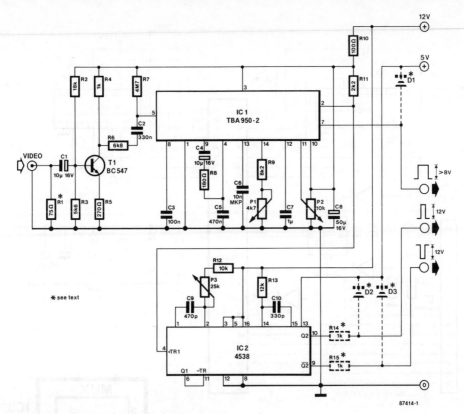

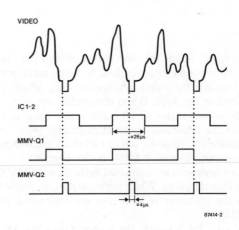

pulse from the TBA950 is fairly wide (26 µs), and its positive edge triggers the first MMV (Q1), whose negative output pulse transition in turn triggers the second MMV in the 4538 package. The line sync pulse for the monitor is available positive and negative at IC₂ outputs Q2 and $\overline{Q2}$, respectively.

Adjust the circuit as follows: set P₂ to the centre of its travel, and adjust the frequency control, P₁, such that the image is stable. Next, position the image by adjusting P₃. If the correct position can not be obtained, the phase control, P₂, must be carefully readjusted, followed by P₃. The vertical sync pulse is available at pin 7 of the TBA950-2. Finally, the dashed resistors and diodes are required if the monitor inputs are designed to accept signals with a peak-to-peak amplitude of 5 V.

088   TWIN KEYBOARD FOR APPLE II

The keyboard supplied with computers is for many applications not the *ne plus ultra* it is claimed to be. Unfortunately, deficiencies normally do not become apparent until the machine has been in practical use for a while. Retailers have long since realized this and often stock improved keyboards that are fully compatible with the computer in question. It is, however, not always clear how the new keyboard can be attached to the computer. One possibility is, of course, to open the computer, remove the existing

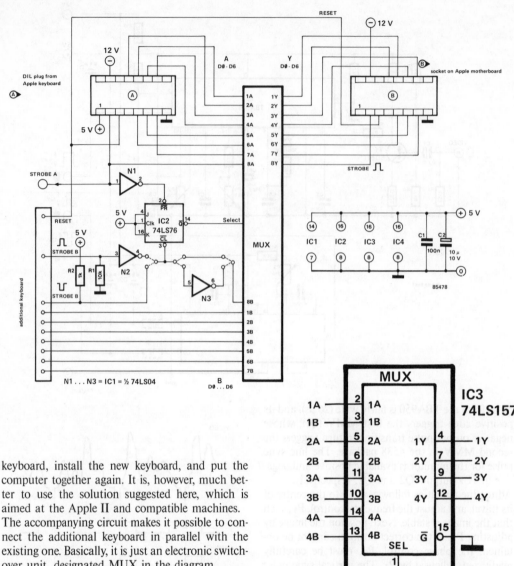

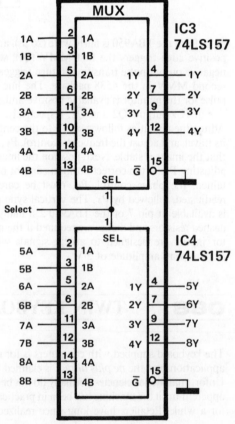

keyboard, install the new keyboard, and put the computer together again. It is, however, much better to use the solution suggested here, which is aimed at the Apple II and compatible machines.

The accompanying circuit makes it possible to connect the additional keyboard in parallel with the existing one. Basically, it is just an electronic switch-over unit, designated MUX in the diagram.

Both keyboards are connected to the input of MUX by their data lines. Which keyboard data are applied to the computer is from now on determined by MUX.

When a key is struck, the keyboard does not only generate data bits, but also a strobe pulse. Depending on whether the strobe pulse emanates from the original or from the additional keyboard, the $\overline{Q}$ output (pin 14) of bistable IC_2 is set or reset. This pulse, therefore, serves as a select signal for the MUX. The electronic switch consists of two type 74LS157 ICs. Each of these ICs contains four 2-to-1 multiplexers, so that all eight input data are available at the output. If the select input of both ICs is logic 0, outputs 1Y...8Y contain the data present at inputs

1A...8A. If, however, the input to the ICs is logic 1, the data from 1B...8B is available at 1Y...8Y.

The Apple II requires a positive strobe pulse, and inverters N_2 and N_3 are, therefore, provided to ensure that this condition is met whatever the strobe pulse from the additional keyboard.

Many computer systems use one clock signal, from which all other timing signals are derived. The frequency of the clock signal determines, among others, the maximum number of characters per line the video controller can display on the monitor screen. This is normally 32 or 40. If more characters per line are required, the clock frequency has to be increased. The clock generator described here makes it possible to switch between frequencies which are related in a ratio of 2:3. The switching is carried out synchronously, so that no bits are lost. The clock oscillator, T_1, is controlled by an inexpensive 3rd overtone 27 MHz crystal, XL_1. The LC circuit connected to the collector of T_1 is tuned to 54 MHz. The 54 MHz signal is converted to logic bits by field-effect transistor T_2 which are then applied to the Q inputs of dual J-K bistable IC_1 ($=FF_1/FF_2$). The ring counter formed by these bistables can be changed over by T_3.

When T_3 is on, the J input of FF_1 is logic high, and the 54 MHz signal is divided by 2. When T_3 is off, the J input of FF_1 is connected to the $\overline{Q}$ output of

FF_2 and the 54 MHz signal is then divided by 3. The output frequency can thus be switched synchronously between 18 MHz and 27 MHz.

If a fundamental crystal is used in the XL_1 position, the oscillator can be modified as shown inset.

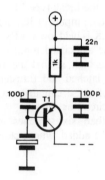

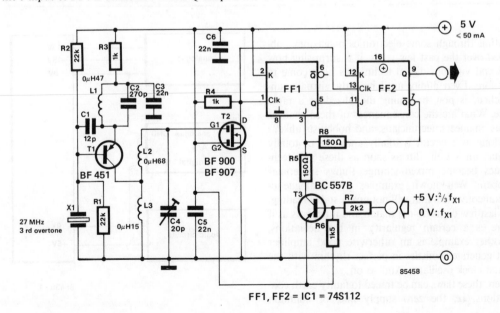

FF1, FF2 = IC1 = 74S112

090 6-WAY CHANNEL SELECTOR

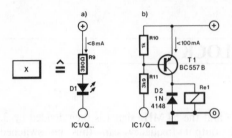

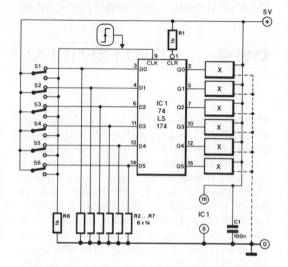

This design proves that a latching 6-way channel selector with debounced switch inputs need not always be based on the use of special integrated circuits.

When none of the break-type SPDT push buttons is pressed, the data inputs of IC₁ are held at +5 V, while input CLK is held low via R₈. When a switch is operated, the associated input of IC₁ goes low, while CLK goes high, so that the logic state of the D₀-D₅ lines is latched and transferred to outputs Q₀-Q₅. Each of these can drive a LED or relay based output circuit as shown.

When more than six switches are required, a 74LS174 may be added, whose clock input is connected to IC₁.

Note that the LS chip may be replaced by a corresponding version from the HC or HCT family. This will reduce the current consumption from about 20 mA to 6 mA. The maximum output current supplied by IC₁ is 8 mA in all cases.

091 ANALOGUE & DIGITAL

Leafing through some electronics magazines published over the past few years, it is surprising how fast and vigorous digital techniques have come to the fore. Even audio, until recently virtually untouched, is now becoming digitalized at a rapid pace. What are the consequences of these changes to us engineers, technicians, and hobbyists alike?
As long as a circuit is totally analogue or totally digital, all is well. But as soon as these two techniques become mixed strange things sometimes happen. Well-known examples are analogue-to-digital converters that will not give a stable reading: the last few digits do not match and it appears as if there is a certain regularity in the deviations. Another example is an otherwise good amplifier that generates whistles in perfect rhythm with the digital clock oscillator. And so on...
Often, these flaws can be traced to faulty earth connections, i.e. the zero supply line, or common

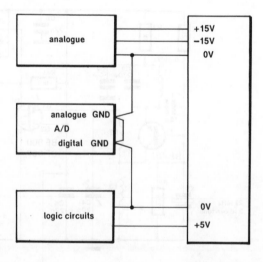

86436 - 1

ground. Because of that, here are a few tips that may prevent these annoying defects.

■ Avoid earth loops.

■ Keep the analogue and the digital earths separated.

■ Interconnect the analogue and digital earths at one point only, for instance, at the analogue-to-digital converter, but NOT at the power supply.

■ If there are more earths, connect these to the same common point.

■ At high frequencies, the impedances of earth lines are not negligible: short, thick wires should, therefore, be used.

An example that gives good results is shown in the accompanying drawing. All sensitive parts of the circuits have been isolated from those parts that carry (large) earth currents. Most converters have, therefore, two earth terminals, or an earth terminal and a differential input (which is the same thing). In audio amplifiers most of us do not dream of wiring the power supply to the output amplifier via the preamplifier. In mixed analogue-digital circuits, such considerations are not so self-evident, although the principle is the same.

Note that in the accompanying drawing the system needs several electrically isolated power supplies: that is unfortunately the price often to be paid for new techniques.

092   BAND-GAP VOLTAGE REFERENCE

It is generally known that the accuracy of measurements in electronic circuits is mainly a function of the stability and reliability of the reference against which the unknown quantity is compared. Therefore, everything feasible should be done to maintain the stability of the reference, i.e., counteract the adverse effects of variations in the ambient temperature, supply voltage, and load current. The zenerdiode in Fig. 1 is a usable reference device for applications where the above three parameters are not subject to appreciable variation. The "super zener" in Fig. 2 features excellent stability and is hardly affected by variations in the supply voltage and the load current. Although the temperature coefficient of the super zener circuit can be optimized by careful dimensioning of the components, there exists a still better way for making a precision voltage reference.

The term *band gap* refers to the difference between two discrete energies of the outer four electrons in a semiconductor atom. Electrons in the highest energy band contribute to the conduction of the material. As the temperature is increased, some electrons gain enough thermal energy to escape from the valence (non-conductive) band, cross the band gap, and enter the conduction band, leaving the valence band unfilled. Thus, conductivity is a function of temperature.

With reference to Fig. 3, the temperature coefficient of current mirror T_1-T_2 is compensated by that of T_3. The following conditions should be met if the circuit is to function optimally: (1): $R_2 \approx 10R_1$; (2): R_3 is dimensioned such that $V_R = 1.204$ V; and (3): the transistors are exactly matched. The latter

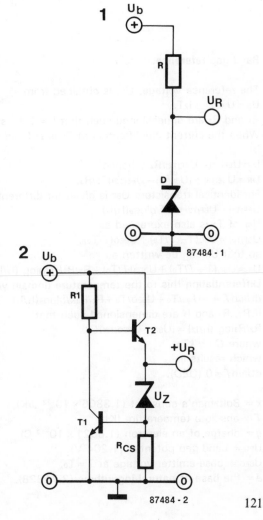

87484 - 1

87484 - 2

condition is probably best satisfied by using transistors on one and the same chip carrier, e.g. those in a transistor array such as the Type CA3083. The value of R depends on the supply voltage and the maximum output current. It should be noted that T_3 carries the output current if the circuit is not loaded, so that the resulting dissipation may give rise to temperature differences on the chip. It is, therefore, recommended to permanently load the band-gap reference. The accompanying calculations prove that the output voltage of the circuit is not affected by temperature variations.

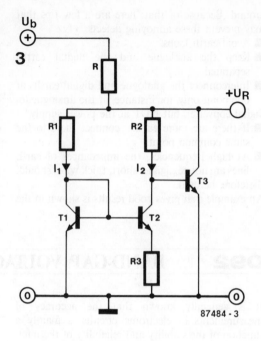

87484 - 3

Band-gap reference.

The reference voltage, U_R, is obtained from
$U_R = U_{BE(T3)} + I_2T_2$.
R_1 and R_2 are dimensioned such that $I_1 = 10I_2$, so that R_3 drops $|U_{BE(T1)} - U_{BE(T2)}|$ volts.
When the current amplification of T_2 is sufficiently high, R_3 carries virtually all current I_2:
$I_2 = U_{BE(T1)} - U_{BE(T2)}/R_3$ whence
$U_R = U_{BE(T3)} + (U_{BE(T1)} - U_{BE(T2)})R_2/R_3$.
For identical transistors U_{BE} is given for different values of I_{BE} as
$U_{BE(T1)} - U_{BE(T2)} = kT/q \log_e(I_1/I_2)$.
U_{BE} of T_3 is also expressed as
$U_{BE(T3)} = U_{BG}(1 - T/T_0) + U_{BEO}(T/T_0)$
so that U_R can be written as
$U_R = U_{BG}(1 - T/T_0) + U_{BEO}(T/T_0) + R_2/R_3 kT/q \log_e(I_1/I_2)$.
Differentiating this to the temperature domain yields
$dU_R/dT = -U_{BG}/T_0 + U_{BEO}/T_0 + R_2/R_3 k/q \log_e(I_1/I_2)$
if R_2, R_3 and I_1 are dimensioned such that
$R_2/R_3 \log_e(I_1/I_2) = (U_{BG} - U_{BEO(T3)})C$
where $C = q/kT_0$
which results in
$dU_R/dT = 0$ (QED).

k = Boltzman's constant $(1.3805 \times 10^{-23}$ J/K).
T = absolute temperature [K].
q = charge of an electron $(1.6021 \times 10^{-19}$ C).
U_{BG} = band-gap potential (1.204 V).
U_{BEO} = base-emitter voltage at $T = T_0$.
e = the base of natural logarithms (2.71828).

Piezoelectric resonators, also referred to as *buzzers*, are frequently used for providing audible signals in all sorts of electronic equipment. Buzzers are small, light, simple to use, and yet provide a loud output signal. They are either of the passive or of the active type. The former are driven by an AF signal source, while the latter feature a built-in oscillator, and require a direct voltage only.

This circuit is a double AF oscillator for driving passive buzzers. It ensures a richer output sound than normally obtainable from a piezo buzzer due to the use of two oscillators, N_1 and N_2, whose output signal lies between 1 and 10 kHz. Gates N_3-N_4 form an S-R bistable which is controlled by the outputs of N_1-N_2, and drives the buzzer direct. The spectral composition of the output signal is fairly complex, due to the presence of both the fundamental notes and the difference and sum frequency. The timbre so obtained varies as a function of the ratio between the oscillator frequencies, which are adjustable with the aid of presets P_1-P_2. Note that diodes D_1-D_2 reduce the duty factor of the oscillator signals to about 25%. Optimum effects are achieved when a simple ratio is set between the oscillator frequencies, e.g. 3:4. The resulting waveform is always composed of rectangular signals, but these differ in

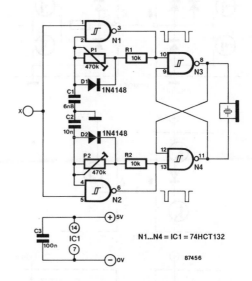

respect of their period to ensure that the buzzer produces a rather agreeable sound.

The buzzer driver is controlled by a logic level applied to point X. The quiescent current consumption is virtually negligible, while about 10 mA is drawn in the actuated state.

Many electronics hobbyists combine all sorts of digital circuits into works to be marvelled at. However, even they sometimes have that uncertain feeling: must they all be powered by one unit or should there be more or can there be more? And in what sequence should they be switched on? Printer first, or computer first?

In digital engineering, which by definition embraces computers, inputs are driven by outputs: information is being transferred. When the IC that drives has a power supply, but the receiving one has not, a current will ensue, whether the circuits are TTL or CMOS. This is an undesirable situation, although it does not normally lead to damage. But the ensuing current may be so large that the IC providing the current does not operate efficiently any more, because its output voltage, owing to the large

current, becomes too low. Particularly bistables can become disorganized by this. It is, therefore, possible that a certain equipment does not work properly because another circuit connected to it does not have a power supply.

That situation can become really critical when several outputs of an IC are terminated in that manner. Normally, an IC can withstand a short at one of its outputs, but if that happens at several outputs, the IC will probably give up the ghost. This may happen, for instance, in the case of a Centronics interface, of which the eight data lines are normally driven by one IC.

And what happens to the IC that is provided with the current? CMOS circuits are generally well protected against this, and TTL devices normally stand up well to them also. But other types may not take

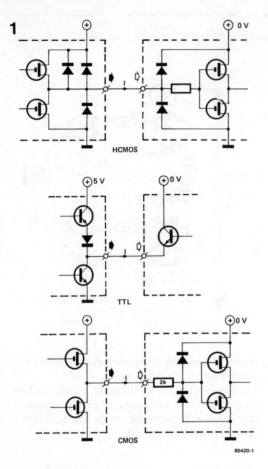

HCMOS

TTL

CMOS

85420-1

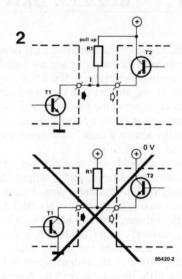

pull up

85420-2

■ Driver ICs, whether TTL or CMOS, must have an open-collector output.
■ All inputs should be provided with additional resistance (pull-up resistors) to the positive supply line.
If these rules are adhered to, current can only flow from input to output (see figure 2). This does not matter, because the collector of transistor T₁ can stand quite a high voltage and nothing will, therefore, go wrong. Make sure that the pull-up resistor is connected at the input side, otherwise it has no effect.
As to the question at the beginning: it does not matter which unit is switched on first, because the IC manufacturers have made sure that the input and output circuits are protected.

so kindly to these currents.
Semiconductor manufacturers have, of course, also been confronted with these problems and have found solutions to them. Anyone designing and building his own circuits should, therefore, heed their experiences and observe the following rules.

095   CURRENT DRIVE FOR STEPPER MOTORS

Stepper motors have either unipolar or bipolar stators. In unipolar models, each stator winding has a centre tap, which enables the magnetic field to be inverted by switching from one to the other half of the winding. Bipolar types have a single stator winding, so that the direction of the current through it must be changed to attain inversion of the magnetic field. From this, it is clear that, given that the two motors are of similar size, the bipolar type will provide a larger couple than the unipolar

model. There is, however, a price to be paid for this larger couple: the drive of a bipolar motor is more complex than that of a unipolar type.
The drive for bipolar motors may, in principle, be obtained by means of a
• full bridge circuit. i.e. four transistors per stator winding;
• half bridge circuit and dual power supply, i.e. two transistors per stator winding;
• half bridge circuit with large output capacitor.

1

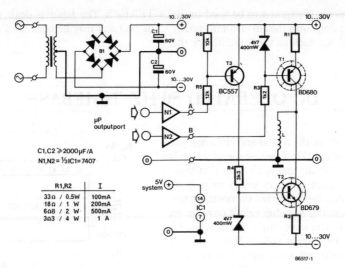

C1,C2 ⩾ 2000 µF/A
N1,N2 = ⅓ IC1 = 7407

R1,R2	I
33Ω / 0,5W	100mA
18Ω / 1 W	200mA
6Ω8 / 2 W	500mA
3Ω3 / 4 W	1 A

86517-1

The last method is totally unsuitable for low stepping frequencies or stand-still. Of the other two, the half bridge is to be preferred in most cases, in spite of the requirement for a dual power supply. In this context, it should be noted that the supply need not be regulated, since constancy of current is guaranteed by a zener diode and emitter resistor, even with variable input voltage. The value of the smoothing capacitors in the power supply is determined by the total stator current, and is a minimum of 2000 µF/A.

Values of R1 and R2 are given for various values of stator current in the table below.

R1 & R2	Is
33 Ω;⅚ W	100 mA
18 Ω;1 W	200 mA
6Ω8;2 W	500 mA
3Ω3;4 W	1 A

Current drive ensures a higher pull-in rate, i.e. permissible starting frequency, because commutation is quicker with an inductive stator winding.

The higher the supply voltage, the more effective the drive, but also, unfortunately, the dissipation in T1 and T2. In practice, a 2×12 V or 2×18 V mains transformer has proved very satisfactory. Note that freewheeling diodes have been included in the darlington circuit to give a good measure of protection against high induced voltages caused by switching.

2

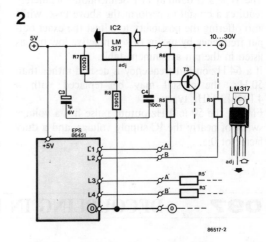

EPS
86451

86517-2

The prototype was used in the first instance for the control of four-phase stepper motors via an eight-bit output port of a microprocessor system. The interface used to obtain TTL levels was a Type 7407 which has 30 V open-collector outputs. The control instructions may be generated as trol instructions may be generated as follows:

Phase	1	2	3	4	
Bit	7 6	5 4	3 2	1 0	
Output byte	1 0	1 0	1 0	1 0	initial position
Auxiliary byte	0 0	0 0	0 0	1 1	XOR with output byte
New O/P byte	1 0	1 0	1 0	0 1	made one step
Rotate aux. byte twice*	0 0	0 0	1 1	0 0	preset for next step

*Direction of turning determines rotational direction of motor.

125

If the stepper motor is required to be used on its own, this may be done with the aid of commercially available control ICs such as the SAA1027 or the TEA1012. The latter is dealt with in Circuit 119 (p. 146) and may be connected as shown in Fig. 2.

096   DC OPERATED 50 HZ TIMEBASE

Many clocks, both of the digital and the analogue type, make use of a 50 Hz timebase signal which is usually derived from the mains. In order that these clocks may also work in places where there is no mains supply available, as in cars, on boats, or, say, on a camping site, this one-chip circuit provides an accurate 50 Hz square wave output signal, while being fed off any DC supply voltage between 6 and 15 V (battery, solar cell array, etc.). Current consumption of the circuit is only 3 mA (max.).

The Type SAF0300 by ITT Semiconductors merely requires a crystal to perform the above task, while also offering the possibility to adjust the exact output frequency by means of seven active low bits as listed in the pin assignment table.

If a 64 Hz output frequency is desired rather than 50 Hz, the crystal may be replaced with a 4.194812 MHz type.

Finally, the 50 (64) Hz output pulse has a voltage swing of nearly the IC supply voltage, and a duty factor of 0.5.

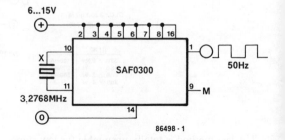

86498 - 1

1 Output 1 (50Hz)
2 Adjustment pin 122 ppm
3 Adjustment pin 61 ppm
4 Adjustment pin 30.5 ppm
5 Adjustment pin 15 ppm
6 Adjustment pin 7.6 ppm
7 Adjustment pin 3.8 ppm
8 Adjustment pin 1.9 ppm
9 Test pin M (fx/4)
10 Cristal connection
11 Cristal connection
12 Bridge output
13 Bridge output
14 Ground, 0
15 Leave vacant!
16 Supply voltage

097   DECOUPLING IN LOGIC CIRCUITS

Failing to heed the importance of adequately decoupled supply rails is one of the most serious mistakes a constructor of digital circuits can make. Two important facts necessitate a reappraisal of the effectiveness of decoupling: the introduction of the fast HC and HCT series of CMOS chips, and the general availability of ever larger dynamic RAM (DRAM) devices. The 41256 256Kbit DRAM and 6264 CMOS SRAM, for instance, have become commonly used integrated circuits, available at relatively low cost. The fast spreading use of the new CMOS series of logic circuits has created the widely heard misunderstanding that these devices can be used without paying the least attention to decoupling of the supply lines. However, a reduced current consumption relative to TTL devices is by no means a carte blanche for designers to skimp on decoup-

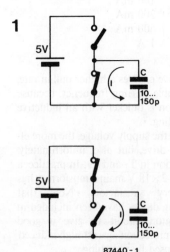

87440 - 1

ling provisions, as will be seen below.

Why does a logic circuit draw current? The current consumption of TTL chips goes mainly on account of indispensable, internal, resistors. CMOS structures are complementary, and theoretically consume no current at all in the *static* mode. As soon as any kind of switching is to be done, both by TTL and CMOS circuits, the charge of the capacitance at the output must be reversed as illustrated in Fig. 1. The switch currents internal to the IC are only a fraction of those required for the load capacitance, and can, therefore, be disregarded, except in the case of counters.

TTL and CMOS circuits thus consume an equal peak current during switch operations. Decoupling capacitors are fitted direct to the IC supply terminals to prevent the instantaneous supply voltage from briefly dropping to an unacceptable level when the switching takes place. The graph in Fig. 2 is reproduced from a Texas Instruments databook, and shows the correlation between the capacitor-to-package distance and the peak amplitude of the spikes on the supply line to a typical HCMOS gate. This shows beyond doubt that decoupling capacitors must be fitted as close as possible to the IC supply terminals, to rule out the stray inductance of supply tracks on the PCB, however neatly these may run in parallel. Often, tuned circuits are designed with long supply tracks and a wrongly placed decoupling capacitor. Any spike is then subject to ringing effects, which further deteriorate the operation of the logic circuit in question. Not surprisingly, Mullard recommend a multipath supply track when it is impossible to fit the decoupling capacitor close to the IC. This solution is called a *grid structure*, and is definitely preferable to creating relatively wide, single tracks—see Fig. 3. The value of the decoupling capacitor must be based on the foreseeable number of IC outputs that are *simultaneously* active. A conventional starting point is 20 to 100 nanofarad for every three ICs.

Further reflection on this theme leads to the conclusion that the supply for a 256Kbit DRAM is far more difficult to decouple than that for, say, a 16 Kbit DRAM. Fortunately, the problems are not as serious as one would expect. In practice, the size of the chip carrier, and hence the parasitic capacitance, is constantly reduced by the manufacturers, whose foremost aim is to ensure optimum response of the device at high operating frequencies. Certain DRAM manufacturers recommend the use of 330n decoupling capacitors (see Fig. 4), but in practice no problems evolved from the use of the standard value of 100n.

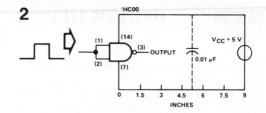

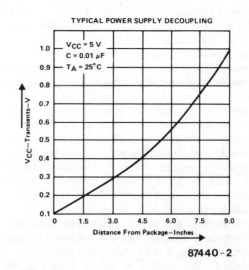

TYPICAL POWER SUPPLY DECOUPLING

$V_{CC} = 5$ V
$C = 0.01 \mu F$
$T_A = 25°C$

V_{CC}—Transients—V

Distance From Package—Inches

87440 – 2

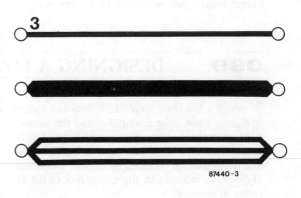

87440 -3

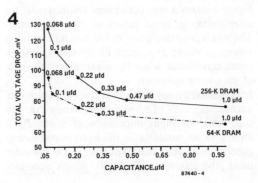

TOTAL VOLTAGE DROP.mV

CAPACITANCE.ufd

87440 - 4

127

Extremely short, unwanted, pulses with a period in the nanosecond range are often referred to as *glitches*, and occur in most, if not all, digital circuits. Whilst the circuit in question can be designed and built with due attention paid to effective suppression of glitches, it is not always possible to foresee the effects of external noise on, for instance, a clock signal. The filter presented here effectively rules out the presence of glitches in a serial data link.

Assuming that counter IC1 is at state nought, and that the data input is logic high, IC2 is configured as an AND gate. Output Q4 of IC1, and hence the output of the deglitcher, goes high after 8 clock pulses. A short negative pulse at the data input merely results in a few more clock pulses being required before Q4 is activated. After another 8 clock pulses, the counter state is 15. This causes the $\overline{\text{CI}}$ (CARRY IN) input of IC1 to be driven high, so that the clock signal remains blocked as long as the data input is logic high. When it goes low, IC2 is configured as a NOR gate, enabling the clock transitions to be counted down in IC1. Output Q4 goes low again after 8 clock pulses, and the counter is blocked after another 8 pulses. Therefore, the filtered output data is delayed by 8 clock periods,

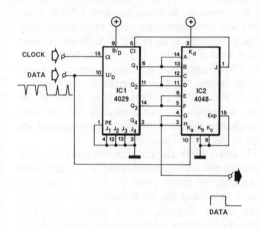

but this is insignificant in the proposed application. The data frequency, $f_{[D]}$, depends on the clock frequency, $f_{[CL]}$:

$$f_{[D]} = f_{[CL]}/16$$

The maximum usable clock frequency is about 8 MHz. The current consumption of this circuit is less than 1 mA.

To design a low noise amplifier, it does not suffice to choose a low noise opamp, because the components associated with the opamp, particularly resistors, are themselves sources of noise. The noise in a resistor, which is caused by random movement of electrons, increases by the square root of the increase in resistance.

Figure 1 shows a very convenient characteristic for determining optimum values of input resistance. The y-axis gives the square of the sum total of noise voltage produced in a circuit (in nV over the bandwidth considered), while the x-axis gives the value of the source resistance.

For instance, a noisy opamp like the 741, which produces some 70 nV of noise over its bandwidth, can cope with an input impedance of some 200 k (higher values would cause the input impedance to generate more noise than the opamp!). On the other hand, the less noisy TCA 520, which generates

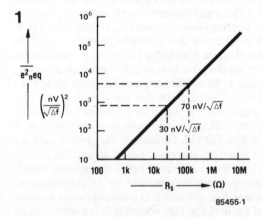

about 30 nV of noise over its bandwidth, should have an input impedance not greater than about 50 k.

It is not always convenient to use such relatively

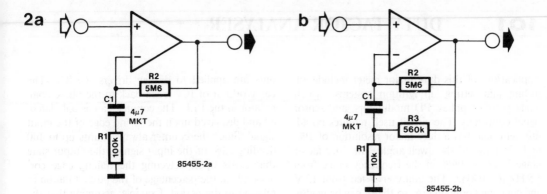

2a

R2
5M6

C1

4μ7
MKT

R1
100k

85455-2a

b

R2
5M6

C1

4μ7
MKT

R3
560k

R1
10k

85455-2b

low values of resistance. For example, the audio amplifier in figure 2a is intended to operate down to 0.3 Hz; because of that, the time constant, $\tau = RC$, must be fairly long. The input (=source) impedance of the opamp is determined primarily by R_1. Lower values of this resistor would require a higher value of C_1 and this is not acceptable on cost grounds. The solution to this problem is shown in figure 2b, where both the DC and AC amplification

are the same as in 1a, but because R_1 is 10 times as small, its noise voltage is reduced by $\sqrt{10}$.

Sources
Figure 1: *intuitive IC opamps*
(T M Frederiksen — National Semiconductor)

Figure 2: *technical note 068*
(Philips)

---

100   DISPLAY INTENSITY CONTROL

This is a light dependent voltage source that regulates the supply to 7-segment displays in accordance with the intensity of ambient light. The regulating action is positive, i.e., a higher ambient light intensity results in the circuit raising the supply voltage to the displays.

Phototransistor T_1 does not conduct when it detects darkness, and the base of T_2 is therefore grounded via R_2 and P_1 This causes the voltage at the emitter of this pnp darlington transistor to be about 1.2 V. The voltage across R_5 is the reference potential, 1.25 V, of the Type LM317 regulator, so that I_{R5} is about 5.7 mA, and the output voltage, U_o, of the circuit is

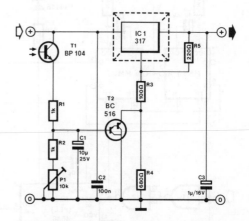

IC 1
317

T1
BP 104

R5
220Ω

R3
100Ω

T2
BC
516

R1
1k

R2
1k

C1
10μ
25V

P1
10k

C2
100n

R4
680Ω

C3
1μ/16V

$$U_o = 1.2 + [5.7 \times 10^{-3}(R_5 + R_3)]$$
$$= 1.2 + 1.82 \approx 3 \text{ volt}$$

when T_1 detects darkness. When it detects a relatively high light intensity, the base and emitter voltage of T_2 increase. When the base voltage of T_2 exceeds 2.7 V, R_4 limits the emitter voltage to 3.9 V due to the constant current of 5.7 mA. T_2 no longer

conducts and the output voltage of the circuit is 5.7 V, because the total resistance between the regulator output and ground is $R_5 + R_3 + R_4 = 1,000 \, \Omega$, and the current through it is still 5.7 mA. The sensitivity of the regulator is adjustable with P_1 The maximum output current is of the order of 700 mA when IC_1 is adequately cooled. The input voltage range of the circuit is 8 to 15 V.

Applications of this duty factor meter include adjusting and setting up ignition systems, switch mode power supplies, PD modulators, and sensor signal converters. The circuit itself requires no adjustment, and has a duty factor resolution of 1%, or 1° in terms of the dwell angle. The duty factor range is 1% to 99% in the frequency range from 1.5 Hz to 10 kHz. The analyser is fed from 12 V and consumes only 50 mA, so that it can be readily used in a car.

The measuring principle is straightforward. A PLL, IC_5, is used to multiply the input signal by a factor 100 and to clock counter IC_6-IC_7, whose BCD out-

puts are applied to display drivers IC_2-IC_3. The carry output of IC7 is fed back to the phase comparator in the PLL. The counter state is only latched and displayed upon the falling edge of the input signal. Since the counter always counts up to 100 (leading edge of the input signal); the output state that exists upon detecting the trailing edge corresponds to the percentage of the pulse duration in relation to the period. Example: assuming that the duty factor of the input signal is 60%, the counter is started at state 00 on the leading edge of the input signal, and is at state 60 when the trailing edge commences, so that '60' is latched and displayed. The

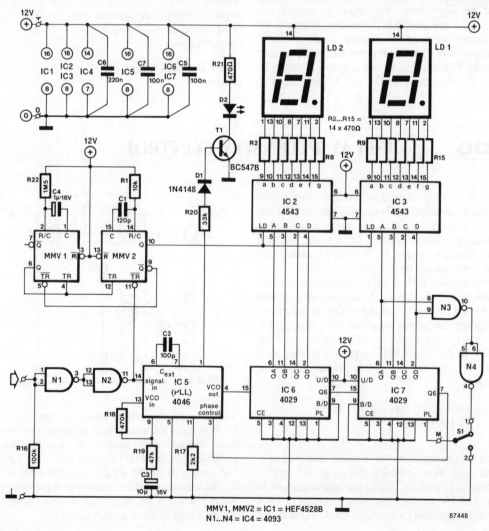

MMV1, MMV2 = IC1 = HEF4528B
N1...N4 = IC4 = 4093

87448

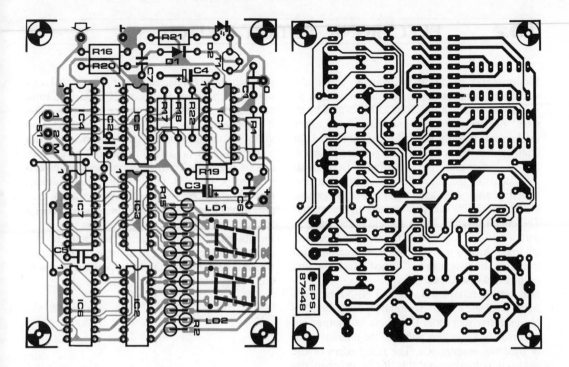

Parts list

Resistors (±5%):

$R_1 = 10K$
$R_2 \ldots R_{15}$ incl.; $R_{21} = 470R$
$R_{16} = 100K$
$R_{17} = 2K2$
$R_{18} = 470K$
$R_{19} = 47K$
$R_{20} = 33K$
$R_{22} = 1M5$

Capacitors:

$C_1 = 120p$
$C_2 = 100p$
$C_3 = 10\ \mu$; 16 V
$C_4 = 1\ \mu$; 16 V
$C_5; C_7 = 100n$
$C_6 = 220n$

Semiconductors:

$D_1 = 1N4148$
$D_2 = $ LED green
$T_1 = BC547B$
$IC_1 = 4528$
$IC_2; IC_3 = 4543$
$IC_4 = 4093$
$IC_5 = 4046$
$IC_6; IC_7 = 4029$
$LD_1; LD2 = $ common anode type, e.g. 7651 or 7766.

Miscellaneous:

$S_1 = $ miniature SPDT switch.
PCB Type 87448

latch pulse is generated with the aid of monostable IC_1 and timing parts R_1-C_1, while R_{22}-C_4 ensure that the display does not flicker when the input frequency is equal or close to the sample frequency. Each display value is so retained for about 0.5 s. Switch S_1 selects between duty factor (position 2, 0-99%) and dwell angle readings (position 1, 0-90°). The latter scale is obtained by programming a divide factor, and hence a PLL multiplication factor, of

90 with the aid of NAND gates N_3-N_4.
The input impedance of the duty factor analyser is 100 kΩ. Input signals should be at least 8 V_{pp}: a suitable preamplifier set up with a switching transistor may be added to increase the sensitivity.

Sooner or later, most types of frequently used multi-way rotary switches develop contact resistance instability or other malfunctions, either caused by internal oxidation or wear and tear of the rotary mechanism. Broadly speaking, the same goes for multi-contact relays. It is, therefore, hardly surprising to encounter the electronic, free-of-wear equivalents of the above devices; n-way electronic switches and solid-state relays are at present available in a wide variety of contact arrangements. The circuit diagram shows the electronic counterpart of a 16-way rotary switch whose pole is connected to earth. Two push buttons have been provided to enable the switch to be "turned" clockwise (up) or anticlockwise (down).

Debouncing bistables N_5-N_6 and N_7-N_8 supply a stable low logic level to monostables N_1-N_2 and N_3-N_4 respectively in order that these can output approximately 3.5 μs long pulses to the relevant input of up/down counter IC_1. The rising edges of the up/down pulse(s) cause this IC to generate the corresponding binary code at its $Q_A \ldots Q_D$ out-

puts, which are connected direct to the $D_1 \ldots D_4$ inputs of latching 4-to-16 decoder IC_2 which, in turn, activates the next lower or higher output $S_0 \ldots S_{15}$ if the relevant control button was activated. Provision has been made to "stop" the switch if this reaches its first or sixteenth position, which conditions cause the down or up monostable respectively to be disabled. Other switch configurations may be defined by using the correct active-low outputs to block gates N_2 and N_4 when the desired stop positions are reached.

Finally, push button S_3 resets the counter IC and consequently causes IC_2 to activate its S_0 output, which is also the default switch position at power-on.

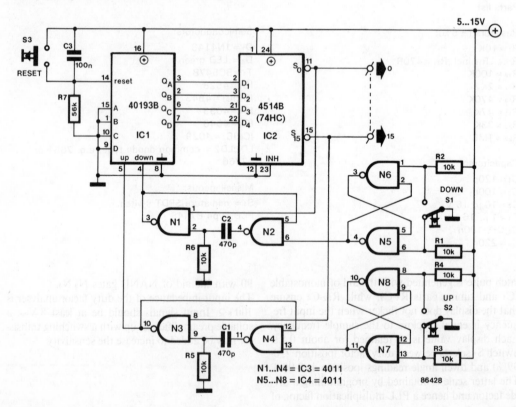

N1...N4 = IC3 = 4011
N5...N8 = IC4 = 4011

86428

The opto-coupler in the normal common emitter circuit at the output of a phototransistor is invariably too slow for use in data communication. Its great advantage remains, of course, the excellent isolation between transmitter and receiver.

To retain the advantage, the phototransistor has been integrated into a cascode circuit, as shown in figure 1. The photograph illustrates data transfer in a conventional circuit (top) and in the cascode circuit — the fast opto-coupler — (bottom) at a frequency of about 30 kHz.

The cascode circuit's faster operation is due to the transistor's internal Miller capacitance being of no consequence as the collector voltage remains constant. The result is a faster transistor.

The base of T_2 is biased at about 1.5 V by voltage divider R_1/R_2. Capacitor C_1 ensures that, even with rapid fluctuations in current, this voltage remains stable. If you consider T_2 as an emitter follower, it is clear that the collector of T_1 is always provided with a constant (direct) voltage, and this causes the Miller (base-to-collector) capacitance to be inactive. A disadvantage of the fast opto-coupler is that its output signal does not go down to 0 V but at best to 1 V. TTL devices like this just as little as they do a supply voltage of 12 V. Basically, the circuit can operate from 5 V, provided R_1 is altered suitably, but it is better to use CMOS devices.

Take care during experimenting not to exceed the maximum LED current (in the TIL 111) of 100 mA (this is the reason for dropping resistor R_v). The value of R_v is calculated from

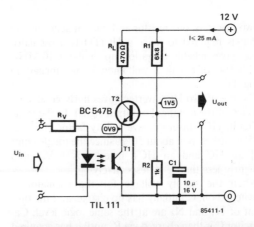

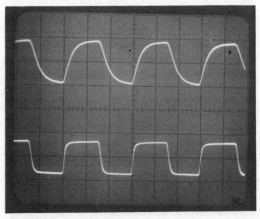

$$R_v = [(U_{in}-1.5)/I_{LED}]\Omega$$

where U_{in} is in volts and I_{LED} in amperes.

When a computer drives external equipment, it is often required that the earths between them are electrically isolated from one another. The simplest way of effecting this is by an isolating transformer. When, however, the system works at high frequencies, it is much better to use an opto-isolator as proposed here because that is capable of following the fast data transfer.

The opto-isolator is driven via a TTL gate. The transistor in the opto-isolator drives comparator IC_1. The trigger threshold of this device is set with P_1. Low-pass filter R_2-C_1 prevents spurious triggering of the comparator by noise pulses.

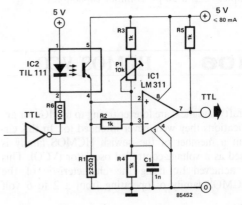

Two inverters, one resistor and one capacitor are all that is required to make a HC(T)-based oscillator that gives reliable operation up to about 10 MHz. This sort of circuit is well-known, and appears in Fig. 1a.

The use of two HC inverters gives fairly good symmetry of the rectangular output signal. In the same circuit, HCT inverters give a duty factor of about 25%, rather than about 50%, since the toggle point of an HC and an HCT inverter is $\frac{1}{2}V_{cc}$, and slightly less than 2 V, respectively.

When the supply voltage for the oscillator is switched on, C initially has no charge, and the output of N_1 and N_2 are at the same logic level. Capacitor C is then charged via R, until it has acquired a charge voltage that corresponds to the toggle voltage, U_s, of N_1. Assuming the output of N_2 initially to be logic low, the waveform of the signal at the input of N_1 is essentially as shown in Fig. 2. When C is charged up to level 1, the output of N_1 toggles, and so does that of N_2. This causes the voltage at the input of N_1 to rise, via C, to about $1.5V_{cc}$, so that C is reverse charged to level 3. From there on, the amplitude changes in a mirror-inverted way to reach the initial state again (level 5 is identical to 1), and the circuit oscillates. In practice, the curve in Fig. 2 is slightly flatter, because the peaks at levels 2 and 4 are clamped to +5 V and 0 V by the protective circuits internal to the inverters.

If the oscillator is to operate above 10 MHz, the resistor is replaced with a small inductor, as shown in Fig. 1b.

The output frequency of the circuit in Fig. 1a is given as about 1/1.8RC, and can be made variable by connecting a 100K preset in series with R. The solution adopted for the oscillator in Fig. 1b is even simpler: C is a 50 pF trimmer capacitor.

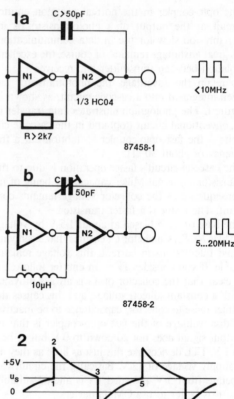

106   HCMOS VCO

Crafty designers are forever trying to use ICs for applications they were never intended for. In this circuit a member of the newish HCMOS family is used as a voltage-controlled oscillator (VCO). This is achieved by using the characteristic of the HCMOS family of operating from a 2 to 6 volt supply. However, at 6 V these ICs are faster than at 2 V.

In the present circuit, a "supply voltage" variable between 1.5 and 5 V is used as the input signal of the oscillator, which consists of three cascaded NAND gates. The VCO operates as follows: a logic

1 N1...N4 = IC1 = 74HC00
N5 = 1/6 74HC04

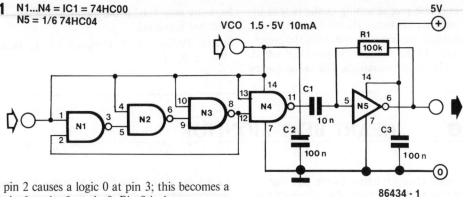

86434 - 1

1 at pin 2 causes a logic 0 at pin 3; this becomes a 1 at pin 6, and a 0 at pin 8. Pin 8 is, however, connected to pin 2, which, therefore, is no longer 1 but becomes 0. This 0, because of the delay times of the gates, appears a little later at pin 2 as a logic 1. And so on: the oscillator works! Gate N4 functions as a buffer for the oscillator output.

Since the peak output voltage cannot be greater than the supply voltage, i.e. the input voltage to the oscillator, its level must be adapted to those at the remainder of the circuit, which normally will be 5 V. This is ensured by inverter N5, which is powered by a genuine 5 V supply. Because of feedback resistor R1, the inverter is arranged as a linear amplifier. It is, therefore, sufficiently sensitive to amplify positive signals between 2 and 5 V adequately.

The characteristic in Fig. 2 shows that the VCO is reasonably linear. Other output frequencies are not possible with the circuit of Fig. 1, unless the

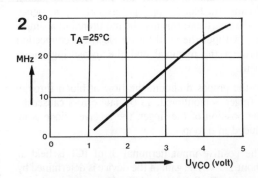

number of gates in the oscillator proper is extended by an even number of identical gates, which increases the total delay times, so that the frequency is lowered. It is also possible to add dividers to the output circuit.

107 HCU/HCT-BASED OSCILLATOR

When frequency stability is not of prime importance, a simple, yet reliable, digital clock oscillator can be made with the aid of relatively few components.

High-speed CMOS (HCU/HCT) inverters or gates with an inverter function are eminently suitable to make such oscillators, thanks to their low power consumption, good output signal definition and extensive frequency range.

The circuit as shown uses two inverters in a 74HCT04 or 74HCU04. The basic design equations are

for HCU: $f = 1/T$; $T = 2.2RC$; $3V < V_{cc} < 6V$; $I_c = 13$ mA

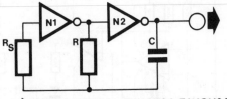

N1, N2 = 1/3 IC1 = 74HCT04, 74HCU04

87437

for HCT: $f = 1/T$; $T = 2.4RC$; $4.5V < V_{cc} < 5.5V$; $I_c = 2.25$ mA

$R_s \geq 2R$; $\quad$ $1K\Omega \leq R \leq 1M\Omega$; $\quad$ $C \geq 10$ nF.
With R_s and R calculated for a given frequency and value of C, both resistors can be realized as

135

presets to enable precise setting of the output frequency and the duty factor. Do not forget, however, to fit small series resistors in series with the presets, in observance of the minimum values for R and R_s as given in the design equations. The values quoted for I_c are only valid if the inputs of the remaining gates are grounded.

Source: *Philips CMOS Designers Guide*, January 1986, p. 105 ff.

108 HEART BEAT MONITOR

The proposed circuit is based on the fact that the degree of translucence of parts of a mammal's body depends, among others, on the flow of blood. Because the blood supply pulsates at the frequency of the heartbeat, this may be monitored in a simple way without the need for an electrical connection between the mammal and the measuring equipment.

In the proposed circuit, the flow of blood through a finger is monitored. To obviate errors caused by the position of the finger, the receiver diode is included in a loop.

The positive input (terminal 3) of IC1 is held at about 2.5 V. The gain of the device is determined by the ratio R_5:R_4. Network R_6-D_2 ensures that the circuit stabilizes rapidly. The amplified signal is rectified by IC_2. Time constants R_8-C_4 and R_7-C_4 are chosen such that the potential at pin 2 of IC_2 has

a sawtooth shape. The CA3130 in the IC_3 position functions as a trigger. The output signal may, for instance, be applied to the input port of a computer. If a computer is not available or deemed necessary, the beat is made audible by a piezo-electric buzzer operated by gates N_1 and N_2.

Circuit IC_5 provides a WAIT indication that shows when the circuit has stabilized and is ready for use. The programme is compiled as follows: wait for a trailing edge, then count until the next trailing edge appears. The count is converted into a number per minute, and this is displayed on the monitor screen. However, the heart beat is not constant, which is quite clear from listening to the buzzer or observing the monitor screen. It is, therefore, advisable to calculate an average over, say, sixty seconds. It is then possible to display the instantaneous value, the average value over 60 seconds, and the trend (rise or fall).

1

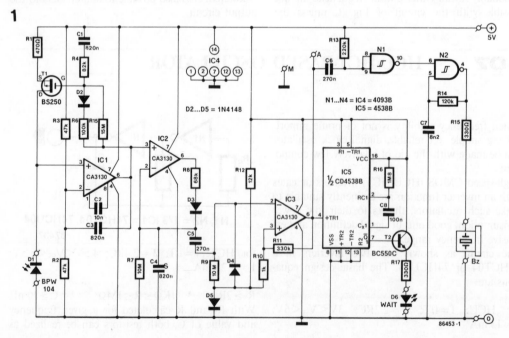

Once the programme is known to work satisfactorily, it becomes interesting to display the actual signal on the screen. If the computer used has an analogue-to-digital converter, the output signal of IC_1 may be used for the display.

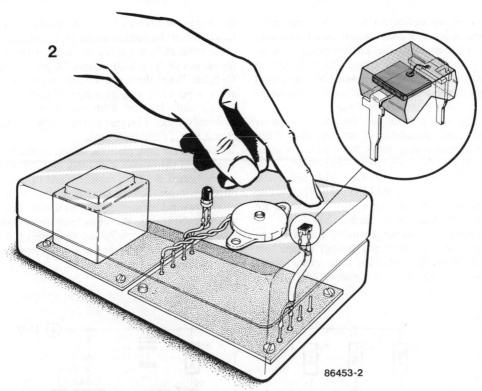

2

86453-2

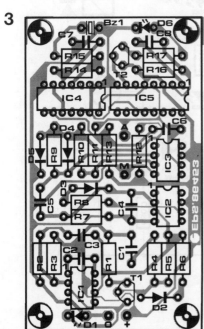

3

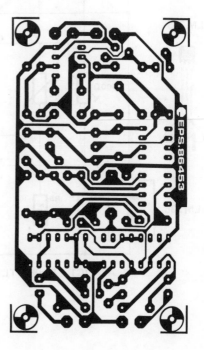

In almost any equipment in which a reasonable amount of energy is consumed, there is bound to be at least one heat sink that enables power semiconductors to get rid of their excess heat. The rating of a heat sink is normally determined on the basis of the maximum allowable temperature of the silicon chip: a rather haphazard method.

The heat sink monitor described here constantly monitors the temperature of the heat sink. When that temperature stays below 50...60°C, the green LED lights; between those temperatures and 70...80°C, the yellow (orange) LED lights; and above 70...80°C, the red LED lights. There is also the possibility of providing a relay with which, for instance, the load can be disconnected.

The circuit is, in essence, a window comparator, in which sensor D_1 provides a control voltage that rises 10 mV per degree Celsius. If the sensor voltage is lower than the voltage at the wipers of P_1 and P_2

the outputs of opamps A_1 and A_2 are low, and D_2 lights. When the voltage across D_1 lies above that at the wiper of P_1, but below that at the wiper of P_2 the output of A_1 is high, so that D_2 goes out and D_3 lights. When the sensor voltage rises above that at the wiper of P_2 also, the output of both opamps is high: only D_5 then lights and transistor T_1 is switched on. Zener D_4 ensures that D_5 lights brightly and that T_1 conducts hard.

To calibrate the unit, place the sensor, together with a calibrated thermometer, in a tray of water, which is then heated. Set P_1 to minimum and P_2 to maximum resistance. Set the cross over from green to yellow (orange) between 50 and 60 degrees Celsius with P_1 Next, set the cross over from yellow (orange) to red between 70 and 80 degrees Celsius with P_2 The sensor can then be fitted permanently onto the heat sink.

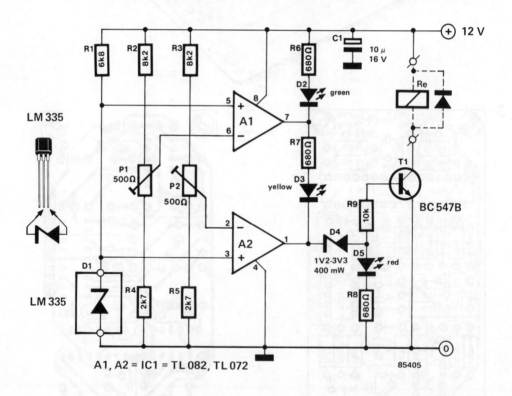

A1, A2 = IC1 = TL 082, TL 072   85405

110   LOGIC FAMILIES

The introduction of new, faster, CMOS techniques has given rise to a considerable increase in the number of available logic families. Understandably, this may cause confusion on the part of designers and users of logic circuits. Up until a few years, 3 families were commonly known: the CMOS 4xxx series; the TTL 74xx series; and the 74LSxx low-power Schottky series. TTL and LS chips are mutually interchangable, but TTL consumes considerably more current at the same switching speed. The 4xxx series is about 10 times slower than the TTL family, but is more economic as regards current consumption. In many cases, TTL chips are no longer considered suitable for new design.

The new HC and HCT CMOS families are just as fast as TTL and LSTTL, and have a greatly reduced current consumption. HCT chips can work in LS based circuits, provided they are not driven from TTL or LS. This is because of the differently defined switching levels. It is, however, possible to use HCT for driving HC. With this in mind, it is possible to replace the LS family by the HC family. This is preferable since the HC family offers the highest noise immunity.

Figure 1 shows the current consumption of a HCMOS gate as a function of the input voltage. The shaded area represents the (logic high) output voltage of an LS chip. From this, two conclusions can be drawn. Firstly, the noise margin is very narrow: the HC gate sees 2.7 V as a logic high level already. Secondly, the current consumption of the gate is a few mA higher than necessary. Although usable in practice, driving HC with LS is, therefore, not recommended.

Another new logic family was recently introduced: FACT (Fairchild Advanced CMOS Technology), also referred to as ACL (Advanced CMOS Logic) by other chip manufacturers. There are 2 versions: AC and ACT. ACT, like HCT, is fully LS compatible, while AC gives the same drive problems as HC. Both series are typically 2 to 3 times as fast as LS or HC.

Figure 2 shows the correlation between the propagation delay, t_p, and the power consumption, P, of various logic families. It will be noted that the modern CMOS families are almost as fast as the ECL series, hitherto renowned for its unbeatable speed. It is expected, therefore, that a CMOS equivalent will soon be available for ECL, and that ECL will gradually become obsolete.

Replacing bipolar chips in existing circuits with CMOS types is not very useful if relatively high frequencies are involved. Finally, a rule of thumb for working with chips of different families in a single circuit: *HCT can replace LS, unless driven by LS*.

For further reading:
RCA CMOS Databook
Fairchild FACT Logic Data Book

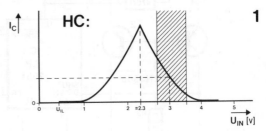

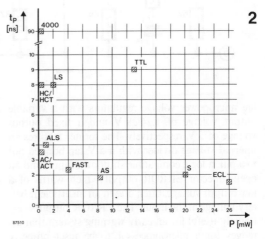

111   LOW VOLTAGE DROP REGULATORS

The fast spreading incorporation of CMOS, HC and HCT chips has created a need for voltage regulators with a very low internal drop to enable

powering CMOS-based equipment from a set of batteries delivering 6 V. The recently introduced Types LP2951 and LP2950 from National Semiconductor

1a)

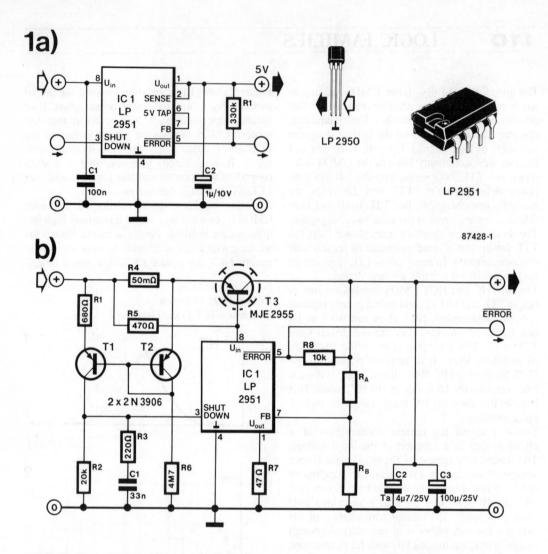

87428-1

b)

are micropower voltage regulators with a variable output voltage of 1.24-29 V and a fixed output voltage of 5 V, respectively. The former features an internal voltage divider with a 5 V tap bonded out to a pin, a logic compatible shutdown input, and an open-collector ERROR output which warns of a low output voltage, often due to an insufficient battery voltage at the input. The ERROR output is extremely useful for an early warning system that arranges for a microprocessor to be reset properly before the supply voltage falls to a level that would upset the operation of the system it controls.

The voltage drop across the LP2951 is only 0.4 V at a load current of 100 mA, so a 6 V battery pack can be used to power a 5 V circuit. The quiescent current drain of the regulator is about 12 mA at an output current of 100 mA. This is fairly high as

compared with a conventional regulator from the 78XX family, and mainly due to the internal series regulator transistor being driven into saturation, which causes it to have a relatively low current amplification factor (the base current flows into the ground return line, instead of into the output load, as with the typical 78XX regulator).

The application circuit shown in Fig. la should be fed from an input voltage of more than 5.4 V, while its maximum output current is 100 mA. Note that both the LP2950 and LP2951 feature internal current and thermal limiting circuits. The decoupling capacitor at the output of the regulator should be a good quality tantalum type, fitted as close as possible to pins 1 and 4. At relatively low output currents, less capacitance is required in this location. For currents below 10 mA, 0.33 μF is satisfactory, while the minimum value is 0.1 μF for currents below 1 mA. These values apply to an output voltage of 5 V; for lower voltages, more output capacitance is needed.

The circuit in Fig. 1b is a 2 A low dropout regulator based on the LP2951. The output voltage is calculated from

$$V_o = (1 + R_A/R_B)1.23V$$

where 1.23 stands for the voltage at the feedback input, pin 7. For an output of 5 V, R_A and R_B may be omitted, and the feedback input pin 7 can be connected direct to the 5 V tap (pin 6) output. The sense input, pin 2, is then connected to the V_o rail. In this application, V_{in} must be at least 0.5 V higher than V_o.

National Semiconductor applications.

112   MAINS ZERO-CROSSING DETECTOR

Both safe and remarkably simple to construct, this circuit detects the zero crossing moments of the mains voltage, in order to provide other circuitry with timing information about the correct instant for switching mains-connected loads; in other words, when the least possible switching dissipation is involved, and, therefore, least interference is induced on the mains lines.

The proposed circuit operates direct off the mains, while comprising no more than two opto-couplers and two resistors. It is seen that photodiodes D_1 and D_2 are connected in antiparallel while being fed with the mains voltage via a resistor, which limits the current through the relevant diode to about 2 mA as it conducts (i.e. lights) during the negative or the positive half wave (D_2 or D_1 respectively) of the mains sinewave; in either case, the circuit output voltage is low, since the associated phototransistor conducts and draws current from + Ub via R_2.

However, at the moment of zero crossing, neither one of the diodes conducts, and the voltage at the circuit output rises to near + Ub level, whence the 100 Hz pulse train.

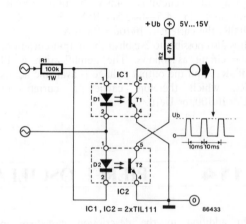

The value of R_2 may be adapted to suit the level of + Ub and the manufacturer-specified typical collector current through the phototransistor. For the Type TIL111, the current should not exceed about 50 mA. The type of optocoupler used in the circuit should not be very critical, but the value of R_1 had best be left at the indicated 100 k so as not to run into excessive diode dissipation.

113   OPAMP-BASED CURRENT SOURCE

A current source based on an operational amplifier alone is likely to be less known than the combination of an opamp and a transistor. This latter circuit can, however, only supply a unidirectional current, and must incorporate a stable reference capable of sourcing the required current. The circuit proposed here is different from the usual design for a current source, because it has a real differential, high impedance, input.

In spite of the small number of components in this circuit, its operation may not be apparent at a glance. An example calculation example may help to clarify how the current source works.

Assuming that 10 V is applied to input 2, and 4.5 V

141

to the output, the voltage drop across R_2 is 0.5 V, and that across R_4 is 5 V. It will be recalled that the output voltage of a current source is determined by the value of the external resistance. The current passed through this gives rise to a voltage drop that need not be constant.

When input 1 is 1 V more positive than input 2, the following circuit potentials can be deduced:

The + input of the opamp is at +9.5 V, because R_2 drops 0.5 V. The operational amplifier starts regulating its output voltage until it detects equal voltages at its + and − input. The voltage drop across R_1 thus rises from 0.5 V to 1.5 V, while that across R_3 is increased tenfold, i.e., amounts to 15 V. The output voltage of the opamp is then 11—1.5—15 = —5.5 V. When it is recalled that the output voltage of the circuit is +4.5 V, the drop across R_5 amounts to 4.5—(—5.5) = 10 V. Since R_5 = 100R, the current is 10/100 = 100 mA.

It is also possible to establish the output current of the circuit as follows. The amplification is 10 (R_3/R_1), and the output voltage is available across R_5, which therefore carries a current of $U_i \times 10/100$, or $U_i/10$.

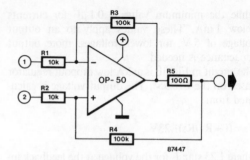

This circuit is probably best operated on the basis of power opamps, such as the Types L149 and L150 from SGS-Ates, which can handle currents of several ampères. The Type OP50 stated in the circuit diagram is suitable for relatively low output currents (I_{max} = 50 mA), and features excellent stability and precision. Its manufacturer, PMI, states that this application of the opamp is capable of handling resistive, capacitive or inductive loads equally well.

Source: *PMI, Analalog Applications Seminar 1986: Current transmitter (Howland current pump).*

114   PIERCE OSCILLATOR

In addition to the description elsewhere in this chapter of HC and HCT based R-C/L-C oscillators for use up to 20 MHz, this design brief concentrates on quartz-controlled oscillators which find applications in digital equipment and microprocessor systems. Such oscillators can only be made with HCU gates, because HC and HCT ones have buffered outputs that make them unsuitable for use as analogue amplifiers.

The circuit diagram shows a Pierce oscillator set up around a single gate in a Type 74HCU04 package. The inverter functions as an inverting amplifier with a phase shift of 180°. The circuit can be modified into a Collpits oscillator by replacing the quartz crystal with an inductor. It should be noted, however, that the use of a quartz crystal is more appropriate because it ensures minimum current consumption and adequate suppression of the third harmonic frequency. Finally, R_2 must be replaced with a 33p capacitor if the oscillator is operated above 4 MHz.

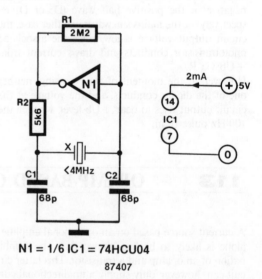

N1 = 1/6 IC1 = 74HCU04

87407

Most designers know that many problems may arise between the paper design and the practical realization of that design. We are, of course, no exception, and one incident that we experienced recently illustrates a problem that is of interest to pass on.

Measurements were being carried out on a circuit that contained some type NE 5532 opamps which were powered from a ±12 V symmetrical supply. When the circuit was switched on, it did not function correctly. Measuring the supply lines revealed that the positive supply was —0.6 V instead of +12 V. When the +12 V line only was switched off and immediately on again, the malfunction disappeared. Switching off the mains and immediately on again made the defect reappear. Using new opamps made no difference.

After some research in relevant literature, it appeared that on switching symmetrical power supplies temporary polarity reversal may occur. Because of the complex internal structure of integrated circuits, it may happen that this polarity reversal causes parasitic components on the chip to be actuated which places the IC in a stable but malfunctioning state.

The book we consulted, *Intuitive IC Opamps*, suggests that the malfunction we experienced was probably caused by a parasitic thyristor being trig-

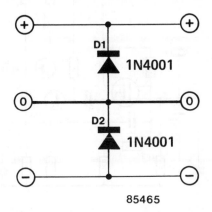

85465

gered owing to the negative supply not rising fast enough. The remedy proposed was to connect two diodes across the supply lines as shown in the accompanying figure: these diodes effectively prevent polarity reversal.

This simple remedy certainly cured the malfunction in our circuit and is probably the simplest protection circuit in this issue.

Literature:
Intuitive IC Opamps
by Thomas M Frederiksen
National Semiconductor Corporation

When designing crystal oscillators, it is good practice to ensure minimum capacitance of the active element(s), since any parasitic loading of the crystal is bound to derate the overall stability to some extent. This forms the underlying principle of the design described here, albeit that good results are also obtainable when an additional load capacitance is connected in parallel with the existing parasitic capacitance, but only if the former is known to possess a low loss factor and a low temperature coefficient, i.e., if it is a very high quality capacitor (and possibly difficult to obtain).

The oscillator proposed here is a Pierce type, in which the crystal operates in parallel mode. The input is formed by a bootstrapped source follower, DG MOSFET T_1, which has a parasitic capacitance of only 1 pF. RF transistors T_2-T_3 are set up as a cascode amplifier. A type BF494 transistor is used in the T_2 position because of its low B-E capacitance (0.15 pF typ.), which ensures a low output capacitance. The oscillator signal is taken from the source of T_1, buffered in T_4, and made logic compatible with the aid of gates N_1-N_3. The optimum inductance of L_1 is approximated with $L_1 = 1/f$, where the inductance and frequency are in milli-henries and megahertz respectively. Example: for f = 10 MHz, L_1 works out at 100 μH. Trimmer C_2 serves to accurately tune the crystal oscillator to the required frequency. The oscillator works well up to about 20 MHz.

Finally, although the dissipation of the crystal is not expected to give rise to instability, it is still a good

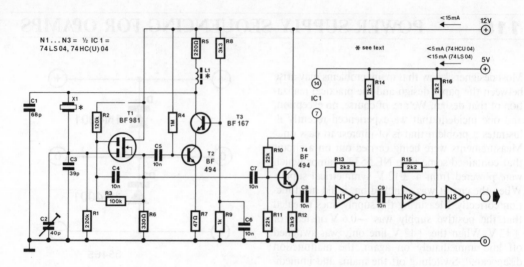

N1...N3 = ½ IC 1 =
74 LS 04, 74 HC(U) 04

idea to keep an eye on its output amplitude so as to preclude the protective diodes in T_1 being activated and causing unacceptable instability. If required, R_7 is altered until the signal amplitude at the emitter of T_4 is less than $1\ V_{pp}$.

117   SMART LED SELECTOR

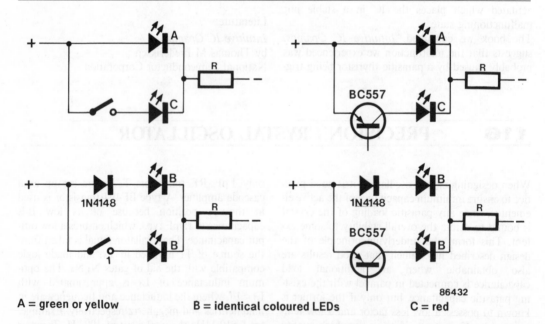

A = green or yellow   B = identical coloured LEDs   C = red

In this tiny circuit, for use in, for instance, a two-lights model railway signal, one of two LEDs may be selected with either a single pole switch or a series transistor, as shown in the circuit diagrams. Note that the LEDs are fed via a common current

limiter resistor, while a switch is connected in series with one of the LEDs.

Why do not both light simultaneously when the switch is closed? Because, apart from their colours, the two LEDs also differ as regards their forward voltage drop; when connected in parallel, therefore, the LED having the lower voltage drop should be fitted with the series switch; this arrangement causes the high voltage drop LED to light when the switch is open and to go out when the switch is closed, at which moment the other LED takes over. Two of the accompanying four small circuits show the use of a series switching transistor rather than a real switch, but the difference hardly requires further detailing, since applying sufficient drive to

the base is in fact the same as closing the switch. Two LEDs of identical colour may also be used as shown, and the additional series diode is seen to create the necessary voltage drop difference to distinguish between the LEDs, which, of course, have roughly the same on/off voltage characteristic. Finally, the value of R is established from the supply voltage level and the typical operating current of the LEDs, which is usually of the order of 20 mA for maximum allowable brightness.

118   SPEED CONTROL FOR DC MOTORS

Simple DC operated motors with a permanent magnetic stator behave as an independently energized motor. The speed of an ideal motor with an infinitely low internal resistance is in direct proportion to the voltage applied, irrespective of the torque. The motor thus runs at a speed at which its reverse electromotive force (e.m.f.) equals the supply voltage. The reverse e.m.f. is directly proportional to the force of the (constant) magnetic field, and the motor speed. In theory, therefore, the motor speed can be held constant with a constant supply voltage. The speed reduction observed in practice arises from the voltage drop across the internal resistance, R_i, of

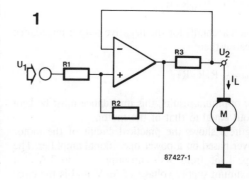

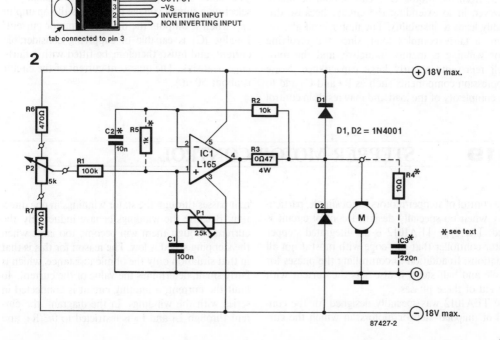

the armature winding. Thus, when the motor is loaded, its current consumption, and hence V_{Ri}, increases, reducing the effective supply voltage. This effect can be eliminated by means of R_i compensation, which essentially entails measuring the motor's current consumption, relating this to the motor's instantaneous drop across Ri, and increasing the supply voltage accordingly. In fact, this calls for a voltage source with a negative output impedance, since it caters for a higher output voltage when the load is increased.

The basic set-up of the supply required here is shown in Fig. 1. The load current is measured as the drop across sensing resistor R_3. The DC transfer function of this amplifier is written as

$$U_2 = U_1 + I_L R_2 R_3 / R_1$$

which accounts for the negative output impedance because then

$$R_{out} = -R_2 R_3 / R_1$$

For optimum results, this impedance must be kept about equal to that of the motor.

Figure 2 shows the practical circuit of the motor driver based on a power operational amplifier. The Type L165 from SGS can supply up to 3 A at a maximum supply voltage of 36 V, and is therefore eminently suitable for the present application. Capacitors C_1 and C_2 suppress noise on the reverse e.m.f. from the motor. Due care should be taken, however, in so extending the circuit, because this readily leads to instability. The motor itself already forms a fairly complex load, since the revolving rotor winding is mainly inductive, and the rotor itself represents a fairly large capacitance. Noise suppression components such as R_4 and C_3 add to the complexity of the load and may result in control instability, which becomes manifest in the motor's tendency to alternately reverse its direction at a relatively low rate. Also, the response to a fast change in the torque may be impaired, and high-frequency oscillation may occur (noticeable as exessive heating of IC_1 and/or R_4). When the circuit was tested with a small PCB drill, best results were obtained by omitting R_4-C_3 and including C_2. If the motor has a noise suppression network, C_2 must be omitted, and R_5 added to protect the opamp inputs against too high differential voltages as a result of commutation voltage peaks. Clearly, D_1 and D_2 have been included with this in mind.

Preset P_1 is adjusted until the motor remains stable. Over-compensation of the motor will give rise to apparently uncontrolled movement. The adjustment of P_1 should be carried out when the motor has not yet reached its normal operating temperature, because its self-heating gives rise to an increase in the internal resistance.

The use of a symmetrical supply (± 18 V max.) enables twoquadrant operation of the motor (cw/ccw rotation), which can then be used to power model trains and the like. The motor is halted when P_2 is set to the centre position. The ground rail may be connected to the negative supply rail if only one direction of revolution is required (PCB drills). The maximum supply is then 36 V, making a greater voltage available for the motor, so that 24 V types can be controlled also, although it is not possible to completely halt these.

The motor can be protected against overloading by selecting a supply voltage that causes the opamp to clip when it outputs the maximum motor current. Finally, IC_1 is capable of supplying considerable current, and must, therefore, be fitted with a fairly large heat-sink. The quiescent current of the circuit is about 50 mA.

119   STEPPER MOTOR CONTROL

The control of stepper motors is not simple, particularly when no specially designed control circuit is used. The Type TEA1012 is an integrated stepper motor controller that can cope with most if not all situations. In addition to controlling the phases for whole and half steps, it also sets the current with the aid of these phases.

The TEA1012 was specially designed for the control of unipolar stepper motors, in which the current passes through the stator windings in one direction. Because the windings behave inductively, the current through them will become too large when the stepping speed is low. The reason for this is that in that situation only the ohmic resistance, which is fairly small, determines the value of the current. To limit the current, a limiting circuit is connected in series with the windings. In the diagram, the current through L_1 and L_2 is restricted to $0.3/R_4$, and

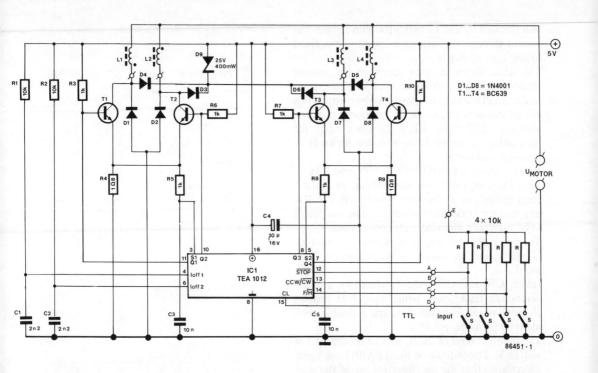

86451 - 1

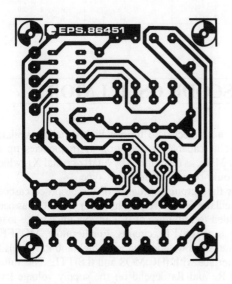

EPS.86451

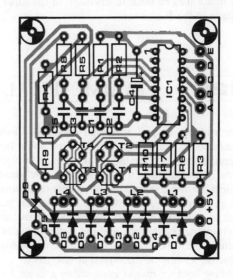

Parts list

Resistors:
$R_1;R_2 = 10$ k
$R_3;R_5;R_6;R_7;R_8;R_{10} = 1$ k
$R_4;R_9 = 1\Omega8$

Capacitors:
$C_1;C_2 = 2n2$
$C_3;C_5 = 10$ n
$C_4 = 10\ \mu;16$ V

Semiconductors:
$T_1;T_2;T_3;T_4 = BC639$
D_1 to D_8 incl. $= 1N4001$
$D_9 =$ zener 25 V;400 mW
$IC_1 = TEA1012$

PCB 86451

that through L_3 and L_4 to $0.3/R_9$. This enables the current through the stator windings to be adapted to any type of motor.

The table shows in what sequence the various phases are driven with full and half step control, as well as for clockwise and anticlockwise control. The stepper motor is arrested in the position it occupies with the STOP input. CL is the clock input: for each pulse, the motor turns one step forwards or one step backwards.

Because inputs CL, $\overline{STOP}$, CCW/$\overline{CW}$, and F/$\overline{H}$ all are TTL compatible, it is not difficult to connect these controls to a computer. Resistors R_{11} to R_{14} incl. and the associated switches, enable the circuit to be manually provided with control data.

The maximum stepping speed depends on the type of motor and on switch-off time-constants $T_{off(1)}$ and $T_{off(2)}$.

Letters CW and CCW signify clockwise and anticlockwise respectively, while input F/$\overline{H}$ enables choosing whole (F) or half (H) steps. A double resolution is, therefore, possible.

The supply voltage of the IC may be between 4.5 V and 15 V. The outputs of the TEA1012 are open-collector, so that the operating voltage of the stepper motor may be made independent of the supply voltage to the IC.

Table

CL-	inputs			outputs			
	F/$\overline{H}$	CCW/$\overline{CW}$	$\overline{STOP}$	Q1	Q2	Q3	Q4
	half	clockwise	run				
1	0	0	1	0	0	0	1
2	0	0	1	0	1	0	1
3	0	0	1	0	1	0	0
4	0	0	1	0	1	1	0
5	0	0	1	0	0	1	0
6	0	0	1	1	0	1	0
7	0	0	1	1	0	0	0
8	0	0	1	1	0	0	1
	half	counter clockwise	run				
1	0	1	1	1	0	0	1
2	0	1	1	1	0	0	0
3	0	1	1	1	0	1	0
4	0	1	1	0	0	1	0
5	0	1	1	0	1	1	0
6	0	1	1	0	1	0	0
7	0	1	1	0	1	0	1
8	0	1	1	0	0	0	1
	full	clockwise	run				
1	1	0	1	1	0	0	1
2	1	0	1	1	0	1	0
3	1	0	1	0	1	1	0
4	1	0	1	0	1	0	1
	full	counter clockwise	run				
1	1	1	1	0	1	0	1
2	1	1	1	0	1	1	0
3	1	1	1	1	0	1	0
4	1	1	1	1	0	0	1

120   SYMMETRICAL CASCODE OSCILLATOR

Free running as well as crystal controlled clock generators in many digital designs are most frequently based upon the use of one or more inverter gates. However easy it may seem to use these devices for the construction of reliable oscillators, the resultant frequency stability is generally not such as might be expected from a look at the relevant quartz crystal data, and this is mainly on account of the rather poorly defined capacitive and/or inductive loading of the crystal at resonance.

Stability, however, may be improved by a factor 3 to 5 by using cascode type inverters in a symmetrical configuration, as can be seen in the accompanying circuit diagram. Two sets of two n- and p-channel MOSFETs, contained in the Type 4007UB IC, have been connected to form a highly stable oscillator circuit capable of operation at frequencies up to 10 MHz, as determined by quartz crystal X_1, which should be a series resonant type.

As the output impedance of the proposed cascode oscillator is relatively high, buffer stage T_1 has been added to minimize drift with low impedance loads such as (LS)TTL circuits. Furthermore, MOSFET T_1 ensures well-defined logic high and low levels to interface with (HC)MOS and (LS)TTL. The values of R_4 and R_5 depend on the supply voltage level (U_b), while the voltage at gate 2 should be between 4 and 6 V to achieve a 5 V output level swing. In case the oscillator is to operate from a 5 V supply, gate 2 of T_1 must be connected direct to $+U_b$.

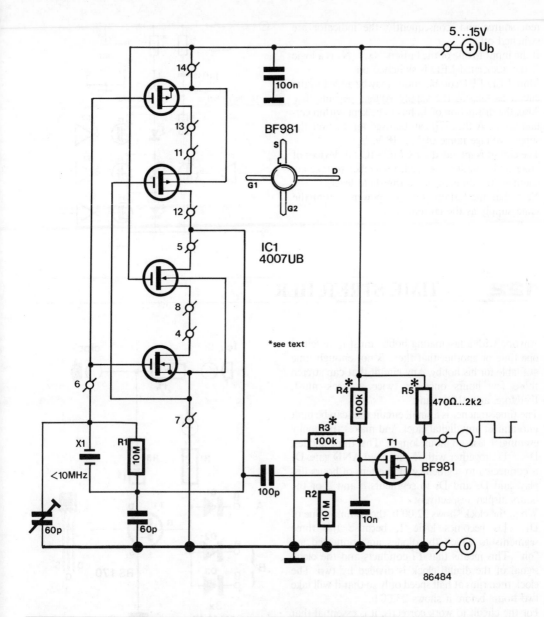

5...15V

Ub

100n

BF981

S

G1

D

G2

IC1
4007UB

*see text

R4*
100k

R5*
470Ω...2k2

R3*
100k

T1

BF981

X1

<10MHz

R1
10M

6

7

100p

R2
10M

10n

60p

60p

0

86484

121   THRIFTY LED INDICATOR

It is often necessary that the current consumption of an essential status indicator is minimal. In the circuit shown, dependent on the level of the supply voltage, a number of LEDs drawing a current of only 10...15 mA may be switched on or off as desired. Moreover, the entire indicator may be switched off if none of the LEDs lights.

The circuit is based on switched current source T_1.

The base current of this transistor is set at c. 15 mA with R_x. The value of this resistor is calculated from

$$R_x = [4 \times 10^6/(U_b - 0.7)] \; \Omega$$

where U_b is the supply voltage in volts.

Transistor T_2 conducts when the input to inverter N_1 is logic 0: when this becomes a logic 1, the current source and, consequently, the indicator are switched off.

If the input to one of the buffers N2...N4 is a logic 1, the associated LED is switched on.

More LED-FET combinations may be added to the circuit as long as the supply voltage permits this. Also, the dissipation of T1 has to be kept within certain limits. A BC557B can be used for T1 over the supply voltage range of 5...18 V.

The circuit is intended for CMOS ICs; if devices of other logic families are used, remember to take account of the different logic threshold levels.

Note that the buffers must be powered from the same supply as the current source.

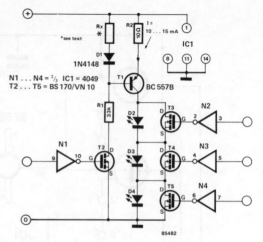

122   TIME STRETCHER

Anyone with a fascinating hobby must have felt at one time or another that there is not enough time available for his hobby. Any circuit that can stretch those few hours once or twice a week must, therefore, appeal to many.

The time stretcher is a small circuit that can be built into almost any digital clock and makes the hobby evening(s) last an hour longer. The three diodes, D1...D3, together with R1, form an AND gate. D1 is connected to segment g of the tens-of-hours display, and D2 and D3 to segments e and g of the hours display respectively.

When the clock shows 22.00 h, the common line of D1...D3 becomes logic 1, because the three segments to which the diodes are connected are "on". This means that T1 conducts and the clock signal of the digital clock is divided by two. The clock then runs at half speed only so that it will take two hours before it shows 23.00 h.

For the circuit to work correctly, it is essential that the clock signal is divided by two exactly, and this means that resistors R2 and R3 must be 1 per cent types. This is also the reason that a BS 170 is used as the switching gate; this MOSFET has no saturation voltage. Using a normal transistor with a certain saturation voltage would not cause the clock signal to be divided by two exactly, so that the clock would be fast or slow by minutes within a few days! The circuit as drawn is intended for common-anode displays; if it is to be used with common-cathode displays, simply reverse the connections of diodes D1...D3.

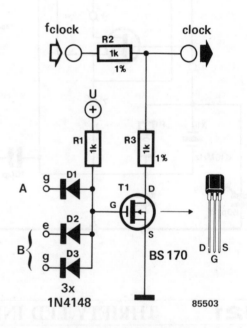

A = tens of hours display
B = hours display

150

The use of comparator circuits in many different appearances and practical realizations is common in a wide variety of electronic control and measurement systems. Usually, the voltage from a sensor device is fed to a comparator which, as its name implies, compares the measured level, U_{in}, with a fixed reference, U_{ref}, and produces a negative output (0) or positive output (1) when $U_{in} < U_{ref}$ and $U_{in} > U_{ref}$, respectively. A *window comparator* can be made by connecting two comparators with different reference levels, which define the upper and lower limit of the switching range.

In practice, these references are usually adjusted with presets to dimension the window as required. This arrangement makes it impossible, however, to automatically shift the window up or down in accordance with, say, ambient light conditions to be measured with a light dependent resistor.

This circuit has no fixed threshold levels, but derives its reference from the measured signal, so that slow changes in this cause the window to track along.

Capacitors C_1 at the inverting input of A_1, and C_2 at the non-inverting input of A_2 store the input voltage. When the voltage at the non-inverting input of A_1 rises, this opamp toggles. The associated inverting input lags this change because of the delay introduced by the capacitor. LED D_1 lights. The process is similar in the A_2 section of the circuit when the input voltage drops. This is indicated by LED D_2 lighting.

Diodes D_3 and D_4 form an OR function to actuate a simple relay driver set up with T_1. The relay is energized when the circuit detects a fast change in the input voltage. The ability of the circuit to accept a variable input voltage makes it suitable for use in burglar alarms—see Fig. 1b. Several break contact arrangements R_{13}-S_1-R_{14} may be connected in series and to the input of the window comparator. Alarm relay Re_1 is activated when either S_1 is opened or S_1-R_{14} is bypassed. To prevent burglars from fooling the alarm, R_{14} must be fitted into S_1, because no alarm signal is given when only S_1 is shorted.

The sensitivity of the tracking window comparator is defined by the ratios R_2/R_3 and R_5/R_6. The relevant component values indicated in the circuit diagram give 1:100 ratio, so that, for example, a fast change of 30 mV is detected when the input voltage is 3 V. The sensitivity also depends on the input voltage. Although the circuit can in principle handle any input between 0 V and the supply level,

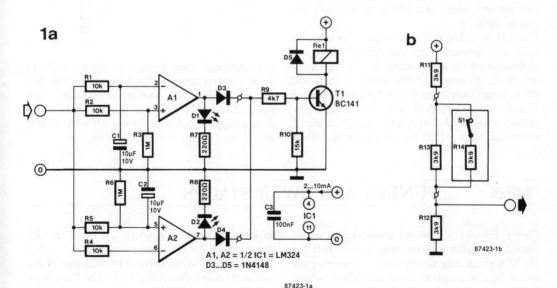

1a   **b**

A1, A2 = 1/2 IC1 = LM324
D3...D5 = 1N4148

87423-1a

87423-1b

the ICs used give reliable operation only when driven between 1 and U_b—1 volt.

The tracking window comparator is preferably fed with a supply between 5 and 15 V. Its current con-sumption, inclusive of the LEDs but exclusive of the relay, is 10 mA maximum (note that the relay can be fed separately).

---

124   TRANSMISSION LINES FOR TTL CIRCUITS

Although cable connections between TTL circuits are normally not as critical as those for, say, RF applications, it is still worth while to reflect on this subject because strange things often happen when a TTL transmission line is not correctly terminated. In particular, this discussion is about terminating coaxial cable and flat ribbon cable. The latter is frequently used for driving Centronics compatible inputs.

A commonly used coaxial cable is RG59B/U, which has a characteristic impedance of 75 Ω and a propagation delay of 5 ns/m. With signal rise and fall times of 4 ns, the cable may be considered electrically long if it exceeds 40 cm. One of the most common terminations used when driving a long coaxial cable with an LSTTL gate is shown in Fig. 1. This set-up is unsuitable for a HCT bus driver, since the termination provides a poor impedance match, and requires a current sinking capability of 20 mA. An improved termination circuit is shown in Fig. 2: this ensures reliable signal transmission for cables up to 15 m. Note that the 1 kΩ pull-up resistor is only required when the driver is an open collector gate or buffer.

Flat ribbon cable often introduces considerable cross-talk between wires, especially when terminated in HC(T) gates, which form a high input impedance. In general, a flat ribbon cable should not be longer than about 60 cm, but longer runs are possible when individual wires are separated by grounded wires (1.8 m max.), or when each wire is terminated with a 1 kΩ pull-up resistor (1.2 m). A

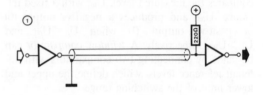

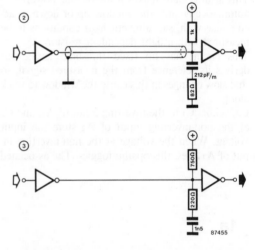

combination of these methods makes it possible to use flat ribbon cables with a length up to 2 m, but this is also attainable without ground wires—see Fig. 3. The combined use of this termination network and grounded wires in the flat ribbon cable should enable a cable length of about 5 m.

---

125   TUNING AF POWER STAGES

Simple, economically priced audio output stages, such as, for instance, those using the hybrid ICs in the STK series, may be improved in a simple manner as regards distortion, noise, and off-set voltage. To this end, the output amplifier is included in the feedback loop of an op-amp. Fig. 1 shows the set-up for inverting output amplifiers, and Fig. 2 that for non-inverting ones (the normal situation).

In the calculations to arrive at the new gain of the output amplifier, determined by R_1 and R_2, it is assumed that the LF356 provides an undistorted signal of 5 V_{rms}; note also that this type of op-amp must work into a load of not less than 5 kilo-ohms to prevent distortion.

For an output power of 50 W into 4 ohms, the output stage must provide a voltage, $U = PR = 14.2$ Vrms. If the amplification of the stage is 3, the op-amp should deliver 4.73 V. For the set-up in Fig. 1, the value of R_2 is then $R_2 = 3R_1$, while for that in Fig. 2, $R_2 = 2R_1$. Note that in both versions only the value of R_1 should be altered. The total amplification may be calculated from the ratio of R_A and R_B as follows: $A = (R_A + R_B)/R_B$. Furthermore, because of the load impedance of the op-amp, $R_1 > 10$ k (Fig. 1); $R_2 > 10$ k (Fig. 2); $R_A > 10\ \Omega$; and $R_C > 10\ \Omega$ (Fig. 1 and 2).

To compensate for the off-set voltage of the output amplifier, the input capacitor should be replaced by a wire link. The capacitor in series with R_1 in Fig. 2 should also be short-circuited. The lower frequency limit of the complete circuit is then determined by $C_B = 1/2\pi f_{lim} R_B$. The off-set voltage is then smaller than 3 mV, provided both R_A and R_c are equal to, or greater than, 100 kΩ. Where greater accuracy is required, P_1 can be used to set the off-set to exactly 0 V.

To ensure that there is no direct voltage at the new input of the amplifier, capacitor C_C should have a value of $C_C = 1/f_{lim} R_C$.

Since the amplification of the output stage has been reduced to 3, its feedback factor has gone up, and the distortion has gone down. The additional feedback of the LF356 reduces the distortion even further. An overall reduction in the distortion from 1 per cent to 0.1 per cent is fairly typical. The altered feedback unfortunately results in a change in stability. If there is a tendency to oscillate, the first thing to do is to bring the upper frequency limit back to its previous value with the aid of $C_Y = 1/2\pi f_{lim} R_A$. If the tendency persists, capacitors

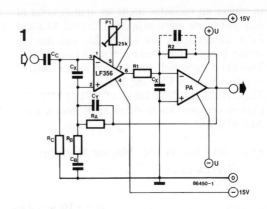

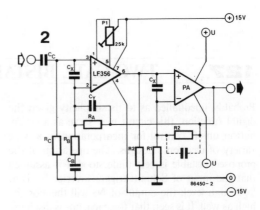

C_X must be used: their value lies between 100 pF and 1 nF. Our prototype (using STK ICs) worked satisfactorily without either C_X or C_Y.

---

126   TWO-FREQUENCY OSCILLATOR

Not so long ago, when semiconductors were still quite expensive, it paid to make a transistor serve more than one function. Although this is no longer necessary because of cost considerations, it is still fun to do so — and it may even have its uses!

The circuit presented here is an *LC* oscillator that changes frequency through reversal of the supply voltage.

When the supply voltage is positive, D_1 conducts

and short-circuits L_1C_1. Oscillations are then maintained by crystal XL_2 and L_2C_2. The DC operating point is set by P_1 in a way which ensures a compromise between faultless starting of the oscillator and low distortion of the output signal.

When the polarity of the supply voltage is reversed, transistor T_1 operates in its inverted mode, i.e., the functions of emitter and collector are interchanged. This means that the amplification is reduced, but, of course, an oscillator needs an amplification of only just above unity to operate. Crystal XL_2 and L_2C_2 are effectively cut out by D_2, and the frequency is now determined by crystal XL_1 and L_1C_1. The circuit lends itself, for instance, for use as BFO switched between USB and LSB.

The crystals may have values of up to 1 MHz. Current consumption in either mode does not exceed 45 mA.

From an idea in the *Master Handbook of 1001 Electronic Circuits*.

$$U = +10 \text{ V} \rightarrow f_{X2}$$
$$U = -10 \text{ V} \rightarrow f_{X1}$$

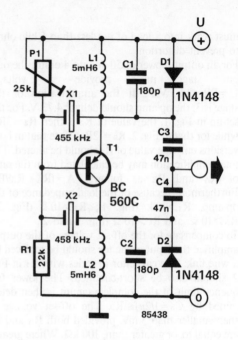

127 TWO-GATE BISTABLE

Probably unequalled as to its simplicity given the digital function, this circuit may serve as a single-button on/off control for incorporation in a wide variety of electronic designs. The operation of the proposed bistable is best understood if it assumed that the input of Schmitt-trigger inverter N_1 is at logic high level; the output of N_2 will therefore be high as well. It is seen that the capacitor is discharged because of the low output level of N_1. Therefore, depression of the button pulls the input of N_1 to logic low level, causing the bistable to toggle; the capacitor is charged via the 1 M resistor, and the circuit will change state again at the next switch action. The indicated resistor values have been found

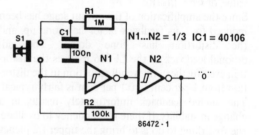

to offer optimum stability of the bistable, while the use of Schmitt-trigger CMOS inverters is essential to the correct operation.

128 UP/DOWN CLOCK GENERATOR

Various designs of clock generators have appeared in previous Summer Circuits issues of *Elektor Electronics*, and this tradition is kept up with the present design which, unlike the other circuits, outputs an up/down indication as well as a rectangular signal over a wide frequency range; 0 Hz to several kHz.

The output signal and the U/D̄ indication are both

controlled by a single potentiometer. If this is set to the centre of its travel, nothing happens; turning the potentiometer in the clockwise direction causes the U/D̄ output to be at logic high level, and the frequency of the output signal rises with turning P_1 further in this direction. The same goes for turning it anti-clockwise, U/D̄ being at low logic level.

154

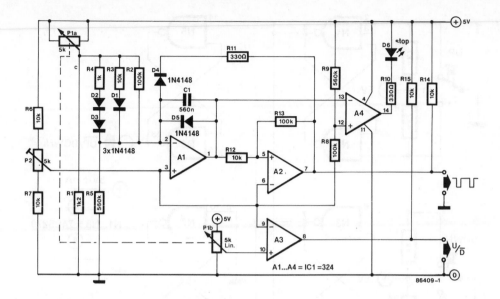

The basic operation of the circuit is as follows. Operational amplifiers A_1 and A_2 together constitute a sawtooth/square wave generator. The falling edge of the sawtooth voltage has a fixed duration of about 200 μs, as defined by the current through D_4. The rising edge time, however, depends on the voltage at the wiper of P_1. The wiper of P_2 is arranged to be at a slightly higher voltage than that at the wiper of P_1, when this is set to the centre of its travel. The STOP LED will light in this condition. If P_1 is turned in either direction, the voltage across R_1 rises and causes a low current to flow through R_2. This current, and therefore the output frequency, is proportional to the position of the wiper of P_1, but this only goes for a limited frequency range. If the voltage across R_2 exceeds about 0.6 V, D_1 conducts and connects R_3 in parallel to R_2. D_2 and D_3 do the same for R_4 at about 1.2 V; this method causes the oscillator frequency to be an exponential function of the voltage, set with P_1; the arrangement ensures a considerable output frequency range for the oscillator A_1-A_2.

Together with one or more universal counter modules (see *Elektor Electronics*, March 1985), the proposed clock generator may offer a neat replace-

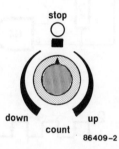

ment of the well-known BCD coded thumbwheel switches; the potentiometer-set value is present at the $Q_1...Q_4$ outputs of IC_2, as well as visible on the seven-segment display.

The U/$\overline{D}$ and clock output of the present generator are connected to the relevant points on the modules, as explained in the above mentioned article, but remember to observe the different supply voltages of clock generator and counter module; keep all points marked +5V at that voltage, except the supply pin of the LM324 and R_{14} and R_{15}, which are connected to the counter module +12 V supply. Current consumption of the present up/down clock generator is modest at about 10mA.

---

129   UP/DOWN COUNTER CONTROL

The up/down binary- or BCD-mode counter is a regularly spotted item in digital circuits of various levels of complexity. The up/down counter simply does what its name indicates; it counts up or down, depending on the logic level applied at the relevant control input, and activates the corresponding out-

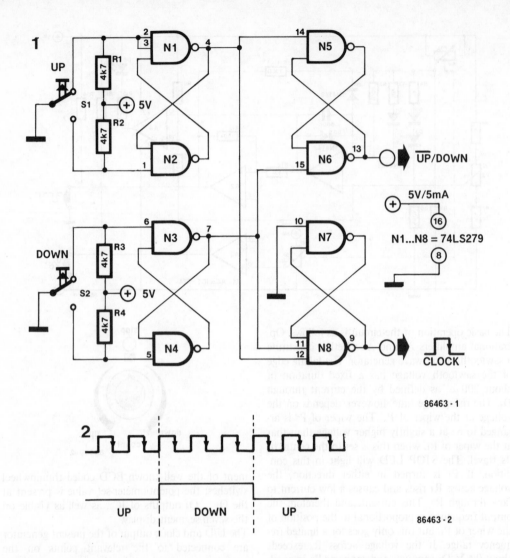

1

2

UP   DOWN   UP

86463 - 1

86463 - 2

put bit pattern at every pulse transition detected at the chip's clock input.

This circuit simplifies the control of up/down counters in that it allows the user to press one button to increment the counter output state, while another decrements it. Each of the changeover type buttons is connected to a two-gate debouncer/bistable (N1-N2 and N3-N4), which supplies a low pulse at its output when the relevant button is pressed. N8, which serves as an OR gate, receives the debouncer pulses and, together with N8, provides the output clock pulse to the up/down counter.

Bistable N5-N6 keeps track of the selected count mode, and provides the relevant logic level to the up/down counter input. It should be noted that the logic level designation of the up/down input to the

counter chip may differ from type to type; it may therefore be necessary to interchange the UP and DOWN keys.

The use of counter chips changing output state on the negative clock transition is to be preferred for use with the suggested circuit, since bistable N5-N6 toggles coincidently with the positive clock pulse transision (see Fig. 2). However a minor disadvantage of the use of negative-edge clocked up/down counters lies in the fact that the circuit acts upon release rather than depression of the UP and DOWN buttons.

Finally, the use of the Type 74LS279 is in no way compulsory; a combination of other types of TTL IC incorporating the necessary NAND gates should work equally well, but note the three-input NAND gate N8!

This simple-looking circuit enables the arbitrary programming of seven outputs in a series of not more than 2048 (2^{11}) steps. The step length may be set as required. The time base is derived from the mains voltage. Transistor T_1 produces a square wave from the mains voltage applied to its base. This square-wave voltage is divided by 10 in IC_1, so that the frequency of the signal at the clock input of IC_2 is 5 Hz. Circuit IC_2 serves as address counter for the Type 2716 EPROM. This means that IC_2, after a reset, counts upwards from $\emptyset$ and runs over the successive addresses of the EPROM. Circuit IC_2 has twelve outputs which would enable the use of a Type 2732 (4096 steps), but, on practical and financial grounds, a Type 2716 is used here since 2048 steps are normally quite sufficient.

The outputs of the EPROM are buffered by a Darlington array, IC_5, so that seven switch outputs are available with a sink capacity of 500 mA at a maximum voltage of 50 V. The eighth output contains the stop-bit that provides the facility of stopping the programme if this is shorter than 2048 steps.

The start-stop circuit is based on bistable N_3-N_4. When the supply is switched on, IC_2 ensures that the bistable resets from the stop state. This means

that both divider IC_1 and counter IC_2 are in position "zero". The first address in the EPROM must, therefore, have a neutral content, because it is addressed in the stop state and thus appears at the output.

The bistable is set, and both resets cleared, when the start button is pressed. Circuit IC_1 then commences to divide, and IC_2 starts to count. With the present time base, the programmed content of successive addresses will appear at the output of the buffers at 0.2 s intervals. Counting continues until a stop-bit appears at pin D_7 of the EPROM, or stop button S_1 is pressed. If required, a HOLD function may be obtained by connecting a switch across capacitor C_1, which enables the time base to be switched off.

Switching on a specific output a....g merely requires the corresponding bit position in the EPROM to be left unprogrammed (logic high); programming a $\emptyset$ disables the relevant output. The stop-bit operates with negative logic: a $\emptyset$ therefore causes a stop.

Finally, the time base may be adapted for the setting of the required step frequency and accuracy.

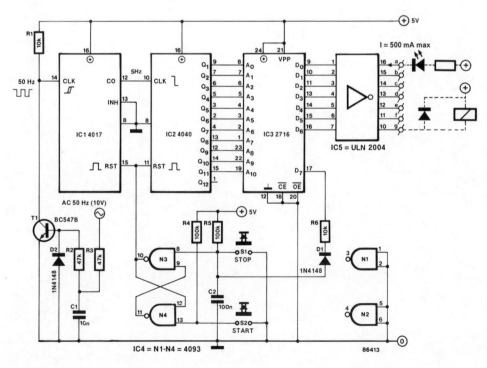

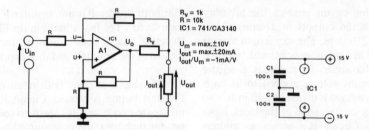

$R_v = 1k$
$R = 10k$
$IC1 = 741/CA3140$

$U_m = max.\pm10V$
$I_{out} = max.\pm20mA$
$I_{out}/U_m = -1mA/V$

The converter proposed here (also called voltage-controlled current source) is based on just one opamp, and provides to, or draws from, ground a current that is dependent on its input voltage. The unit can convert negative as well as positive voltages into negative currents (from ground) and positive currents (into ground) respectively.

When a Type 741 or CA3140 is used in the A_1 position, $R_v = 1$ k, and $R = 10$ k, $U_{in} = \pm 10$ V max.; $I_{out} = \pm 20$ mA max.; and $g_m = -1$ mS. It is, of course, possible to change any or all of these values as required by using a different opamp and altering the values of the resistors. The maximum output current is always dependent on the opamp used. To make such changes, the following formulas may prove useful.

$$U+ = U-- = (U_{in}-U_{out})/2 + U_{out}$$

$$U_o = 2[(U_{in}-U_{out})/2 + U_{out}] = U_{in} + U_{out}$$

$$I_{Rv} = U_{in}/R_v$$

$$I_{out} = I_{Rv} + I_R = U_{in}/R_v + (U_{in}-U_{out})/2R$$

If $R >> R_v$ (the usual case),
$$I_{out} = U_{in}/R_v.$$

132 BLOW THAT SYNTHESIZER!

Circuits for generating electronic music are usually controlled by key switches. Not only do keyboards offer the simplest technical solution for producing fast changing, reproducible tones over a wide frequency range, but they also enjoy tremendous popularity because they are considered to be easier to learn to play than string or wind instruments.

Because of that, we have not tried to create an electronic oboe, flute, or clarinet with the present circuit. In any case, the technical intricacies associated with such instruments would make their electrophonic counterpart prohibitively expensive.

So, what we have got here is the relatively simple facility of converting breath power into a proportional analogue voltage with which the volume of a music synthesizer can be controlled; the tones remain controlled by the keyboard switches. No doubt, many of you, ingenious readers, will be able to think of various other applications of the converter.

The circuit does not operate direct from the exhaled breath, but from the noise generated by this. A thin, flexible tube, to which a mouthpiece may be attached, leads into a closed box, in which not only the

circuit, but also an inexpensive microphone have been fitted.

The noise received by the microphone is amplified in IC_1, the gain of which can be adjusted with P_1 and subsequently rectified by IC_2-D_1-D_2. An active low-pass filter removes most of the ripple from the output voltage.

To keep the circuit as simple as possible, we have opted for a compromise between input sensitivity and output ripple: the relation between these two properties can be adjusted with P_2

If you have an oscilloscope with slow sweep, calibration of the converter should present no problems.

First, adjust the value of P_1 so that the output voltage with hard blowing into the tube just does not cause full drive (dependent on the sensitivity of the following instrument).

Second, adjust P_2 so that the output signal is relatively free of ripple, while the converter still reacts to normal breathing. A steeper filter would have been better here, but that would have increased the cost.

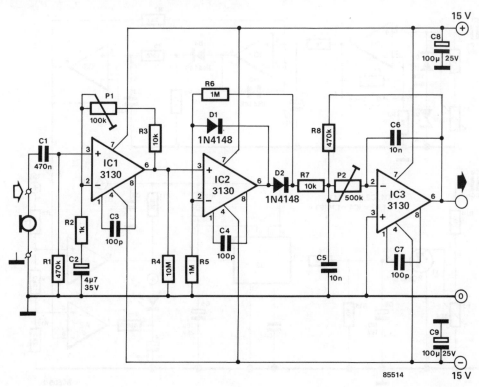

85514

The environmental nuisance value of discos is in direct proportion to their sound level. The circuit proposed here cannot be disabled by the disc jockey, since it is built into the output amplifiers used in the disco. Its operation is amazingly effective: if the preset sound level is exceeded, the input of the amplifier is short-circuited for a few seconds. Any disc jockey whom that has happened to a couple of times soon gives up trying to break the sound barrier.

The power amplifier output is connected to the metering input of the present circuit (C_1). This signal is applied to low-pass filter R_4-C_2 via P_1 (which sets the maximum volume) and buffer IC_1. In case of line inputs, this opamp can be given a gain of 20 dB by the omission of the wire link across R_2.

The signal from the low-pass filter is rectified (half wave) by IC_2 and IC_3. The resulting direct voltage is applied to A_1 and A_2 which compare it with two reference voltages derived from potential divider R_8-R_9-R_{10}. When the first threshold is exceeded, D_5 lights to warn that maximum sound level has

almost been reached. When the sound level then increases by 6 dB, A_1 also toggles, which triggers monostable IC_5.

The input signal to the power amplifier (via C_9, R_{16}, and P_2) is then short-circuited to ground via T_1. Resistors R_{14} and R_{15}, and capacitor C_8, obviate any "plops" from the loudspeakers.

Power for the present circuit may be derived from the output amplifier. The normally quite high supply voltage there is reduced to ± 15 V by two complementary power transistors. Current consumption of the circuit is about 40 mA.

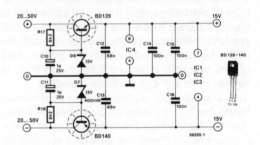

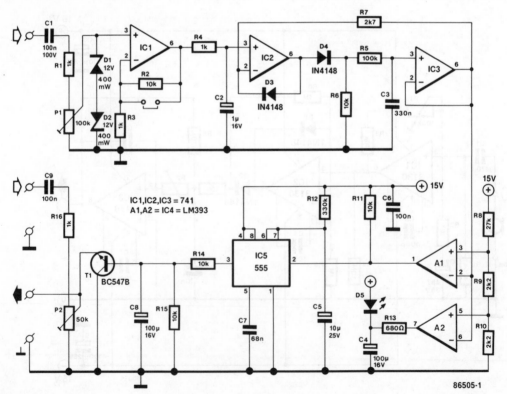

86505-1

The fuzzbox, fuzzer, tube screamer, or whatever other name there may exist for the controlled guitar sound distortion unit, is a well-known item in the electrophonic field, which is of common interest to both musicians and electronics enthusiasts.

The majority of fuzz units are simply opamp configurations with some form of maximum input level control, which determines the degree of overdrive by the guitar input signal, and, consequently, the amount of audible distortion, generally referred to as the object "sound" the player has in mind as his very own musical visiting card.

This is probably one of the few fuzz units to feature controllable symmetrical clipping facilities, which means that the limit for distortion-free amplification may be separately defined for both the negative and positive portions of the input sinewave(s), the peaks of which may be clipped by means of shunt transistors T_1 and T_2 respectively, each with its own clipping level control potentiometer (P_1; P_2). The transistors, when driven, pass the signal from input opamp IC_1 to the positive supply or to the ground rail, before buffer IC_2 can

pass the "fuzzy" guitar sound to the connected amplifier.

Preset P_3 determines the minimum gain of the fuzz unit; the desired level may be set with P_4 turned to its minimum resistance position. Next, P_4 is adjusted to suit the maximum input level that can be expected from the guitar. P_3 and P_4 may then be alternately adjusted to hit the correct compromise between these two signal levels.

Finally, note the three-pole changeover switch which allows easy bypassing of the fuzzer while simultaneously switching it off to preserve battery power.

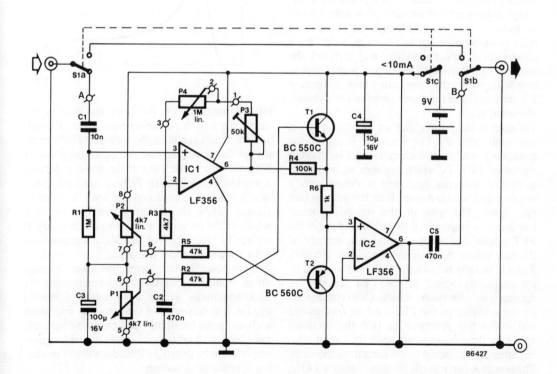

86427

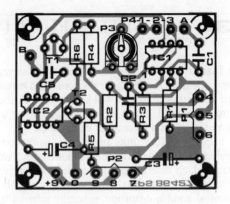

135   LIMITER FOR GUITARS

The basic dynamic characteristic of a chord can be analysed as a fast rising, needle-shaped pulse with a virtually exponential decay—see Fig. 1. This typical amplitude characteristic can only be faithfully reproduced by an amplifier if this is operated well below its overload margin, and that, many guitar players know, generally results in too low an average sound level. Also, when it is desired to use a high volume setting, the distortion soon rises to an unacceptable level. Although the above difficulty is widely remedied by means of a tightly set compressor or limiter, the sound may then lack the required agressiveness. This circuit is expected to give better results than most other limiters, because it is only active in the upper range of the dynamic characteristic.

The gain of the preamplifier set up around IC_1 is adjustable with P_1 The inverting input of the opamp is grounded via the drain-source junction of n-channel FET T_1, which operates as a voltage-controlled resistance here, and is driven with a negative gate voltage derived from the limiter's output signal. The gain of the opamp is therefore inversely proportional to the gate voltage of the FET, whose drain-source resistance is reduced as the gate voltage becomes more negative. Network R_5-C_4 effectively reduces the distortion incurred by the regulating action of the FET. It may be necessary to redimension R_5 and C_4 to compensate for the tolerance on the FET—use an oscilloscope and a function generator to find the optimum values for these components while the circuit is being arranged to operate at maximum compression. The limiter is fairly simple to align. Apply a 1 kHz,

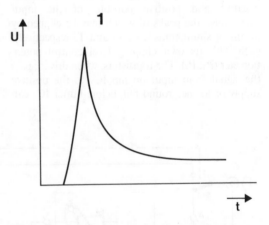

150 mV input signal to the input, and monitor the output signal with an oscilloscope. Adjust P_1 such that maximum amplification is obtained with virtually no distortion. Increase the input amplitude to 300 mV: this is likely to make some distortion noticable. Carefully turn P_1 back until the distortion is reduced to an acceptable level. In some instances, when the distortion remains too high whatever the setting of P_1, it may be necessary to replace T_1, since the Type BF256C is manufactured with a relatively loose tolerance.

The proposed limiter leaves the lower dynamic range unaffected, while slightly compressing the peak amplitudes in the input signal. Optimally aligned, it suffers none of the notorious side-effects such as "noise breathing" and clipping commonly associated with other units, while it enables guitar amplifiers to be driven 3 dB harder without producing appreciable distortion.

<5mA 9V

IC 1 TL 071

(Top schematic circuit diagram with labels: R3 820k, R1 10k, C1 47n, IC1 TL071, R8 100Ω, C6 1µ/16V, R9 10k, R10 1k, P1 5k, R4 150Ω, IC1, C3 100µ 16V, C2 100µ 16V, R5 820k, C4 10n, R6 100k, D1 AA119, D2 AA119, P2 50k log., S1, R2 1M2, T1 BF256C, R7 1M, C5 22n, C7 10n, C8 68p, R11 4M7)

136 MELODIC SAWTOOTH

Even in this era of programmable, polyphonic synthesizers, interest in simple, monophonic keyboard instruments remains. Many FORMANT owners are still proud of their, probably first, home-built synthesizer and are still on the look-out for new circuits for the generation of exotic sounds. For all those, here is an easy-to-build circuit that can convert a sawtooth signal at its input into an output of double the frequency and half the peak value of the input signal (figure 1).

Comparator IC_1 transforms the sawtooth signal into a rectangular signal (see figure 2). Adder IC_2 combines the original input signal and the rectangular signal.

An additional LFO (low frequency oscillator) connected as shown provides pulse-width modulation of the rectangular signal, which has a greatly beneficial effect on the output signal.

When switch S_1 is set to position b, it is possible to inject a rectangular signal whose frequency is independent of the sawtooth frequency, which greatly increases the number of melodic variations, as anyone acquainted with synthesizers knows.

Power requirements can be met direct by the FORMANT or any other ±15 V symmetrical supply. Current consumption is not higher than 10 mA.

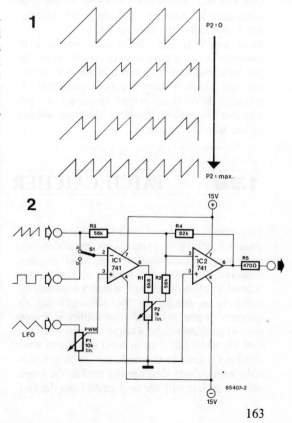

1

P2 = 0

P2 = max.

2

(Circuit diagram with labels: R3 56k, R4 82k, 15V, S1, IC1 741, R1 6k8, R2 56k, IC2 741, R5 470Ω, P2 1k lin., LFO, PWM, P1 10k lin., 15V, 85407-2)

The objective of this circuit is to obtain a synthesizer-controlled equivalent sound as produced by such metal indefinite pitch percussion instruments as cymbals, gong, and anvil. Fig. 1 shows that the generator comprises four independently tuneable VCOs which supply rectangular output signals to a combination of XOR gates.

One of four identical KOV (keyboard output voltage) driven VCOs is shown in Fig. 2. The use of fast opamp types ensures linear VCO operation well up to 4 kHz, while FET T_1 improves upon the linearity of the voltage-frequency curve relevant to the combination of integrator and comparator. With the VCO constructed four times over and connected as shown in Fig. 1, drive controls $P_1 \dots P_4$ allow the user to set the output sound as desired. The outputs of buffer opamps $A_1 \dots A_4$ (IC$_1$, Type TL084) should measure 0 V offset with the KOV rail grounded. If this can not be attained, the IC will have to be exchanged with a more stable type.

Linearity of each of the VCO circuits is set with the preset at the drain of the FET, P_5 and T_1 respectively in Fig. 2. Use a scope to check whether the rectangular VCO output signal has a 50% duty factor; if not, adjust the relevant preset.

As the four VCOs lack a linear to exponential KOV converter at their inputs, it is not possible to use the present circuit with a keyboard of the 1 V per octave type. However, many keyboards provide an exponential KOV signal whose frequency doubles with every octave and which are, therefore, suitable for use with this generator.

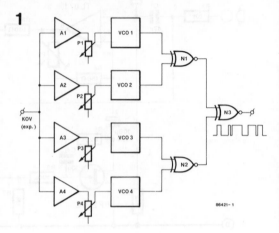

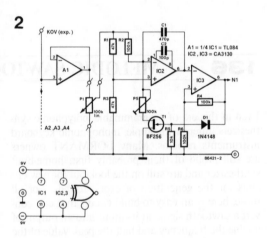

This circuit facilitates switching between programmed settings on synthesizers, expanders, and other electrophonic instruments. Most of these have some provision for storing or saving user-defined instrument settings, which are usually referred to as *patches* in the electrophonics enthusiasts' jargon. Although this facility is a great asset to many musicians, a problem arises when patches are to be called up in rapid succession while playing. On some instruments, this problem is solved by a pedal that, when pressed, enables the instrument to operate with the next patch from the user-

defined file (patch increment pedal). In practice, however, the increment function of the pedal may still be considered cumbersome. Assuming that the relevant instrument supports the use of eight patches, the pedal needs to be pressed no less than seven times to switch from, say, patch 3 to 2. This is obviously a distracting additional task when the keyboard is to be played simultaneously.

This circuit uses a relay whose contact is connected to the pedal input on the instrument. The user presses a key numbered 1-8 to select the relevant patch, and the circuit arranges for the relay contact

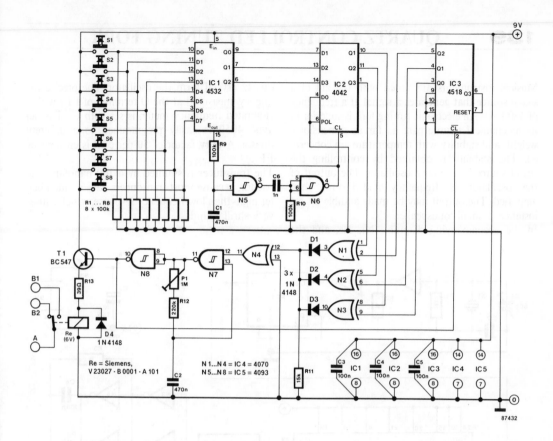

87432

to be automatically actuated, simulating the number of pedal operations that would be required otherwise. With reference to the circuit diagram, IC1 is a priority encoder whose outputs Q0-Q2 supply the binary code of the pressed key S1-S8. The pulse at therminal Eout is delayed in R9-C1 and fed to N5-N6 which serve to clock 4-bit latch IC2. Outputs Q1-Q3 of this chip are applied to the inputs of XOR gates N1-N3, together with the outputs of counter IC3, whose binary output state is initially assumed equal to that of IC2. Pressing one of switches S1-S8 causes the output of IC2 to change, and one of the XOR outputs to go high. This enables oscillator N7, so that its output pulses, inverted in N8 and buffered with T1, energize the relay and increment the patch number on the instrument. The oscillator pulses are also applied to binary counter IC3, which is set up to count from 0 to 7 because its Q3 output drives the RESET input. After a maximum of 7 pulses, the logic levels applied to each of the XOR gates are equal again, so that the oscillator is disabled via N4.

The choice between the make or break contact of the relay is governed by the type of pedal this circuit

is to replace. Preset P1 is adjusted such that the instrument is just capable of reliably following the actions of the relay. After turning on the equipment, it is necessary to first press S1, then select the first program on the instrument, and finally make the appropriate connection between this and the patch catcher.

The circuit, exclusive of the relay, consumes only a few milliamperes. The prototype, fitted with the stated Siemens relay, drew a mere 50 mA from the 9 V supply.

Musical instruments are tuned with the aid of a signal source that generates a signal at a frequency of 440 kHz. An electronic tuning fork is superior to its mechanical counterpart as far as dimensions, weight, and stability with temperature are concerned. The stability is obtained by controlling the signal source by a quartz oscillator. The output of the oscillator is frequency-divided and then amplified. The output may be made audible by, for instance, a small loudspeaker.

In the accompanying diagram, N_1, N_2, and the

quartz crystal form the oscillator. The precise frequency, measured at the Q terminal of FF_2 with a calibrated frequency meter, is set with C_1. Divider Type 4059 is easily programmed to a different divisor. A duty factor of 50 per cent is ensured by FF_2.

The transducer is shunted by a 100 nanofarad capacitor, because most transducers have a much better high- than low-frequency response, which causes very shrill sounds.

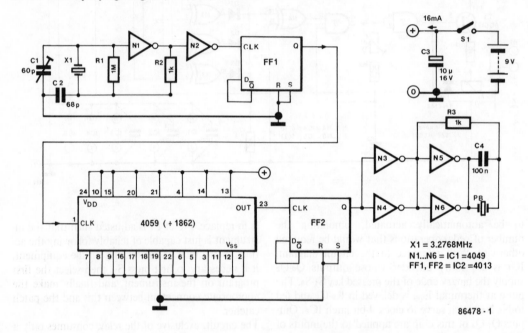

X1 = 3.2768MHz
N1...N6 = IC1 =4049
FF1, FF2 = IC2 =4013

86478 - 1

This novel indicator is ideally suitable for use in a discotheque. It consists of eight equi-distant columns of eight LEDs arranged in a starlike pattern, so that corresponding LEDs in the eight columns form concentric circles, as shown in figure 1b. The higher the sound level, the more circles light, giving the impression of a star of constantly varying brightness.

As can be seen in figure 1b, the eight LEDs in any one of the eight circles are connected in series. Each

of these series chains is driven by a transistor: $T_1 \ldots T_8$ in figure 1a. Dropping resistors are not required: the positive supply voltage provides just over 1.8 V per LED, which is a perfect value for red LEDs to show up nicely.

Transistors $T_1 \ldots T_8$ are driven by differential amplifiers $A_1 \ldots A_8$, which compare the audio-dependent direct voltage across C_2, which is buffered by A_{12}, with the potential determined by D_{11} and $R_{11} \ldots R_{18}$. If the result of the comparison is

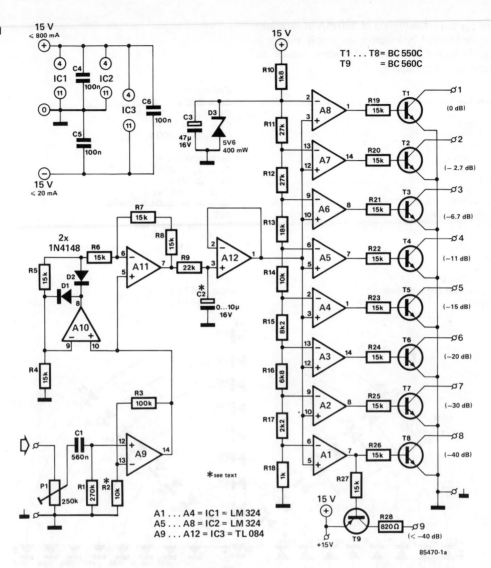

1a

T1 ... T8 = BC 550C
T9 = BC 560C

A1 ... A4 = IC1 = LM 324
A5 ... A8 = IC2 = LM 324
A9 ... A12 = IC3 = TL 084

* see text

85470-1a

(0 dB)
(− 2.7 dB)
(−6.7 dB)
(−11 dB)
(−15 dB)
(−20 dB)
(−30 dB)
(−40 dB)
(< −40 dB)

positive, the associated driver transistor is switched on, and the appropriate circle of LEDs lights. The LED in the centre, D4, is driven by T9 and only lights when the sound level is very low.

The direct voltage across C2 results from full-wave rectification in A10 and A11 of the input signal after this has been amplified in A9. The input sensitivity is about 600 mV for saturation, i.e., to light all sixty-four LEDs; it can be increased by lowering the value of R2.

The speed with which variations in sound intensity are indicated depends on the value of C2: if this is 10 μF, the light pattern changes slowly, whereas when the capacitor is omitted, it reacts instantly to different sound levels.

The indicator is constructed on two printed circuit boards (figures 2 and 3). The LED board in figure 3 has not been provided with a component layout because of aesthetic considerations. The layout is, however, given on the PCB in figure 4 for those who want to use it all the same. The two boards can be fitted together with the use of spacers: appropriate holes have been provided for this in a manner which ensures that the 11 terminals for interconnections on the boards are opposite one another.

An interesting optical effect arises when a sheet of red perspex is mounted in front of the LED board. Refraction in this material causes the LEDs to show up as sources of diffused, rather than pinpointed, light.

The current consumption of 800 mA at saturation may be reduced by lowering the supply voltage to, say, 12 V, but this will, of course, reduce the brightness of the display.

Parts list

Resistors:
R_1 = 270 k
R_1^*, R_{14} = 10 k
R_3 = 100 k
$R_4 \ldots R_8, R_{19} \ldots R_{27}$ = 15 k
R_9 = 22 k
R_{10} = 1k8
R_{11}, R_{12} = 27 k
R_{13} = 18 k
R_{15} = 8k2
R_{16} = 6k8
R_{17} = 2k2
R_{18} = 1 k
R_{28} = 820 Ω
P_1 = preset potentiometer, 250 k

Capacitors:
C_1 = 560 n
C_1^* = 0 . . . 10 μ/16 V
C_3 = 47 μ/16 V
$C_4 \ldots C_6$ = 100 n

Semiconductors:
$T_1 \ldots T_8$ = BC550C
T_9 = BC560C
D_1, D_1 = 1N4148
D_3 = zener diode 5V6/400 mW
$D_4 \ldots D_{68}$ = LED red
IC_1, IC_1 = LM324
IC_3 = TL084

* = see text

PCB 85470-1
    85470-2

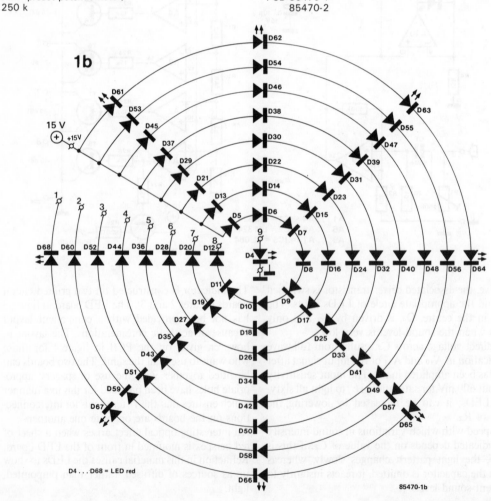

1b

15 V

D4 . . . D68 = LED red

85470-1b

168

2

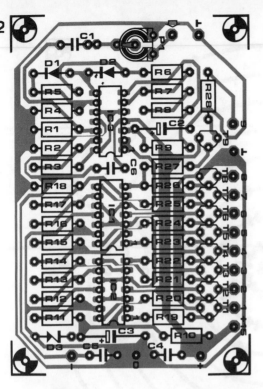

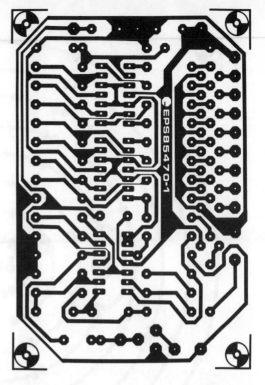

3

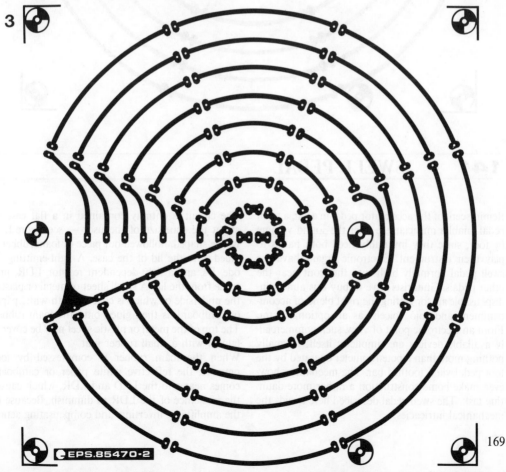

EPS.85470-2

169

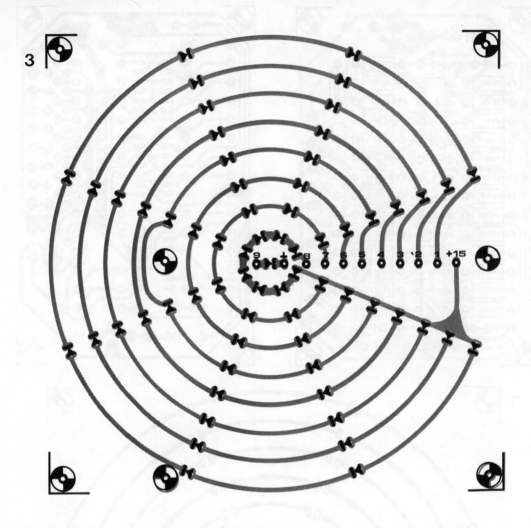

141   SWELL PEDAL

Reminiscent of the accelerator pedal in a car, a swell pedal enables musicians to alter the sound volume by foot, since they invariably need both hands to play their instrument. Electronic organs have the swell pedal normally built into the front near the other pedals. Guitarists have to buy this almost indispensable aid for getting the right blend of accompaniment and solo voice(s) as an optional extra. From an electronic point of view, such commercially available devices are simplicity itself: normally nothing more than a potentiometer operated by the foot pedal via a toothed bar. The mechanics, however, make home construction a rather more daunting task. The swell pedal described here avoids the mechanical intricacies.

The circuit is entirely contained in a flat case of about the shoe-size of the user — see figure 1. A wedge-shaped, hollowed-out piece of foam rubber is glued onto the lid of the case. A light-emitting diode, D_5, and a light-dependent resistor, LDR, protrude from the lid. A small sheet of metal or plastic, the underside of which is covered with white paper or cardboard, is then glued onto the foam rubber. The top of the metal or plastic sheet may be covered (glued) with a small rubber mat.

When the foam rubber is compressed by foot pressure, the reflective white paper or cardboard comes nearer to the LED and LDR, which causes the resistance of the LDR to diminish. Because of the amplifying, inverting, and compensating action

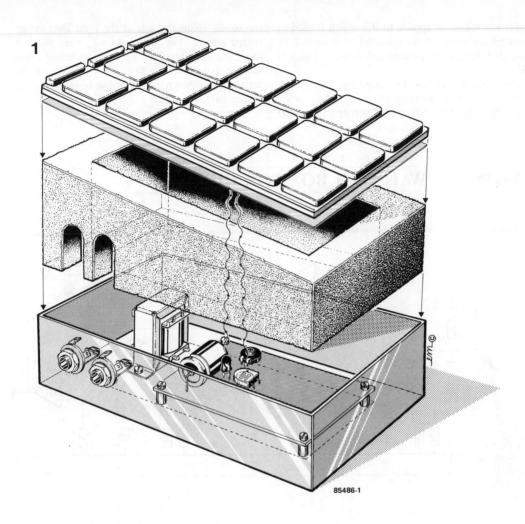

1

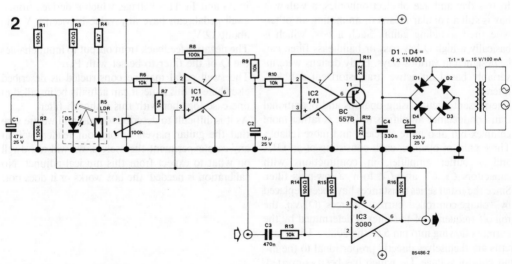

2

R1 100k
R3 470Ω
R4 4k7
R8 100k
R9 10k
R10 10k
R11 2k2
D1 ... D4 = 4 x 1N4001
Tr1 = 9 ... 15 V/100 mA

R6 10k
R7 10k
IC1 741
IC2 741
T1 BC 557B

C1 47µ 25 V
R2 100k
D5
R5 LDR
P1 100k
C2 10µ 25 V
R12 27k
C4 330n
C5 220µ 25 V
D1 D2
D3

R14 100Ω
R15 100Ω
R16 100k

C3 470n
R13 10k
IC3 3080

85486-2

85486-1

171

of IC$_1$, a voltage is applied to IC$_2$ which is used to control the drive current provided by transistor T$_1$ for OTA (operational transconductance amplifier) IC$_3$.

After the pedal box has been glued together, so that the electro-optical components are in a light-proof chamber, adjust P$_1$ so that with non-operated pedal the sound volume is just at the right level for accompaniment. For solo playing, the pedal is depressed as required to obtain the increased sound volume. It is advisable to fit P$_1$ in the side of the pedal case as shown, so that it can be re-adjusted at a later date if required.

142   WAH-WAH BOX FOR GUITARS

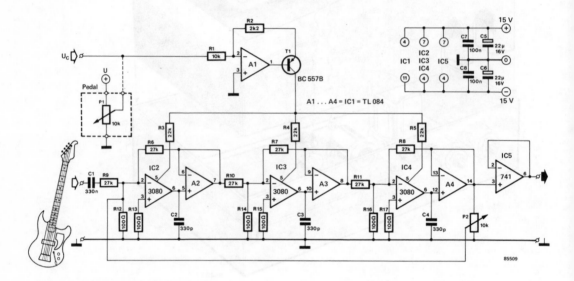

In this day and age of electrophonics, a wah-wah box is still a popular means of animating an otherwise tired sounding guitar. Such a box, which is basically a high-Q low-pass or band-pass filter, can be designed in various ways. Early designs were invariably based on active (transistorized) double-T filters.

The present circuit, using opamps and operational transconductance amplifiers (OTAs), is rather more complex but also more efficient and more reliable. Three pairs of opamps, each consisting of an OTA and a buffer amplifier, in conjunctions with capacitors C$_2$, C$_3$, and C$_4$, form a low-pass filter. Since the usual series resistances have been replaced by voltage-controlled current sources (OTAs), the roll-off frequency of the filter is determined by the currents flowing into pin 5 of the 3080s. These currents are themselves directly proportional to the input control voltage, U$_c$, which has been converted

in A$_1$ and T$_1$. This voltage, which is derived from a swell pedal, can have any value between 0 V and about 12 V.

The negative feedback from output to input enables the Q of the filter to be set with P$_2$

The swell pedal may be constructed as described elsewhere in this issue: it can actually be installed in one case together with this wah-wah filter!

As it is difficult to describe sounds, and we are sure that the guitar players among our readers will in any case experiment themselves, we will not dwell on what to expect from this musical adjunct. No calibration is needed: the box works or it does not!

172

143 ELECTRONIC VHF/UHF AERIAL SWITCH

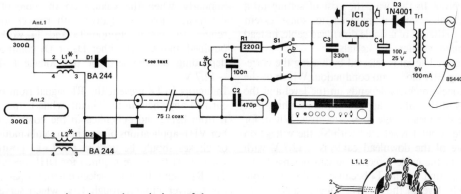

There are many situations where it is useful, or downright essential, to be able to switch between two VHF/UHF aerials at the aerial mast without introducing losses in the signal paths. The switch proposed here does all this over the usual coaxial down lead.

The switch and its small associated power supply are fitted near the relevant receiver. The power supply, consisting of a small mains transformer, a rectifier diode, and a three-pin voltage regulator, provides a direct voltage of 5 V, the polarity of which can be reversed by DPCO (double-pole change-over) switch S_1. The poles of the switch are connected to the coaxial cable via decoupling network L_3-C_1. Resistor R_1 serves as a current limiter for p-i-n diodes D_1 and D_2. Whichever of these diodes conducts depends on the polarity of the voltage across the coaxial cable. The signal from the aerial connected to the conducting diode is passed to the input of tuner or receiver, while the other signal is blocked.

A p-i-n diode is a semiconductor diode that contains

a region of i-type semiconductor between the p-type and n-type regions. They are invariably used as switching diodes. Their most important property is a very low self-capacitance, while at high frequencies they are virtually purely resistive (see *Elektor*, June 1983, p. 6-36).

Choke L_3 is made from four turns enamelled copper wire of 0.3 mm dia. around a ferrite bead. If the aerials have no 75 Ω termination, this may be provided by L_1 and L_2 which convert the 300 Ω balanced aerial impedance to the asymmetrical 75 Ω required by the receiver input. These inductors are made by winding 7 turns of two-core flat cable on a T50-2, T50-3, or T50-6 toroid as shown in figure 2.

If the switch is mounted in the open, it should be well protected from the elements: potting in araldite is best.

144 FOUR-WAY AERIAL SWITCH

In many cases it may be necessary to switch between two or more aerials with minimum loss in the RF signal. Though this is not generally a problem at low frequencies, it becomes a serious one when the relevant signal is in the VHF/UHF range (50-960 MHz). The electronic switch described here keeps the switching losses minimal by making use of PIN diodes. PIN diodes are essentially current

controlled resistors with properties that make them suitable for switching and attenuating RF signals. They differ from most other types of diode in that rectification of the input signal only occurs below a certain limiting frequency. Above this frequency, the resistance of a typical PIN diode will change from 1Ω to 10,000Ω when the control current is reduced from 100 mA to 1 μA.

The circuit can switch up to four aerials, and is composed of two functional parts: the RF switching section, mounted onto the aerial mast, and the power supply & control section, kept near the receiver. In this way, the cost of setting up a multi-aerial system is reduced to some extent thanks to the use of a single downlead cable, instead of as many as there are aerials.

The required aerial is selected by biasing the corresponding PIN diode into conduction. Which of the four diodes conducts depends on the level and the polarity of the voltage applied to the switching unit via the downlead cable to the receiver. When, for example, input 1 is selected with S_1, the voltage on the core of the downlead cable is $+12.7$ V with respect to the cable screen, and can not reach the circuit around T_3 and T_4 because D_6 does not conduct. The level of the positive voltage causes zener diode D_7 to conduct, and so provides a bias for T_1, driving it into saturation. T_1 in turn provides the requisite bias for PIN diode D_1, and at the same time prevents T_2 from conducting. Input 1 is thus connected to the common output of the switching unit, through D_1. If S_1 is set to position 2, the supply voltage on the downlead cable falls to 8 V, which is insufficient for D_7 to conduct. T_1 now remains switched off, and T_2 is driven into saturation, providing the required bias current for the associated PIN diode, D_2. Diodes D_8 and D_9 prevent D_1 from being biased through R_2 and the base-emitter junction of T_2. Input 2 is thus connected to the common output through D_2.

Similarly, when the voltage on the core of the downlead cable is negative with respect to the screen, the circuit around T_3 and T_4 works as outlined above, with either D_3 or D_4 conducting, depending on the level of the voltage (-8 or -12.7 V).

Inductors L_1-L_6 prevent the RF signal from being earthed anywhere in the circuit, while L_7 prevents it from being short-circuited in the power supply. For VHF applications of the circuit, 5 μH inductors or chokes should be used in the L_1-L_7 positions, while 2 μH types are required for UHF operation. The RF signal from the selected aerial is passed to the receiver input through C_{19}, which serves to block the direct voltage. In case balanced aerials are to be switched, their outputs must first be made unbalanced and, if necessary, transformed to 75Ω, using a balun.

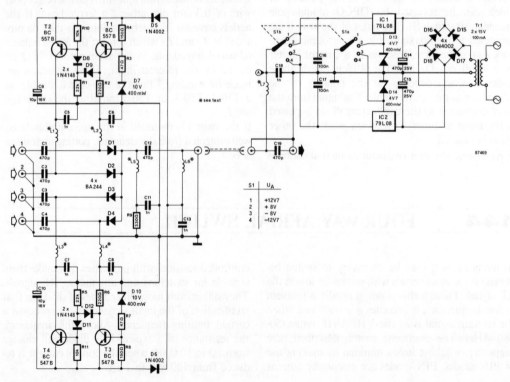

S1	U_A
1	+12V7
2	+ 8V
3	− 8V
4	−12V7

Among the most important technical characteristics of a VHF preamplifier are the noise figure, and the large signal handling capability. Although these are in principle conflicting requirements, a compromise can be found in the use of high-quality RF components. The receiver's ability to withstand high input levels can be enhanced by providing sufficient selectivity ahead of the active element(s). This is especially important for the mixer, since it generates most intermodulation products.

In this FM tunerhead, the aerial signal is first passed through a slightly overcritically coupled band filter, amplified with the aid of low noise UHF transistor T_1, and again filtered. The overall gain between the aerial input and the mixer input is about 12 dB at 87 MHz, and 17 dB at 108 MHz. The difference is caused by the adopted method of filter coupling. A wideband Schottky DBM (double balanced mixer) is used for the mixer in this design. The Type SBL-1 (LO = +7 dBm) is probably the best available of the 3 DBMs stated. Tuneable local oscillator T_2 produces very little phase noise, and DG MOSFET T_3 provides a LO power of 50 to 100 mW at a drain current of about 25 mA. FET T_4 enables driving a prescaler or a synthesizer with the LO signal. Series network R_9-C_{20} is fitted at the input of the IF amplifier because any passive DBM should be correctly terminated on at least two of its ports. To compensate for the 6 dB conversion loss in the DBM, and to ensure some spare IF gain, medium power RF J-FET T_5 is dimensioned to provide a gain of about 12 dB at a drain current of 25 mA.

The proposed front-end gives fairly good results: its third-order intercept point is better than 0 dB when a mixer is used with IP = +20 dBm, while the noise figure is about 4 dB. This sort of performance should enable the reception of quite weak transmissions even with a powerful transmitter within a few miles from the receiver.

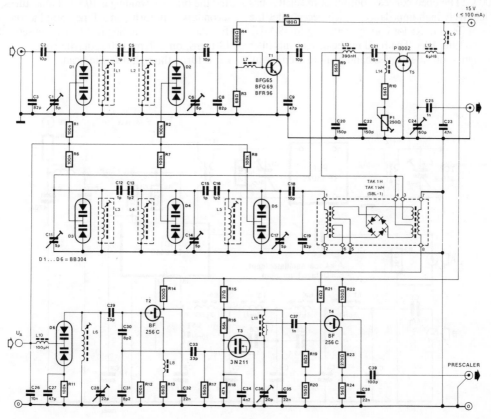

87493

Finally, due account should be taken of the fact that the IF output easily delivers 10 mW, which may well give problems if the IF amplifier is not properly dimensioned.

Inductor data for this project:

$L_1 \ldots L_5$ incl. = E526HNA10014 (Toko).
L_6 = E526HNA10013 (Toko).

$L_7 \ldots L_9; L_{14}$ = 6 turns 36SWG ($\varnothing$ 0.2 mm) enamelled copper wire through a ferrite bead.
L_{11} = 9 turns 24SWG ($\varnothing$ 0.6 mm) enamelled copper wire on a T25-12 ferrite core; tap at 3 turns from C_{35}-R_{15}-R_{16}.

146   FRONT-END FOR SW RECEIVER

There are many conflicting technical requirements for a good-quality front-end in an SW receiver. The noise figure and the intermodulation level should be low, the RF insulation between ports LO, RF and IF should be high, and some amplification is desirable. The Type SL6440 high level RF mixer from Plessey ensures a noise figure of around 10 dB, and offers sufficient suppression of the LO signal. The signal applied to the RF input (B) of the front-end is passed through a low-pass filter with a cut-off frequency of 32 MHz and an output impedance of 500 Ω. The open collector output of mixer IC_1 has a relatively high impedance, which necessitates the use of Tr_1 and R_5 for correct matching to 48 MHz crystal filter FL_1. The fixed impedance of this filter for signals outside its pass-band helps to keep the in-

termodulation distortion low. Trimmers C_{13} and C_{14} are aligned for a maximum flat pass-band at minimum loss. The mixer's intermodulation characteristics can be optimized by careful dimensioning of R_1 and R_2, provided the amplitude of the local oscillator signal is stable. A third-order intercept point of 33 dBm was achieved in a prototype. The mixer IC gets fairly warm, and should be cooled with a heat-sink.

The RF transformers are wound as follows (use 30SWG enamelled wire):

Tr_1: the primary winding is 10 + 10 bifilar turns, the secondary is 10 turns, on a Type T50-12 ferrite core.
Tr_2: the primary winding is 2 turns, the secondary 18 turns, on a Type T50-12 ferrite core.
L_6: 6 turns through a ferrite bead.

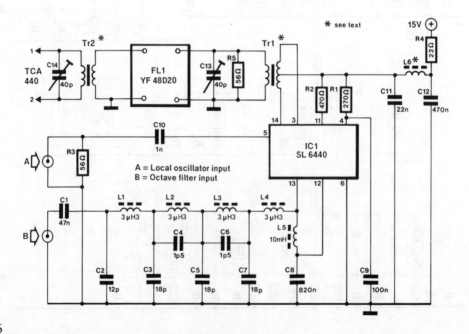

HIGH LEVEL PASSIVE DBM

The mixer is one of the most important sections in any good-quality SW receiver, since it determines to a large extent the sensitivity and the dynamic range. The so-called switching mixer is often used, because it has none of the technical imperfections of active mixers. The most commonly found switching mixer is the diode-based double balanced type (DBM), which is, unfortunately, a notoriously expensive component, especially when a high intercept point is required to ensure low levels of intermodulation. The application of active devices, such as bipolar transistors and J-FETs, in a passive mixer is less well established. And yet, these components enable the mixer to remain relatively simple, since the RF input signal can be thought of as electrically insulated from the local oscillator output. The present design is based on a pair of well-known UHF transistors, which require no supply voltage or bias circuits.

The input and output transformers are wound on two-hole ferrite cores (Baluns). The primary of Tr₂ is 8 turns with a centre tap for the RF input, the

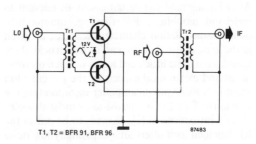

T1, T2 = BFR 91, BFR 96.   87483

secondary is 4 turns. Tr₁ is wound such that the indicated LO amplitude is available at the secondary. Only the RF input or the IF output requires correct termination on 50 Ω, the other connections are then fairly uncritical. The input intercept point of this mixer is excellent at between 31 and 36 dBm, while the noise figure and conversion loss are acceptable at about 6 dB. The LO rejection is roughly 25 dB, and depends mainly on the construction. The mixer is suitable for RF and IF signals up to 30 and 50 MHz respectively.

148   HIGH LEVEL WIDEBAND RF PREAMPLIFIER

A linear RF amplifier can be made in two ways: (1) with the aid of a linear active element, or (2) with a non-linear element operating with negative feedback. This circuit is of the second kind, using an RF power transistor as the active element. Feedback is also required to ensure correct termination (50 Ω) of the aerial, since bipolar transistors normally exhibit a low input impedance. Also, the noise figure is not increased because virtually no signal is lost.

The common-base amplifier is based on a UHF class A power transistor Type 2N5109 from Motorola. The feedback circuit is formed by RF transformer Tr₁. The input and output impedance of the preamplifier is 50 Ω for optimum performance. Network R₃-C₅ may have to be added to preclude oscillation outside the pass-band, which ranges from about 100 kHz to 50 MHz. The gain is approximately 9.5 dB, the noise figure is between 2 and 3 dB, and the third-order output intercept point is at least 50 dBm.

The input/output transformer is wound on a Type

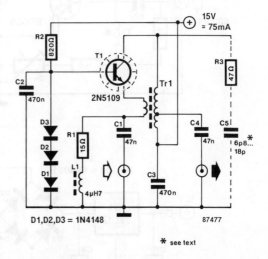

D1,D2,D3 = 1N4148   87477

* see text

FT37-75 ferrite core from Micrometals. The input winding is 1 turn, the output winding 5 turns with a tap at 3 turns.

After having read the design essentials relevant to wideband amplifiers, RF filtering, intermodulation/crossmodulation characteristics, etc., as given in the articles listed at the end of this article, there would seem to be little need for us to dwell on functional and electronical aspects of the present ultra low-noise, wideband preamplifier incorporating the wonderful Type BFG65 transistor, which, although already introduced in [3], deserves to be put in the RF limelight as it offers an exceptionally low noise figure at more than satisfactory strong signal response, thanks to the relatively high collector current ($F_{dB}=0.8$ dB at 5 mA, for instance).

Since the important points to observe in RF construction have been covered in [1] and [2], the large earth plane on the component side of the ready-made PCB Type 86504 need not cause any wonder;

all parts are soldered direct onto the relevant copper fields; the holes merely serve to aid in locating the parts correctly. The hole for T_1 should be drilled to dia 5 mm for the transistor to be seated and soldered with the shortest possible lead length.

Additional holes have been provided to enable the input and output coax cables to be secured by means of screw-on clamps, although soldering screen and core should also be possible.

It is seen that the ready-made PCB consists of an RF and a supply section, which may have to be separated by cutting if it is desirable to fit the units at different locations, as is the case with a masthead mounted amplifier and the supply located at the nearest mains outlet, e.g. on the attic. On the other hand, if is more convenient to cut the download cable immediately as it appears indoors, amplifier

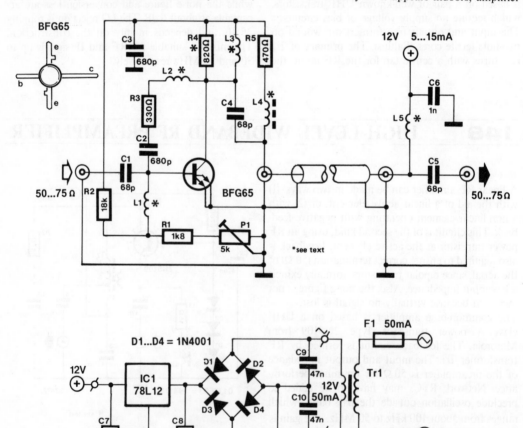

86504

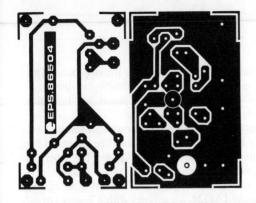 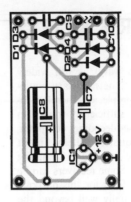 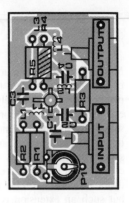

and supply may be left to form one unit for insertion in the coax cable. As in that case the amplifier may be fed direct rather than via the coax cable core, L4, L5, C5 and C6 are rendered unnecessary and may be removed; the free lead of R5 should then be connected to the +12 V terminal on the supply section of the board.

The optimum collector current for T1 is adjusted by means of P1, which should be set for a value between 5 and 7 mA if the amplifier is to handle relatively weak signals, such as may be received in fringe areas. The indicated collector current corresponds to 2.3 to 3 V voltage drop across R5; higher values (10 to 15 mA; 4.6 to 6.1 V respectively) should be set when receiving two or more strong (local) transmissions in the 80...800 MHz band.

If masthead-mounted, the amplifier should be fitted in a waterproof enclosure, carefully treated with silicone spray to preclude corrosion of the solder contacts.

Finally, the coils are wound as follows, using dia 0.3 mm (30 SWG) enamelled copper wire:
L1: 8 turns, closewound, internal dia 3 mm.
L2: 4 turns, closewound, internal dia 3 mm.
L3: 5 turns on R4.
L4;L5: 4 turns through 3 mm ferrite bead.

Literature references:
[1] *VHF filters*
    (EE, March 1986, p. 50 ff).
[2] *VHF amplifier*
    (EE, April 1986, p. 40 ff).
[3] *Wide band amplifier for satellite
    TV receivers*
    (EE, April 1985, p. 66 ff).
[4] *Aerial amplifiers*
    (EE, February 1980, p. 27 ff).

Parts list

Resistors:
$R_1 = 1k8$
$R_2 = 18 k$
$R_3 = 330 \Omega$
$R_4 = 820 \Omega$
$R_5 = 470 \Omega$
$P_1 = 5 k$ preset

Capacitors:
$C_1;C_4;C_5 = 68 p$
$C_2;C_3 = 680 p$
$C_6 = 1 n$
$C_7 = 1 \mu;16 V$; electrolytic
$C_8 = 470 \mu;25 V$; electrolytic
$C_9;C_{10} = 47 n$

Semiconductors:
$D_1 ... D_4 = 1N4001$
$IC_1 = 78L12$
$T_1 = BFG65$ (Philips/Mullard)

Miscellaneous:
$L_1 ... L_5 =$ see text.
$Tr_1 = 12 V;50 mA.$
$F_1 = 50 mA$; fast.
PCB Type 86405.
4 soldering pins.

Morse, or CW (continuous wave), is still widely used thanks to the fact that the necessary equipment can be kept relatively simple, and therefore inexpensive, if the operator is sufficiently trained in selective listening. A morse decoding computer, however, requires an adequately filtered input signal, because it lacks the noise discriminating capability of the human ear. Some receivers can be upgraded with a 250 Hz IF filter for this purpose, but such an extension is usually well beyond the financial reach of most radio amateurs. The filters discussed here operate in the audible frequency range, and compare favourably with far more expensive types for 455 kHz. Figures 1 and 2 show the circuit diagram and the typical response of an eighth-order inverse Chebishev filter which has been optimized for non-computer using listeners. The filter of Fig. 3 is less complex, and intended for driving a computer. The associated frequency response is shown in Fig. 4. Both filters were designed with *Eldesign IIe*, an advanced filter design program for the BBC micro. The inverse Chebishev response gives a smooth pass-band, while the characteristic ripple ends up in the stop band. This ensures the required phase stability in the pass-band, which is a must for processing burst-like signals such as morse.

Prototypes of the filters gave excellent results: normally hardly audible signals could be recovered for reliable decoding. The supply for the filters is preferably a symmetrical 15 V type to ensure an optimum dynamic range. Do not use any other opamp than the LM324, since types with a higher cut-off frequency may give rise to oscillation. Note that C_1 in Figs. 1 and 3, and C_2 in Fig. 1, is a parallel combination of two capacitors from the E12 range of values, while all resistors used are from the E96 range. Should any of the filter sections persist in its tendency to oscillate, either one of the even-numbered opamps may have to be dimensioned for a slightly different roll-off point by connecting a 100 pF capacitor across the output and the — input, and a 390 Ω resistor between the — input and junction C_3-R_5-(-A_1) (example refers to opamp A_2).

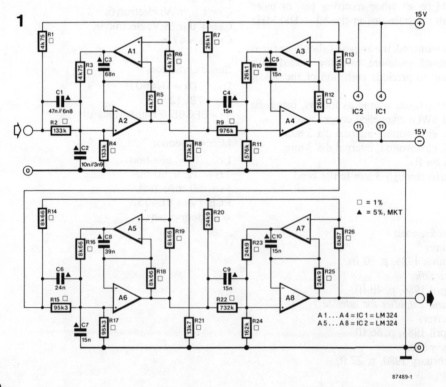

87489-1

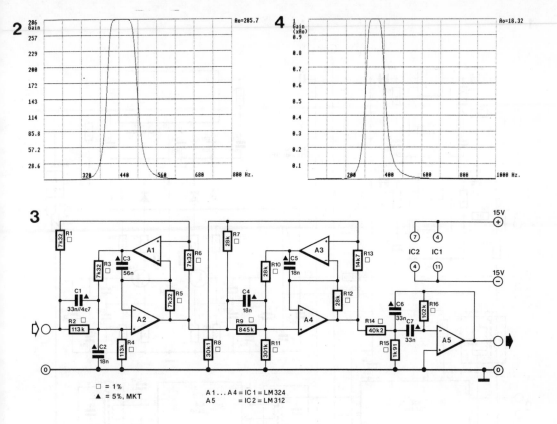

151   MULTI-MODE μP-CONTROLLED IF MODULE

The intermediate frequency (IF) module shown in Fig. 1 accepts 48 MHz, and is suitable for receiving AM, FM and SSB transmissions. CW reception should also be possible in the SSB mode when a sufficiently narrow bandfilter is included (BW<500 Hz). For radio-teletype (RTTY), it is best to drive a comparator from the FM detector output. There is no need for a high level mixer to convert the input down to 455 kHz, since the 48 MHz signal has already been filtered and occupies a bandwidth of only 12 kHz. The RF and mixer stages in the TCA440 operate up to 50 MHz, while the built-in AGC has a dynamic range of about 100 dB. The mixer output is fed to diode switches to enable digital selection of the appropriate bandwidth.

The proposed selection circuit ensures a filter separation of the order of 80 dB. The choice of the 455 kHz filters is governed by the particular appli-

cation and the financial means available. The CLF-D12 and CLF-D2 are for FM/AM and SSB respectively: the number in the type indication stands for the bandwidth. The Type CLF-D4 or CLF-D6 can be used equally well for communication quality AM. Unfortunately, narrow-band filters for CW and RTTY are difficult to obtain, but "add-on" 500 Hz or 250 Hz filters for commercially available receivers and transceivers (Yaesu, Kenwood) can be used here with excellent results.

The IF output from IC2 is rectified for the AM and AGC sections, and inductively fed to FM detector IC4 as well as to product detector IC3. Note that in general no AGC action is required in the FM and RTTY mode. The BFO for the product detector is based on USB and LSB ceramic resonators, which are found in most SW receivers of Far Eastern origin, but may be difficult to obtain as a one off. The circuit around T4 is a voltage-controlled

181

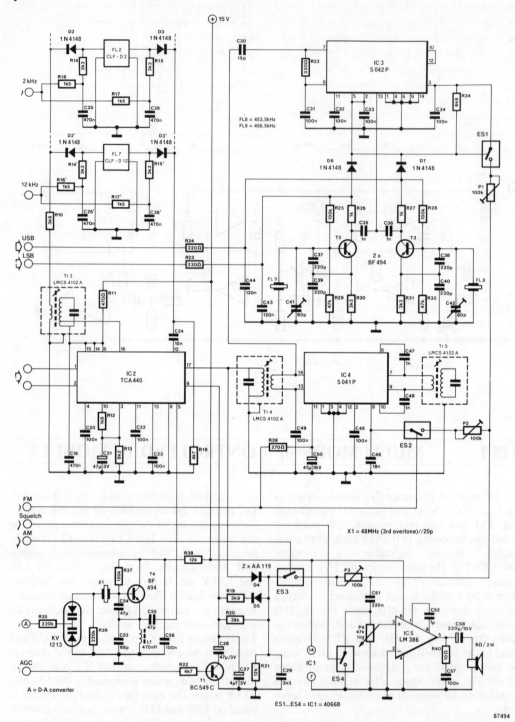

2

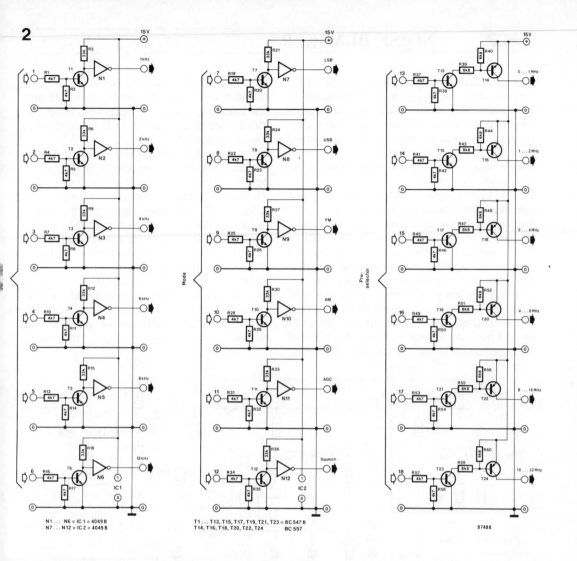

N1 ... N6 = IC 1 = 4049 B
N7 ... N12 = IC 2 = 4049 B

T1 ... T13, T15, T17, T19, T21, T23 = BC 547 B
T14, T16, T18, T20, T22, T24   BC 557

87488

48 MHz crystal oscillator (VCXO) that operates in the parallel mode, requiring due attention to be paid to the correct output frequency if a common, series-resonant crystal is used. The synthesizer for tuning the proposed receiver outputs 1 kHz steps, so that a D-A converter is required for driving the VCXO input. A resolution of 10 Hz should be adequate to ensure smooth and reliable tuning.

The computer interface for controlling the receiver is shown in Fig. 2. This is essentially a 5 V to 15 V logic level converter with TTL/CMOS compatible control inputs. The remote control of the receiver obviates the need for this to be housed in a neat enclosure. Albeit that the receiver therefore need not have a "desktop" appearance with all the controls fitted on a front panel, it is, of course, still

necessary to provide for adequate screening and thermal stability. Sufficient AF power is available from IC_5 to drive a relatively long cable to the loud-speaker enclosure, which is located near the computer.

The receiver can be controlled from any computer that has three 8-bit output ports based on, for instance, Type 74LS374 octal latches. A receiver function is enabled when a logic 1 is written to the respective input. Example: 4 kHz bandwidth is selected by driving BANDWIDTH input 4 high, and the remaining five low. Writing a computer program for controlling the receiver should not be too difficult if the following sequence is observed: 1. actuate the squelch; 2. reset all bits on the relevant control port; 3. set the required bit; 4. turn off the squelch.

A noise blanker is indispensable for improving the reception of very weak signals on the SW bands. In most communication receivers, the selectivity of intermediate frequency (IF) filters cause interfering pulses to be widened, blotting out the wanted signal. It is useful, therefore, to suppress interference before this can wreak havoc in the IF ections of the receiver.

The 455 kHz IF signal is first buffered in T_2, and then processed separately in two circuits.

The lower section of the circuit is a TCA440 based receiver for the interfering pulses. The TCA440 is in itself a virtually complete receiver, since it comprises an RF amplifier, a mixer, and an IF amplifier. All stages in the latter are used since pin 4 is grounded here. The pulse receiver has its own AGC (automatic gain control) to ensure effective suppression of relatively weak interference also. Preset P_1 and potentiometer P_2 enable precise adjustment of the noise blanker for various levels of interference.

The circuit can be controlled digitally via R_{23}; a logic high level renders the noise blanker ineffective. The interfering pulses are made logic compatible with the aid of opamp IC_2. LED D_3 lights when noise is detected.

In the upper section of the circuit, the IF signal is first delayed in FL_1 to compensate for the processing time in the pulse receiver. ES_1 is opened when a sufficiently strong interfering pulse is recognized, so that the IF signal is no longer applied to output buffer T_2. Also, the gate of this FET is then grounded for RF signals via ES_3-C_4, while ES_2 is closed to maintain correct termination of FL_1.

Properly constructed, this circuit achieves noise suppression of the order of 85 dB. Alterations to suit operation at an IF other than 455 kHz involve L_1 and FL_1, although due account should be taken of the parasitic capacitance of the electronic switches at relatively high frequencies.

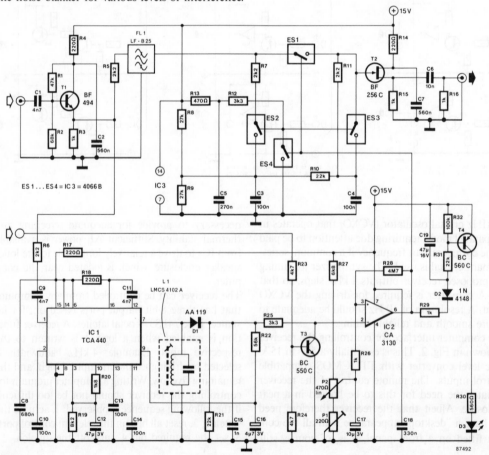

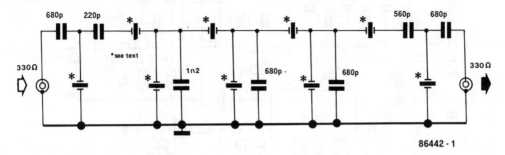

680p   220p   *   *   *   *   560p   680p

*see text

330Ω   *   *   1n2   *   680p ·   *   680p   *   330Ω

86442 - 1

Since good crystal filters are expensive, there is a constant search for (less expensive) alternatives. One of these is the ceramic filter, now widely used as IF filter in short-wave receivers. The somewhat poorer temperature characteristics of ceramic filters (as compared with those of crystal filters) are normally not of much consequence.

Numerous experiments have finally led to the circuit of Fig. 1, which uses five 455 kHz ceramic filters. As computer crystals can be obtained cheaply nowadays, it would also be possible to construct a similar filter with a number of such crystals.

The result of our experiments is a 3 dB filter bandwidth of about 800 Hz; the attenuation outside the pass-band is of the order of 60 dB.

A possible application is its use in a receiver with variable bandwidth for SSB, AM, and FM operation.

Another application is as input filter in a receiver whose dynamic frequency range is inadequate (but the IF should then not be 455 kHz).

Finally, note that correct matching of both the input and output impedance (330 ohms) is imperative.

154   NAVTEX RECEIVER

NAVTEX, the international maritime service that provides navigational and meteorological information via RTTY (radio teletype) on 518 kHz, makes use of FECTOR. This is a system in which the information is transmitted twice, with a particular interval between the first character and the repeat. FECTOR is decoded automatically by a microprocessor that is coupled to the ship's medium wave receiver.

It is, of course, not desirable that the decoder is taking up the medium wave receiver continuously. On the other hand, navigational officers, and many amateur radio listeners, do not want to miss one iota of NAVTEX information. Obviously, a second receiver is the answer, and this can, of course, be coupled to the decoder night and day. Since only one frequency, 518 kHz, and one type of transmission, FSK (frequency shift keying), needs to be received, the circuit can be kept quite simple.

The circuit is based on a type TCA440. The AGC (automatic gain control) provided by this IC is not

used because the IF amplifier, due to its internal symmetry, is already an excellent limiter for FSK signals.

The internal oscillator is not used either: it is replaced by a crystal oscillator, T_1, operating on 5185 kHz, that is followed by a decade scaler, IC_2. The exact frequency of the crystal depends on the requirements of the decoder; trimmer C_3 enables it to be varied by a few kHz, i.e., a few hundreds of Hertz at the output.

Thanks to the TCA440, the remainder of the receiver is fairly simple without the need of special components. Standard chokes can be used in the $L_2 ... L_4$ positions; L_1 consists of 6 turns enamelled copper wire of 0.3 mm dia. on a ferrite bead.

Sensitivity of the receiver is good at a few μV.

Calibration is very simple: adjust input trimmers C_1 and C_2 for maximum output, and then turn C_3 until the output frequency matches the decoder.

The crystal should be suitable for parallel resonance with a capacitance of 30 pF.

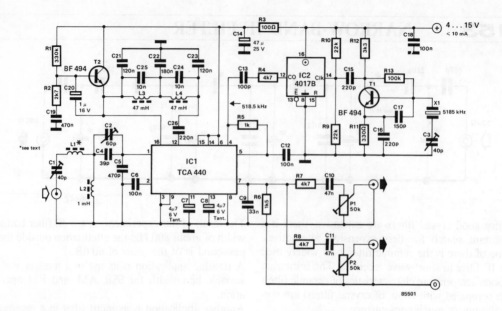

Current consumption is not greater than 10 mA. The supply voltage may be 4...15 V.
It is, of course, a fairly simple matter to make the receiver suitable for use on other maritime medium wavelengths.

155   RTTY CALIBRATION INDICATOR

To calibrate an RTTY (radio teletype) decoder correctly in accordance with the marks and spaces, an oscilloscope is needed. The mark and space signals are applied to the X and Y inputs of the instrument respectively, when, on correct calibration, the screen of the oscilloscope displays the well-known RTTY cross.
If an oscilloscope is not available, the circuit shown here can be used. It consists of two amplifiers with high-impedance input, T1 and T8, that are followed

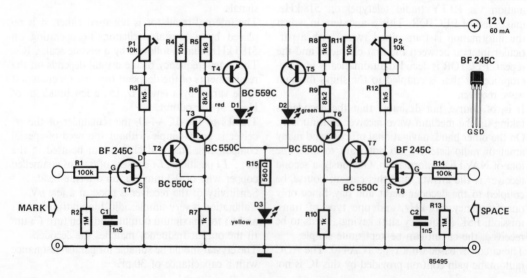

186

by driver stages $T_2 \ldots T_4$ and $T_5 \ldots T_7$. The driver stages control three LEDs, $D_1 \ldots D_3$ direct. Diode D_1 (red) is the mark indicator, D_2 (green) is the space indicator, and D_3 (amber) indicates whether the decoder has been calibrated symmetrically.

Preset potentiometers P_1 and P_2 determine the amplification of the field-effect transistors. Proper setting of these components enables the indicator to be matched with the filter outputs of any RTTY decoder.

After the indicator has been coupled to the RTTY decoder, that unit can be calibrated as follows:

■ tune the short-wave receiver to the marks; the BFO knob must be adjusted until the red and amber LEDs both flash brightly;

■ the RTTY decoder is then adjusted to the correct frequency deviation, indicated by the flashing of the green LED. If the amber LED lights continuously, the decoder has been calibrated correctly. Otherwise, the above procedure should be repeated carefully.

---

156   RTTY/CW FILTER

An appreciable part of short-wave radio traffic takes place via morse and radio teletype transmission. To ensure optimum reception of these types of transmission, a practical bandwidth of about 300 Hz is required in the receiver. Such a bandwidth allows for some drift of both transmitter and receiver, and also for the frequency shift of RTTY signals. As commercially available filters meeting these requirements are still rather expensive, it pays to build your own: a suitable one is shown in the accompanying diagram.

The crystals used are inexpensive types, commonly found in computer systems.

Inductor L_1 is made by winding 2 times 20 turns enamelled copper wire of 0.3 mm diameter onto a

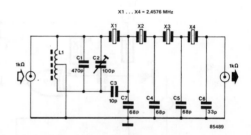

T50/2 RF toroid (available from Cirkit).
Some parameters of the filter are:
■ bandwidth at —6 dB points : 300 Hz
■ bandwidth at —60 dB points : 1100 Hz
■ insertion loss : 7 dB
■ ripple in pass-band : 1 dB

---

157   S METER

Since many amateur receivers are fitted with an S meter that functions far from logarithmically, the proposed circuit should be a welcome extension of such receivers.

Although ICs such as the CA3089 or the CA3189 are not in common use any more, they serve a useful purpose in the meter circuit, because, apart from a symmetric limiter, a coincidence detector, and an AFC amplifier, they contain a very good logarithmic amplifier-detector.

As is seen, the circuit is fairly simple, but remember that these ICs operate up to about 30 MHz, so that the wiring of the meter, and also its connections in the receiver, should be kept as short as possible.

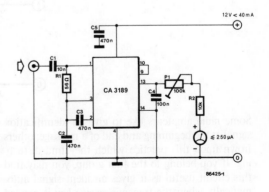

Note further that
■ the input of the CA3189 must be terminated by 50 Ω;
■ the connection to the input of the CA3189 should be in screened cable;
■ if it is not possible to obtain the input signal from a low-impedance source, a source follower should be used between it and the meter circuit.

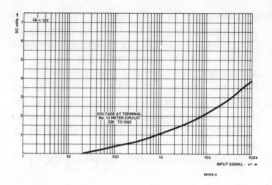

158   SEND/RECEIVE IDENT

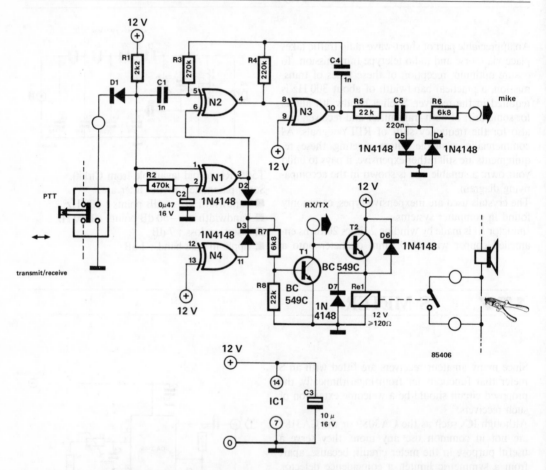

Some radio amateurs like to give an identification signal at the beginning and end of a message; others frown upon this practice which they find disturbing. If you belong to the first group, you may find this circuit useful as it gives an ident signal automatically when the transmit/receive key is pressed

and just after this has been released again. The two signals are identifiable by being slightly different in frequency.

XOR gate N₁ functions as a monostable, whose output is high for a short time after its inputs either change from high to low (at the onset of a transmission), or from low to high (at the end of a transmission). Its output is applied to an oscillator, N_2/N_3, and to the transmit/receive switching section. When the input pin 6 of N_2 is high, this XOR gate functions as an inverter, so that the oscillator generates a short tone in the medium audio range which is fed to the microphone via limiter D_4/D_5. The frequency determining network is earthed via C_1 and D_1 or via C_1 and R_1, depending on whether the transmit/receive key is pressed or has just been released.

During transmission, the rx/tx output is low: this output is intended to be connected to the corresponding input of the transceiver. Transistor T_2 is on, so that relay Re_1 is actuated: its contact(s) may be used, for instance, to disconnect the loudspeaker during transmissions.
Current consumption, ignoring the relay current, amounts to about 15 mA.

---

159   SIMPLE FIELD STRENGTH INDICATOR

A practically proven small circuit that is very popular with many model fliers, as it enables them to verify that their remote control transmitter is actually transmitting. Any doubt as to whether a fault lies in the receiver or transmitter is also quickly resolved.
The only active element in the circuit is a transistor that is used as a controlled resistance in one of the arms of a metering bridge. The base of the transistor is connected to the wire or rod aerial. The increasing HF voltage at the base of the aerial drives the transistor so that the bridge is brought out of equilibrium. A current then flows through R_2, the

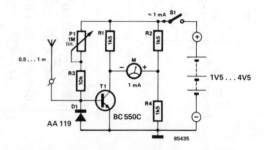

mA meter, and the collector-emitter junction of the transistor. The meter should be zeroed with P_1 before the transmitter is switched on.

---

160   SPOT FREQUENCY RECEIVER

Monitoring a number of frequencies in the short-wave band, such as the international shipping distress frequency, is a fascinating pastime. Since only a limited number of stations is normally monitored, and their frequency is invariably fixed by international treaty, the receiver needs only to be capable of being switched between those spot frequencies.
The receiver works on the direct conversion principle, i.e., the oscillator frequency is equal to the received frequency, so that the intermediate frequency is zero.
The aerial signal is fed to tuned RF amplifiers T_1 and T_2 via a switched preselector. The RF amplifiers are coupled to an S042P type mixer. There are three crystal-controlled local oscillators, which are switched into circuit in accordance with

the preselector.
The output of the mixer is the audio signal, which is fed to AF amplifier IC_2 via low-pass filter $R_{11}...R_{13}\text{-}C_{28}...C_{30}$. The gain of IC_2 is about 60 dB.
Part of the output of IC_2 is rectified in D_1 and D_2 and used for AGC (automatic gain control) of T_1 and T_2.
The output of IC_2 is fed to power amplifier IC_3 which drives a loudspeaker or headphones. There is also a tape output. Volume control is provided by P_1.
Inductors $L_1...L_3$ are each wound on a T50/2 toroid as follows:
- $L_1 = 115$ turns enamelled copper wire of 0.15 mm dia. with tap   at 11 turns;
- $L_2,L_3 = 90$ turns enamelled copper wire of

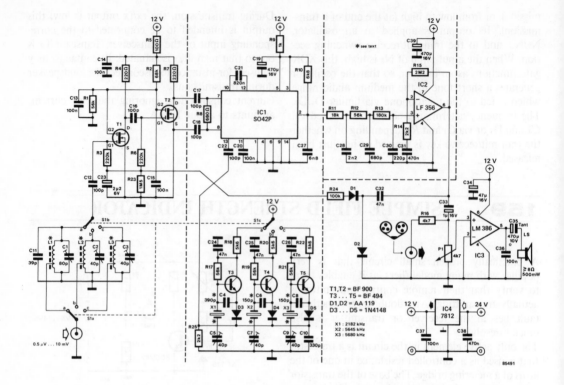

0.2 mm dia. with tap at 9 turns.

If different frequencies from those shown are required, one or more of the crystals must, of course, be replaced, but at the same time L_1, L_2, or L_3, as appropriate, must also be modified. The change in the number of turns and the tap is directly proportional to the change in frequency. If, for instance, a frequency of 2600 kHz instead of 2182 kHz is wanted in position 1 of switch S_1, the number of turns, n, of L_1 should become

$n = 115(2182/2600) = 97$ turns and the tap should be at

$n = 11(2182/2600) = 9$ turns.

Oscillator capacitors C_4, C_6, and C_8 should have a higher value if the frequencies are chosen at the low end of the short-wave band.

When the receiver has been built correctly in accordance with HF requirements (short connections, ample decoupling), it should work up to about 18 MHz. The dashed lines in the circuit diagram represent earthed screens between the various sections.

The receiver is calibrated by adjusting C_5, C_7, and C_9 for zero beat, and then adjusting C_1, C_2, and C_3 for maximum audio output.

161 SWITCHABLE BANDSELECTOR

In many older types of SW receiver, intermodulation in the mixer was generally avoided by including a tuneable, often automatically tracking, preselector. In a computercontrolled preselector, the use of varactor diodes for tuning the inductors often leads to considerable intermodulation distortion. A different approach is therefore used in this design.

The circuit diagram shows the use of PIN diodes Type BA244 for selecting one of 5 bandfilters followed by a low-pass section. Selection of a filter is effected by having the computer drive the associated input high. An impedance transformer is provided at the input to enable connection of 50 Ω as well as 500 Ω aerials. For most purposes, the 500 Ω

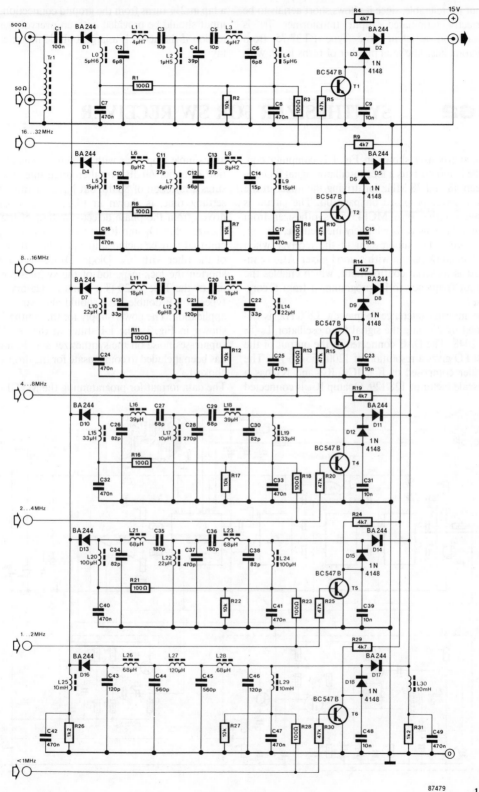

87479

191

input is preferable, since it allows short aerials to be correctly terminated. Input transformer Tr1 is wound on a ferrite core Type FT37-75 from Micrometals. The total number of turns is 19, with a tap at 2½ turns from the ground connection. The input should be provided with an overvoltage protection if the aerial is a large, outside mounted, array.

162   SYNTHESIZER FOR SW RECEIVER

The synthesizer shown in Fig. 1 is computer controlled, and outputs a local oscillator signal (LO) between 48 and 78 MHz for driving the mixer in the SW receiver proposed on page 00. The circuit is based on the Type MC145156 synthesizer from Motorola. This IC is relatively inexpensive, and ensures good LO suppression in the receiver when used in combination with a good mixer. Also of interest is its serial control input, which enables the output frequency to be programmed from a computer.

The internal reference frequency, 1200 Hz, is obtained by dividing the signal from oscillator T_5-T_6 by 2048. The DAC connected to the output of the first LO gives a resolution of $1200/255 \approx 5$ Hz. The divider composed of IC_1, IC_2, IC_3 and N_1 has a prescale factor of 128/129. Opamp IC_6 is connected as a simple loop filter with a reference signal rejection of about 60 dB. An alternative filter that ensures a rejection of 80 dB, but has a slightly longer settling time, is shown in Fig. 2. This circuit is driven from the phase detector output of the synthesizer chip. Opamp IC_1 is used in a speed-up circuit that may be included to equal the settling time of the filter with IC_6. Diodes D_1-D_2 also serve to shorten the lock-in period of the synthesizer. The use of the Type E420 (T_1) is not obligatory: other types of AF double FET should also work in this application. The power supply for the synthesizer is shown in Fig. 3. The L-C filter in the +5 V rail suppresses noise on the synthesizer supply, and D_2 has been included to compensate for the drop across choke L_2.

The data format for programming the MVC145156

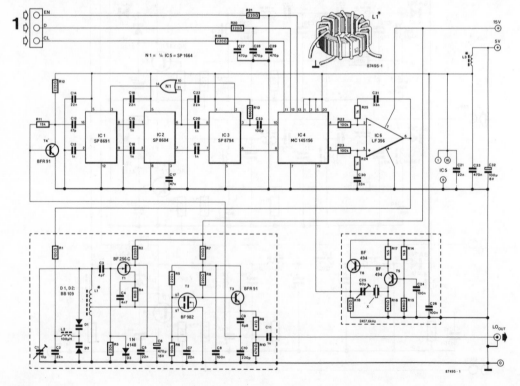

2

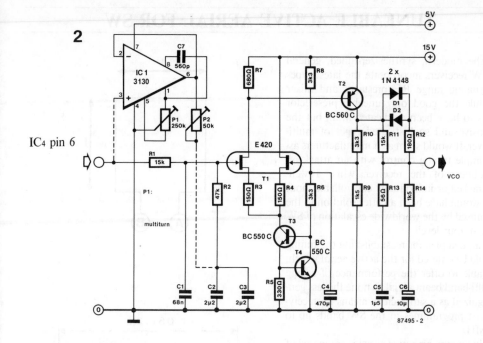

IC4 pin 6

87495 - 2

3

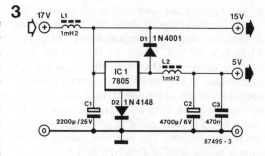

87495 - 3

is shown in Fig. 4. Bits SW₁ and SW₂ control the switching outputs, and are not used here. The synthesizer divides by 128N + A: when counter A reaches state 127, N is increased by 1, and A becomes 0. Data is latched into the synthesizer on the trailing edge of the clock signal. When the control word is complete, the enable signal is briefly made high to transfer the data from the shift register to the programmable dividers. The squelch is then enabled to suppress locking and tuning noises.

The construction of this synthesizer requires some experience in building RF circuits. The ECL dividers and the synthesizer chip should lie upside down on an unetched board to enable effective grounding and cooling. The chips are interconnected with the shortest possible wires. Great care should be taken in the construction of the VCO and the TXO. These sections should be screened and

built such that mechanical stability is ensured at all times. VCO inductor L₁ is especially critical in this respect: make sure that the wire turns are secure on the core.

Finally, the winding data for the home-made inductors in this circuit: (use enamelled copper wire): L₁ (VCO): 14 turns 22SWG (∅ 0.8 mm) on a T50-12 core, tap at 4 turns from ground; L₃ (+5 V rail): 8 turns 30 SWG (∅ 0.3 mm) through a ferrite bead.

4

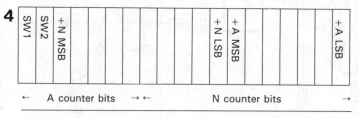

SW1	SW2	+N MSB						+N LSB	+A MSB					+A LSB

←   A counter bits   → ←   N counter bits   →

↑ Last data bit in (Bit no. 16)   First bit in (Bit no. 1) ↑

Many of the modern, synthesizer-tuned, general coverage SW receivers incorporate the latest types of high dynamic range RF prestages and mixer devices, while the good old tuneable preselector stage seems to have been eradicated in all but the most expensive and sophisticated types of multi-mode receiver. It would seem as if manufacturers associate a simple tuning control with an attack on user friendliness of the receiver, while a well-designed, tracked or individually controllable input attenuator would have been a better solution to the problems caused by the worldwide escalation of SW transmitter output levels.

A likewise argued plea for reestablishing the tuning control could be entered for the active aerial which, while not able to offer the performance of a long wire or multi-band beam aerial, is none the less generally recognized as a satisfactory means for receiving broadcast programmes in the SW bands up to about 15 MHz.

As generally known, an active aerial is composed of an aerial proper and associated amplifier. As to the latter, the ciruit diagram shows that the design has a varactor-tuned, symmetrical input using two FETs Type BF256C which are fed over the coax cable to the receiver. Opamp IC1 functions as a fast symmetrical to asymmetrical converter capable of operation up to about 30 MHz. Note that the varicap diode set is tuned over a separate cable; twin-lead 75 Ω coax cable is, of course, ideal for the present purpose. The indicated varicap set ensures a tuning ratio of about 1:2 to 1:3.

When constructing the aerial to this design, it should be noted that neither the circumference of

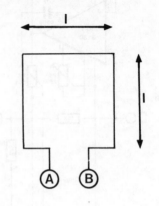

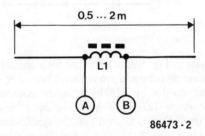

86473 - 2

the loop aerial nor the total length of the dipole must be in excess of one tenth of the relevant wavelength in order to ensure the correct directivity characteristics, especially in the case of the loop

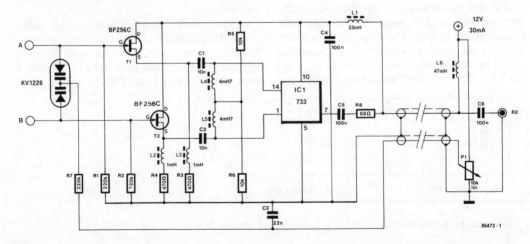

aerial; the dipole will typically fail to match the amplifier input impedance and thus cause problems in getting the device tuned properly.

Table 1 summarizes the aerial construction data, given a number of possible operating frequencies. The aerial should be mounted in such a position as to receive a minimum amount of man-made, short range interference; the amplifier's symmetrical input should ensure sufficient aerial directivity to find a dip for the interfering source.

The loop aerial is uncritical as to the height above ground, but not so the dipole, which is bound to act as a vertical rather than horizontal aerial when mounted at less than a quarter wavelength above ground.

Table 1.

Fmin [kHz]	L1 [µH]	turns n	l [m]
150	2200	32	1
		51	0.5
350	390	13	1
		20	0.5
1000	47	4	1
		6	0.5
2000	12	2	1
		3	0.5
4000	3.9	1	0.5

164 TUNEABLE FM BOOSTER

This FM band (88-108 MHz) preamplifier has been designed to come round the problems associated with wideband as well as narrowband aerial boosters. Most commercially available boosters are wideband types with relatively poor selectivity and adjacent station rejection, while the (more expensive) narrowband types are rather impracticable when it comes to receiving stations well removed from the (fixed) frequency of peak amplification. This proposed design is the best of both worlds,

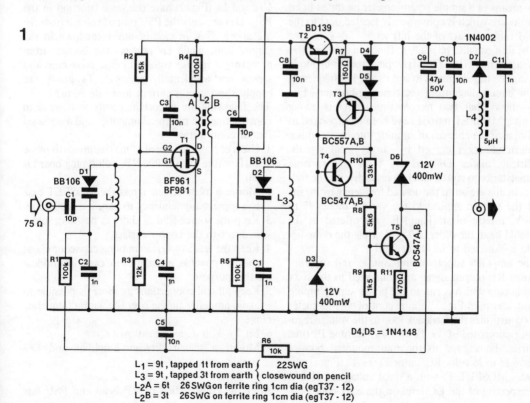

L₁ = 9t , tapped 1t from earth ⎰ 22SWG
L₃ = 9t , tapped 3t from earth ⎱ closewound on pencil
L₂A = 6t   26SWG on ferrite ring 1cm dia (egT37 - 12)
L₂B = 3t   26SWG on ferrite ring 1cm dia (egT37 - 12)

2

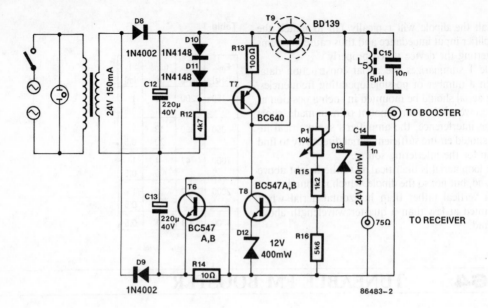

86483-2

since it features good selectivity and strong signal handling, as well as a relatively low noise figure and sufficient amplification over the entire FM band. Tuning the preamplifier is done in the living room, by means of a simple potentiometer mounted in an enclosure which is conveniently located next to the FM tuner as part of the hifi set.

The unit can also be made to function as a 2 metres amateur band (144-146 MHz) preamplifier by modifying the tuned circuits to suit the higher frequency. The circuit diagram of the tuneable booster—Fig. 1—shows that two remote tuned circuits, along with a MOSFET tetrode have been incorporated to minimize the chances of running into cross- and/or intermodulation caused by strong local signals. Varicap diodes D_1 and D_2 form the variable capacitance to coils L_1 and L_3 respectively. The tuned circuits are set to the desired frequency by means of the voltage applied to the varicap diodes (3 to 24 V, reverse bias). The RF gain offered by T_1 should be of the order of 25 dB, while the noise figure is expected to be about 2 dB.

The amplifier supply/tuning voltage and superimposed RF output signal are connected to the coax cable core which is run to the power supply/tuning unit, shown in Fig. 2. Tuning control potentiometer P_1 constitutes the feedback loop to the voltage regulator composed of T_7, T_8 and T_9. Turning P_1 thus varies the voltage to the mast-mounted booster form 15 to 36 volts. Regulator T_2-T_3-T_4 (Fig. 1) provides MOSFET T_1 with a fixed voltage of 11.4 V, irrespective of the DC level on the coax core. Sub-

traction of 12 V from the 15-36 V input voltage is by means of zener D_6 and current source T_5. RF output voltage and DC supply are coupled to the download cable through C_{11} and L_4 respectively. C_{14} and L_5 (Fig. 2) have the same function in the PSU. D_{13} prevents the PSU output voltage from rising above 37 V in case of any breakdown in the supply unit, while D_7 protects the booster from accepting a reverse voltage in case coax core and screen are accidentally reversed. T_6 limits the supply short circuit current to a safe 60 mA.

The following are important points to observe in constructing the masthead amplifier and associated indoor control unit:

1. Use a copper-clad board of maximum earth plane surface (the Type 85000 RF prototyping board is ideal).
2. Mount a metal screen across the MOSFET case to suppress any tendency to parasitic oscillation.
3. Keep the source lead as short as possible; solder it direct to the copper surface.
4. Keep the leads of G_2 decoupling capacitor C_4 as short as possible; a ceramic disc capacitor is ideal for this purpose.
5. Keep all coil connections as short as possible to avoid amplifier tuning over the wrong frequency range.
6. Fit T_9 with a small heatsink.
7. Mount a screen between amplifier and DC supply section.

After the construction of RF head and PSU has

been completed, the latter is tested by verifying the presence of the variable (15.6 to 36.6 V) supply and tuning voltage on the coax cable core. The voltage across R_{14} should be lower than 0.4 V with the amplifier connected at the far end of the cable. Turning P_1 should cause the voltage at the collector of T_5 to vary between 3 and 24 V.

The voltage at the emitter of T_2 should be constant at 11.4 V with respect to ground, irrespective of the tuning voltage set with P_1 Drain resistor R_4 should drop between 0.7 and 2 V. Set P_1 to the centre of its travel.

Optimum RF performance of the booster can be achieved by carefully stretching or compressing L_3 for maximum amplification at about 95 MHz; tune the receiver to a weak transmission at this frequency and align for maximum S meter deflection or optimum audibility of the signal above the noise level. Do the same for signals at either extreme end of the band and set P_1 accordingly. Ensure that the tuning potentiometer can be set to give optimum

amplification for every frequency in the 88 to 108 MHz band and mark the tuning scale on the indoor unit in steps of 1 MHz. In case it is not possible to obtain equal amplification across the band, L_3 may be adapted carefully by increasing or decreasing the number of turns. The tap, however, should remain at 3 turns from ground.

Those constructors striving for utmost perfection may fit a 40 pF trimmer capacitor instead of C_1, in order that the amplifier may be tuned for optimum (i.e. lowest) noise figure, which is not the same as tuning for optimum amplification.

Finally, the coil data for the tuneable booster are as follows:

L_1 = 9 turns 22 SWG (0.7 mm dia) enamelled wire, close wound, coil diameter 7 mm. Tap at 1 turn from ground.

L_3 = the same, tap at 3 turns from earth.

$L_{2a};L_{2b}$ = 6 and 3 turns respectively, 26 SWG (0.5 mm dia) enamelled copper wire on dia 10 mm ferrite ring Type T37-12.

165   VLF CONVERTER

Strictly speaking, the VLF (very low frequency) band stretches from 3 kHz to 30 kHz, and the LF (low frequency) band, often called the long-wave-band, from 30 kHz to 300 kHz. The converter described here covers the frequency range

10...150 kHz and falls, therefore, half-way between being a VLF and an LF converter.

Frequencies between 10 kHz and 150 kHz are converted to 4.01...4.15 MHz which can be fed to any short-wave receiver capable of accepting those fre-

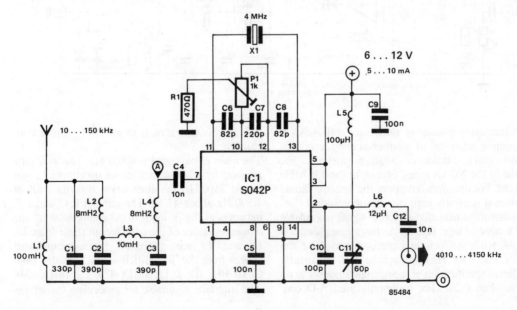

quencies. The converter is connected to the aerial input of the receiver via coaxial cable.

Many converters suffer from break-through of the mixer/oscillator frequency in the output signal, which is normally caused by the mixer being asymmetrical. Because of that, the present converter uses the well-known S042P frequency changer, the symmetry of which can be set accurately with a 1 k preset potentiometer connected between pins 10 and 12.

To prevent reception of image frequencies, the aerial signal is first applied to an *LC* band-pass filter, before it is fed to the frequency changer.

The output of the frequency changer (pin 2) is applied to an *LC* circuit that is tuned to the frequency range 4.01...4.15 MHz. This circuit, consisting of a 100 μH inductor in parallel with a 100 n capacitor

and a 60 p trimmer, effectively suppresses any spurious signals produced in the frequency changer. The 60 p trimmer is used to tune in to the desired transmitter in the 10...150 kHz range (loudest reception!). The symmetry of the frequency changer is set by tuning the short-wave receiver to the frequency of the quartz oscillator, i.e., 4.00 MHz, and then adjusting the 1 k preset for minimum output from the converter, that is, minimum deflection of the S meter, or other field strength indicator, on the receiver. During this calibration, the input of the frequency changer, point A in the diagram, should be short-circuited to earth. All inductors are standard RF chokes. The value of the output inductor, 12 μH, is not critical. The aerial should be as long a wire as possible.

166 WEATHER SATELLITE INTERFACE

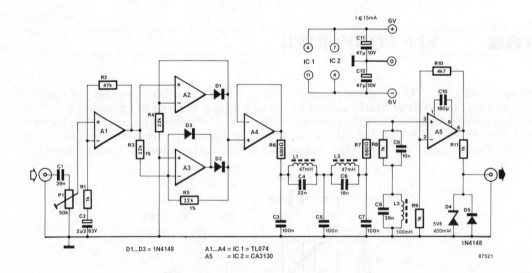

An increasing number of electronics enthusiasts is becoming interested in weather satellite reception. Most non-geostationary weather satellites, like those in the NOAA series, operate in the 138 MHz carrier. For optimum reception, the detector should feature a relatively high carrier suppression.

It is assumed here that a picture signal is available on a cassette tape. Opamp A_1 has an amplification of 48, while A_2-A_3 form a precision two-phase rectifier. The 2,400 Hz ripple arising from the slightly different specification of the opamps amounts to no more than 0.2%. For commonly used A-D con-

verters, this corresponds to an error smaller than ½ (LSB).

The main ripple signal is 4,800 Hz. This is readily removed by a double π filter set up around L_1 and L_2. At 2500 Hz, the attenuation is baout 3 dB, at 4,500 Hz about 45 dB. The parallel R-C and L-C networks at the + input of A_5 compensate for the ohmic resistance of the inductors in the π filter. L_1, L_2 and L_3 are preferably ferrite-encapsulated chokes from the Toko 10RB series, available from Cirkit PLC (L_1 & L_2: 181LY-473. L_3: 181LY-104). The interface is suitable for processing carrier frequencies up to 4,800 Hz, so that it is possible to play the tape at double speed for reading into the computer (provided, of course, the program can handle this). Components R_{11}, D_4 and D_5 protect the A-D converter against voltages higher than 5 and lower than 0 volt. The use of the Type CA3130 BiMos opamp ensures an output voltage swing of 5 V when a ± 6 V supply is used. The maximum supply level and current consumption are ± 9 V and 15 mA respectively. The input signal amplitude should be greater than 68 mV$_{rms}$ for a 5 V$_{pp}$ output.

This circuit is intended as a replacement for the electronics in a partly or wholly defective autofocus driver in a slide projector. The mechanical parts in the autofocus system are assumed to be still functional.

Most automatic focusing systems in slide projectors are based on the use of an optical module, which comprises a small lamp, a few lenses and mirrors, and a light sensor made from two series-connected light dependent resistors (LDRs), which function as a potential divider. As shown in Fig. 1, lamp La projects a narrow beam onto the centre of the slide, A, whose surface reflects it onto the LDRs. When the slide surface bulges inside or outside, the projected image on the screen is blurred, and the beam from L is received on the surface of one of the LDRs (point 2 or 3). This is detected by a motor driver circuit, which ensures that the focal distance between the objective, O, and the slide surface is corrected to maintain a sharp image, i.e., the objective is moved until the circuit detects that the reflected beam from L falls exactly in between the LDRs (point 1).

1

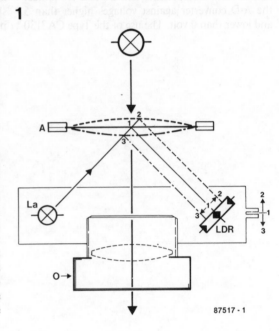

87517 - 1

2

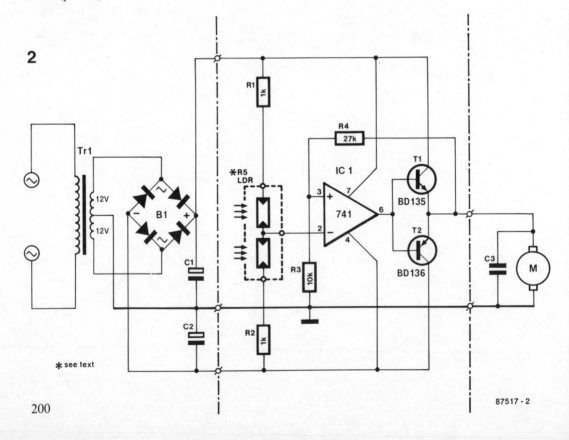

* see text

87517 - 2

The circuit is based on the use of an existing set of LDRs as part of the optical module in the slide projector. The symmetrical supply shown to the left, and the motor plus decoupling capacitor, are also part of the projector. The inverting input of opamp IC_1 is at ground potential when the above mentioned test beam falls in between the LDRs. The output of the opamp keeps the non-inverting input at 0 V as well, so that no motor voltage is available at the emitters of power drivers T_1-T_2. Should the reflected beam illuminate either one of the LDRs,

the circuit arranges for the motor to move the objective glass towards the correct focal position, until no voltage difference between the LDRs is detected. The feedback gain of the circuit has been kept relatively low to keep the motor from continuously moving the objective glass past the target position, causing the system to oscillate slowly. Resistors R_3 and R_4 may have to be dimensioned differently than shown to achieve optimum response as regards speed and stability.

168   DIGITAL JOYSTICK INTERFACE

The BBC and Electron computers produced by Acorn have a joystick port to which only analogue joysticks can be connected. For many purposes, a digital joystick, i.e., one with four contacts, is much

more suitable. The interface suggested here enables a digital joystick to be used with the two computers mentioned.

The joystick port is provided with a voltage of 1.8 V

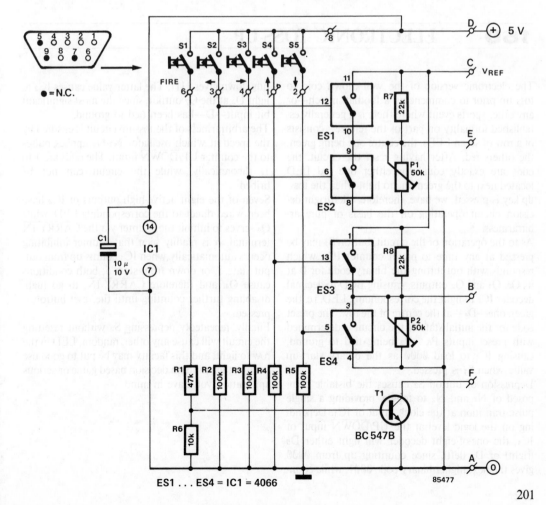

ES1 ... ES4 = IC1 = 4066

85477

when the analogue joystick is set to the left or top positions, 0 V with the joystick in the right or bottom positions, and 0.9 V with the joystick in neutral. The 1.8 V is the reference voltage of the analogue-to-digital converter in the computer.

As can be seen from the circuit diagram in figure 1, the various voltages can simply be provided by four sets of contacts or switches. Each of the sets of contacts controls an electronic switch. The 0.9 V for neutral is obtained from a potential divider. The electronic switches are required because the contacts in the joystick have a common connection and can, therefore, not be used direct for shorting resistors in the potential divider. The fire button is connected to the $+5$ V line by a junction in the joystick, and thus produces a logic 1 when it is pressed, whereas the computer expects a 0. The signal is, therefore, inverted by transistor T_1.

The interface is calibrated with the aid of a small auxiliary program: REPEAT PRINT ADVAL(1) ADVAL(2): UNTIL0 Potentiometers P_1 and P_2 should be set to the centre of their travel.

Connect the joystick and the interface to the computer, start the auxiliary program, and adjust the potentiometers so that the two numbers on the screen are as near as possible 32768.

Table 1.

Interconnections interface to computer

terminal	joystick 1	joystick 2
A	8 (gnd)	8 (gnd)
B	7 (ch.1)	4 (ch.3)
C	11 (Uref)	11 (Uref)
D	1 (+5 V)	1 (+5 V)
E	15 (ch.0)	12 (ch.2)
F	13 (PB0)	10 (PB1)

169   ELECTRONIC TOSS-UP

The electronic version of the well-known coin to toss up prior to commencing a football match—or any other sports event where there is a generally established formality on part of the referee—consists of a row of seven LEDs, the centre one being green, the others red. After having reset the circuit, the odds are exactly equal for either one red LED located next to the green one to light when the toss-up key is pressed; we have, therefore, a left/right decision circuit operating on the basis of pure arbitrariness.

As to the operation of the circuit, button S_1 may be pressed at any time to preset counter IC_1, which responds with outputting the binary code for 0 at its Q_0, Q_1 and Q_2 outputs, causing BCD-to-decimal decoder IC_2 to light the corresponding LED, i.e. the green one—D_4—at the centre of the row. The preset code for the initial state of the circuit is determined with preset inputs $P_6 \ldots P_3$ being tied to ground, causing IC_1 to load 0000 as the binary start-up value when S_1 is pressed.

Depression of button S_2 causes the bistable composed of N_1 and N_2 to toggle, providing a single pulse transition at the clock input of IC_1. Depending on the logic level at the UP/$\overline{DOWN}$ input of IC_1, the one-of-eight decoder will light either D_5 (right) or D_3 (left), since counting up from 0000 gives the next higher binary code 0001, while counting down gives 1111. The latter value causes IC_2 to light D_3 at the Q_7 output, since the most significant bit input—D—has been tied to ground.

The arbitrariness of the toss-up circuit is ensured by the speed at which oscillator N_3-N_4 applies pulses to the counter UP/$\overline{DOWN}$ input. The odds are 1 to 1, theoretically, while the circuit can not be bribed . . .

Seven of the eight active-high outputs of IC_2 have been wired direct to the corresponding LED, while Q_4 serves to inhibit the counter via the $\overline{CARRY\ IN}$ terminal. It is readily seen that counter inhibiting occurs automatically when IC_1 counts up from output state 3, or down from state 5; both conditions cause Q_4, and therefore $\overline{CARRY\ IN}$, to go high, disabling further counting until the reset button is pressed.

Finally, repeatedly depressing S_2 without resetting the circuit will cause any other, random, LED in the row to light, and this facility may be put to good use in any other, random decision based game or serious application you have in mind.

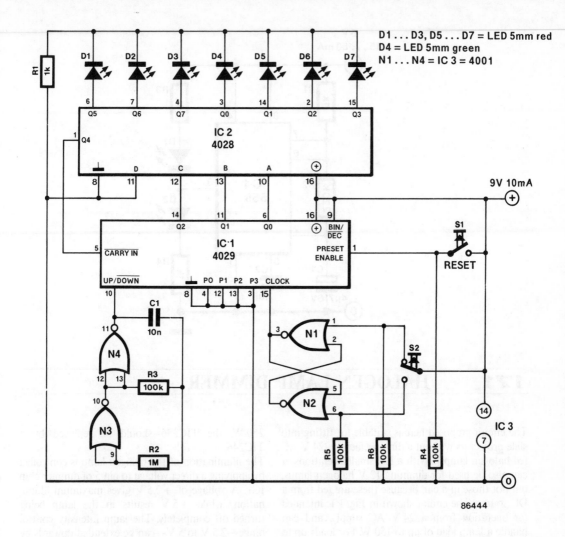

D1 ... D3, D5 ... D7 = LED 5mm red
D4 = LED 5mm green
N1 ... N4 = IC 3 = 4001

86444

170   FLASHING LIGHTS

This application of the well-known Type 555 timer is intended for model railway enthusiasts wishing to construct a two-lamp flashing beacon with a minimum of components.

With reference to the circuit diagram, the number of LEDs need not be restricted to two: several may be connected in parallel to achieve a higher light intensity, but a total current consumption of 200 mA should not be exceeded to prevent the destruction of the output stages in the 555. Each LED added should have its own current limiting resistor, similar to D₁-R₃ or D₂-R₄.

The flashing rate is defined with C₁. The stated value of this component is likely to be optimum for

applications in model railways. The supply voltage for the circuit is not critical, but should remain within the range from 5 to 10 V. With two LEDs fitted and a 5 V supply, the flashing circuit should consume less than 50 mA. The intensity of the LEDs can be adapted to individual preference by changing R₃ and R₄, but too low resistance values should be avoided to prevent the destruction of the LEDs.

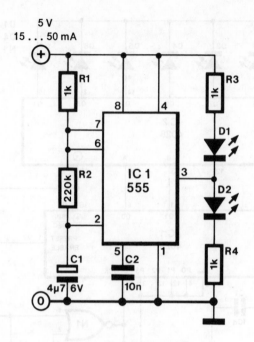

171   HALOGEN LAMP DIMMER

The circuit proposed here is suitable for fitting into slide projectors without a dimmer facility (24 V AC fed halogen lamps). With a few small alterations, it can also be used for dimming 12 V halogen lamps, but not those in a car, because these are fed from a DC source. The circuit shown in Fig. 1 is intended for operation from a 24 V AC supply, and can handle a lamp load of up to 150 W. For loads up to

250 W, the TIC236 should be replaced by a TIC246.

The illumination of the halogen lamp is controlled by applying a direct voltage to pin 5 of dimmer chip IC₁. A voltage of +2.5 V gives maximum illumination, while +5 V results in the lamp being turned off completely. The lamp intensity control range—2.5 V to 5 V—can be extended upwards by

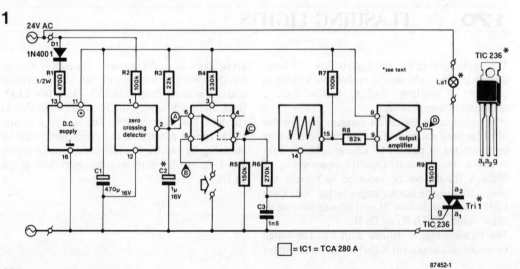

1

87452-1

204

2

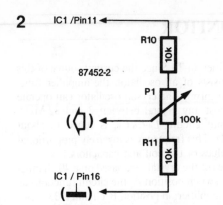

IC1 /Pin11

R10 10k

87452-2

P1 100k

(⟨⟩)◄

R11 10k

IC1 / Pin16

(▬)◄

3

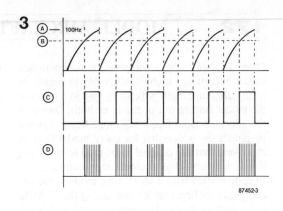

(A) — 100Hz

(B) ---

(C)

(D)

87452-3

4

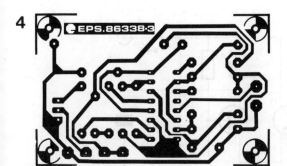

EPS.86338·3

+ C2   + C1

R2

R3

R4   Tri 1

R6

R5

C3   La1

Parts list

Resistors (±5%):
R_1 = 470R; 0.5 W
$R_2; R_7$ = 100K
R_3 = 22K
R_4 = 330K
R_5 = 150K
R_6 = 270K
R_8 = 82K
R_9 = 150R

Capacitors:
C_1 = 470μ; 16 V; axial
C_2 = 1μ; 16 V; axial*
C_3 = 1n5

Semiconductors:
D_1 = 1N4001
Tri_1 = TIC236 or TIC246*
IC_1 = TCA280A

Miscellaneous:
PCB Type 87452
Heatsink for Tri_1.

* See text

decreasing the value of C_2.

The TIC246 should be used when the circuit is to control a 12 V lamp that consumes more than 50 W. Figure 2 shows details of the connection of a potentiometer to the intensity contro! input of the TCA280A. Voltage divider R_{10}-P_1-R_{11} is fitted externally and can be fed from the stabilized voltage available at pin 11 of IC_1. The minimum and maximum intensity of the lamp are determined by R_{10} and R_{11}, respectively, so that the control range can be dimensioned to individual preference. When po-

tentiometer control is used, C_2 must always be 100n.

Figure 3 shows the signal waveforms at various points in the circuit.

The halogen lamp dimmer is constructed on a printed circuit board as shown in Fig. 4. When the lamp power is greater than 15 W, the triac should be fitted onto a heatsink, and the tracks to the a1 and a2 terminals should either be covered with solder, or strengthened with short lengths of wire.

Older, i.e., not using a computer, radio controlled model aircraft are highly vulnerable to breaks in radio communication, which can lead to a crash or the model landing out of reach, or both. Owing to the allocated radio frequency range being usurped by pirates, its is essential for every model flyer to make sure that the channel to be used is free. Even if it is, it is advisable to continue monitoring it.

In combination with a short-wave receiver, the circuit presented here enables monitoring the 27 MHz radio control band. The aerial signal is filtered (26...41 MHz) and applied to the input of differen-

tial amplifier T_1-T_2 Since the current source of this stage consists of an oscillator, the amplifier functions as a mixer. The crystal oscillator can operate with almost any crystal between 2 and 32 MHz. The output circuit, L_4-C_5-C_6, is tuned to about 27.2 MHz. This frequency is inversely proportional to the values of the coil and capacitors.

The values of the crystals are based on a 40-channel set-up. In switch position A, the circuit functions as an aerial amplifier; in position B, channels 38...49 are converted to 8...19; in position C, channels 50...53 are converted to 20...23; and in position

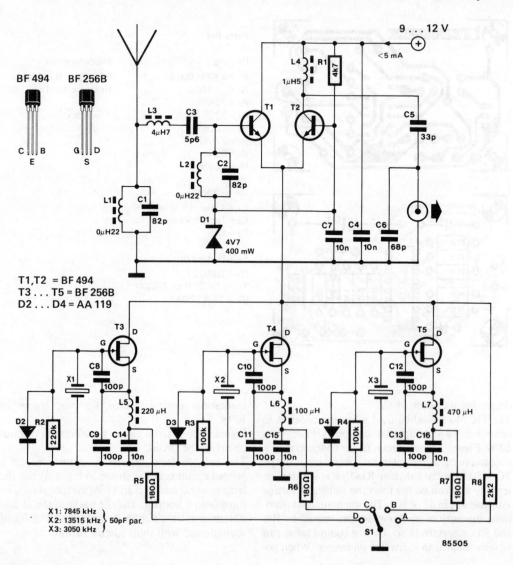

D, channels 61...79 are converted to 21...39. The receiver into which the monitor is coupled need not be suitable for FM reception: an AM re-ceiver can work on FM by detuning the monitor a few kHz.

173 MODEL RAILWAY MONITOR PANEL

Many railway modellers would love to have a track monitor panel, but, unfortunately, the few commercially available types do not justify their cost. It is, however, not too difficult to make one yourself. The reproducing of the track diagram and the mounting of the monitor lights on the panel can be

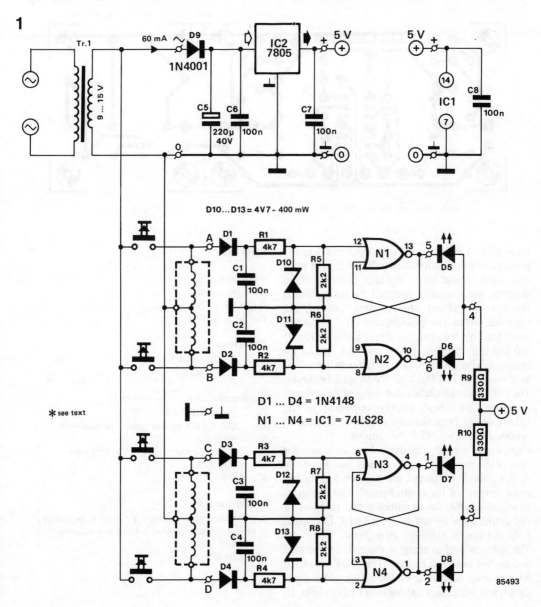

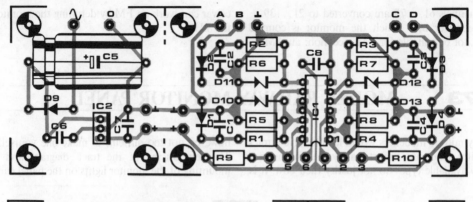

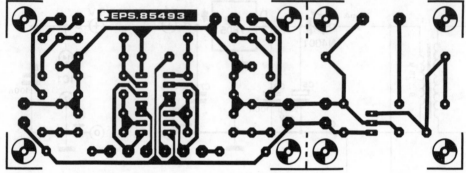

EPS.85493

accomplished without too much trouble. There is a problem, however, in indicating the position of turn-outs and colour-light signals, because these elements are normally operated by spring-loaded switches to prevent the burning out of the solenoids. After the push-button on the control panel has been released, the supply line is no longer live and can, therefore, not be used for lighting an indicator. This problem can, fortunately, be solved by a couple of R-S bistables (NOR gate latches).

The push-button switches and solenoid coils shown in figure 1 are those already contained in the railway set-up. Note that the system is assumed to operate from a 9...15 V AC supply.

Each signal normally requires three lines: one for each of the two coils and a common line. Terminals A, B, C, and D in figure 1 are connected to the relevant outputs of the control panel. The circuit as shown is suitable for monitoring two turnouts or two colour-light signals via A-B and C-D respectively, but can be extended as required.

The voltages used to energize the coils are rectified and applied to an R-S bistable. This NOR gate latch is set or reset, depending on the nature of the input signal, and this causes the relevant LED to light. If,

Parts list

Resistors:
$R_1 \ldots R_4$ = 4k7
$R_5 \ldots R_8$ = 2k2
R_9, R_{10} = 330 Ω

Capacitors:
$C_1 \ldots C_4, C_6 \ldots C_8$ = 100 n
C_5 = 220 µ/40 V

Semiconductors:
$D_1 \ldots D_4$ = 1N4148
$D_5 \ldots D_8$ = LED (red or green, as required)
D_9 = 1N4001
$D_{10} \ldots D_{13}$ = zener diode, 4V7/400 mW
IC_1 = 74LS28
IC_2 = 7805

Miscellaneous:
Tr_1 = mains transformer, 9...15 V secondary (if not already available from the existing system)
PCB 85493

for instance, pin 8 of N2 is high, pin 10 of this gate is low, and D6 lights.

The circuit as shown has a current consumption of about 30 mA per R-S bistable branch.

Not all monitor LEDs will correctly show the position of the relevant turnout or light signal immediately upon switching on the supply. Briefly pressing one of the two push-buttons of each turnout or light signal will correct this situation.

The circuit is most conveniently built on the printed circuit board shown in figure 2. This board can accommodate two monitor channels as shown in figure 1. If more are required, these can be built on additional PCBs. The section containing C_5, IC_2 and D_9 may be cut off subsequent boards, but if many additional PCBs are used, make sure that the power requirements are still met! The $+5$ V and 0 V terminals on all boards should be interconnected.

174   "ON THE AIR " INDICATOR

In radio and television studios it is customary to indicate to all concerned when the microphone or camera is "on the air". This is normally done with a red light at or near the relevant camera or microphone. The circuit described here is intended as an auxiliary for a DIY mixer unit.

To make the circuit automatic in action, stereo slide potentiometers are used at the audio inputs. When one section of these potentiometers is connected to the $+15$ V line, the potential at the wiper of this section is a measure of the potentiometer setting.

This potential is amplified in opamp A_1 and applied to the inverting input of A_2. The latter opamp toggles as soon as the level at its inverting input exceeds that at its $+$input, which has been set with preset P_1.

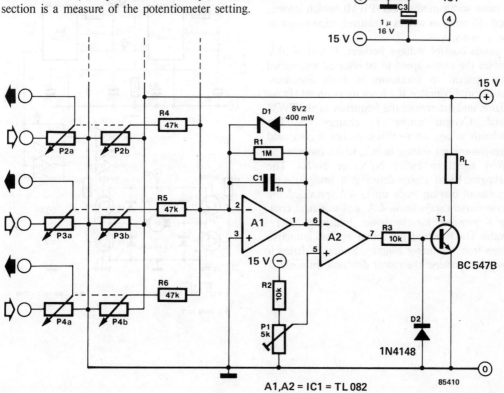

A1,A2 = IC1 = TL 082   85410

The slide potentiometers for this purpose are always logarithmic types, so that the voltage rise at the beginning of their travel is always pretty small. To ensure correct operation of the circuit even at these settings of the potentiometers, the gain of A_1 has been arranged fairly high, about 26 dB.

Opamp A_1 also serves as a summing amplifier that monitors a row of audio inputs. If it is required that each audio input has its own monitor, the two opamps must be repeated for each input, but P_1 of course, continues to provide the non-inverting potential for all opamps in the A_2 position.

The output of the indicator is provided by a type BC 547B transistor, which can switch up to 100 mA. This current is sufficient to light a signal lamp or light-emitting diode (LED) with bias resistor, or to drive a relay.

Current consumption with the BC 547B off amounts to not more than 10 mA.

If low-resistance stereo potentiometers are used, the direct current through the "indicator section" may be too high; if that is so, it is advisable to use a dropping resistor in series with the section.

175 PWM DRIVER FOR DC MOTORS

The speed of DC motors is relatively simple to control. For independently energized motors, the speed is, in principle, a linear funtion of the supply voltage. Motors with a permanent magnet are a subcategory of independently energized motors, and they are often used in toys and models. In this circuit, the motor supply voltage is carried by means of pulse width modulation (PWM), which ensures good efficiency as well as a relatively high torque at low motor speeds.

A single control voltage between 0 and $+10$ V enables the motor speed to be reversed and varied from nought to maximum in both directions. Astable multivibrator IC_1 is set up as an 80 Hz oscillator, and determines the frequency of the PWM signal. Current source T_1 charges C_3. The sawtooth voltage across this capacitor is compared with the control voltage in IC_2, which outputs the PWM signal to buffer N_1-N_3 or N_4-N_6. The darlington-based motor driver is a bridge circuit capable of driving loads up to 4 A, provided the run-in current stays below 6 A, and sufficient cooling is provided for the power transistors T_2-T_5. Diodes D_2-D_5 afford protection against inductive surges from the motor winding. Switch S_1 makes it possible to reverse the motor direction instantly.

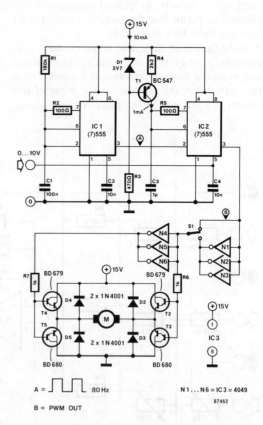

This section indication system may be just the thing you have been looking for when you own a fairly large model railway with tunnels and tracks at several levels, and are sometimes at a loss to find the whereabouts of a particular train. This circuit uses LEDs to indicate the train's position. Each track block is split up into 8 sections, whose starting points are marked with reed contacts (S_1-S_8). A ninth reed contact is fitted at the end of the block, to enable turning off the indication for the relevant length of the track.

The circuit is composed of 8 set-reset (S-R) bistables, which drive a LED each. All SET inputs are combined in a NOR gate, N_1, which drives a pulse shaper and buffer to reset the bistables with a brief

pulse to ensure that only the LED for the last passed track section is lit. The reed contacts are actuated with the aid of a small magnet fitted to the underside of the engine. Depending on the most suitable location of the magnet, the reed contacts are fitted in between the tracks or alongside the left or right hand rail.

Several of these section indication systems may be fitted in series to enable making a control panel with many lights to indicate the train positions. Observing the direction of travel of the trains, section junctions are fitted with S_9 (end of previous section) and S_1 (begin of section) located next to each other.

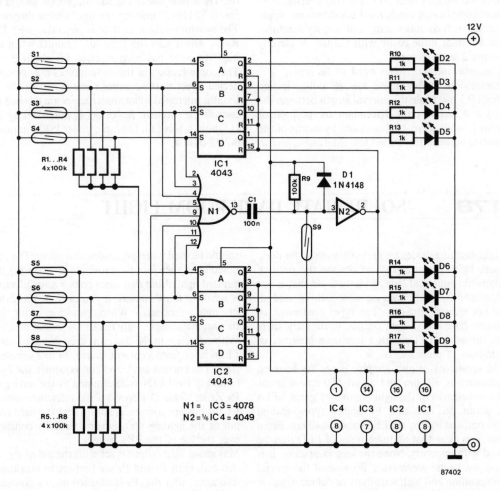

211

Over the past few years, robotics and cybernetics have become new fields of interest for many an owner of a personal micro, equipped with the necessary add-on boards to effect peripheral control. However easy it may seem to write robot control programs and to build the associated computer hardware, the construction of accurately operating mechanical parts (or, if you like, limbs) often poses unsurmountable problems, since a miniature set of gears, ball bearings, spindles and cog-wheels are in no way readily made items for those skilled in programming and soldering.

Despite their limitations as to precision of movement, servo-motors used in model aircraft or boat construction may offer an interesting alternative to more complicated mechanical constructions; applications such as robot arms and sorting machines can be made quite easily with the use of cleverly mounted servo-motors.

A number of wait loops need to be programmed to supply active low (0) pulses lasting about 0.5 ms, while the interval length between the first and second pulse determines the position of servo 1, while servo 2 is positioned by means of the interval between the second and third pulse, and so

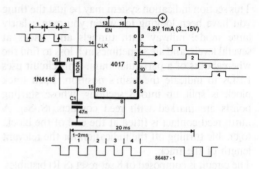

on. The repeat rate of the control process should be about 50 Hz (20 ms); see the inset timing diagram. The synchronization interval is generated with D_1-R_1-C_1, which reset the Type 4017 counter when no negative pulse has been received for about 3 ms. The control inputs of the servo-motors may be connected direct to the counter outputs.

Finally, interested robot constructors are advised to consult the excellent *Robot book*, published by W H Smith & Son Ltd, Leicester, under ISBN number 0-7112-0414-4.

Light-emitting diodes are perfectly suitable for dark-room light, because they (a) obviate the need of filters; (b) emit cold light; (c) have a life that is not shortened by continuous on-off switching; and (d) do not radiate infra-rays. The types used must, of course, have a high light output; fortunately, there are nowadays LEDs with a luminous intensity of hundreds of millicandela.

The sensitivity of photographic paper lies between wavelengths 300 nm and about 550 nm, whereas the wavelength of the light emitted by green LEDs is about 565 nm; that by amber types around 585 nm; and that by red LEDs about 640 nm. From this, it is clear that all three types of LED may be used with impunity. None the less, in practice, it is best not to use green ones. Because of the special composition and high sensitivity of colour negative paper, only yellow LEDs with reduced light output

should be used when processing this paper. The proposed light, therefore, has provision for reducing the emitted light. *Note that since colour reversal paper is sensitive to all colours, it can only be processed in total darkness.* When working with orthochromatic paper, only red LEDs should be used. With reference to the diagram, each group of three LEDs is fed from a current source, T_1 to T_6 respectively. The current level, and consequently the light output of the LEDs, is determined by the setting of P_1 Zener diode D_{19} provides the reference voltage for the current sources, ensuring that the light output of the lighting unit remains virtually constant over the life of the PP3 battery.

Maximum light output is set with the aid of P_2. To this end, both P_1 and P_2 are first set to maximum resistance; after this, P_2 is adjusted until a potential of 0.2 V is measured at point A. The maximum cur-

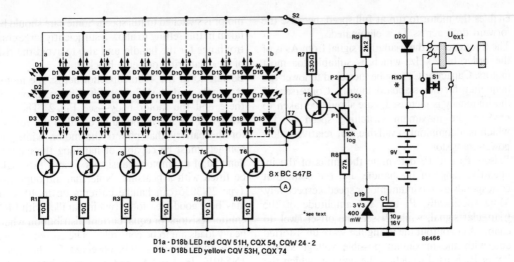

D1a - D18b LED red CQV 51H, CQX 54, CQW 24 - 2
D1b - D18b LED yellow CQV 53H, CQX 74

rent through the LEDs is then about 20 mA.
As the photograph shows, the unit has been constructed so that S_1 is easily operated. Since this switch is a press-to-make type, the light will switch off as soon as it is put aside, thus preserving the battery. It is possible to have the light on continuously by connecting an external battery to U_{ext}. In that case, R_{10} must be matched to this source according to

$$R_{10} = (U_{ext} - 9)10 \ [k\Omega]$$

but only if NiCd batteries are used. If standard cells are used, D_{20} and R_{10} must be omitted.
If a variety of photographic paper is processed, it may be useful to be able to switch between red and amber LEDs. For that purpose, each of the eighteen original yellow LEDs is duplicated by a red LED, shown in dashed lines. Switch S_2 may be used to select the relevant bank of LEDs (red or yellow) as required for the specific application.

179   SPEED CONTROL FOR R/C MODELS

The speed and direction of rotation of a motor in a radio controlled model aeroplane or boat is generally controlled by pulse width modulation of the supply voltage to the motor driver stage.
In the present circuit, shown in Fig. 1, bistable FF_1 is set up rather unconventionally to function as a monostable multivibrator, whose period is set with R_1-C_1-P_1 This period determines the toggle point at which the motor's direction of rotation is reversed. Output $\overline{Q}$ of FF_2 goes high when the pulse at the D input (PWM signal) is shorter than that at the CLK input (signal from FF_1). This causes T_1 to actuate Re_1, so that the motor direction is reversed. The PWM control signal applied to the circuit is also fed to N_2, whose output pulse width is the difference between that of the input signal and that

from FF_1. The pulse width at the output of N_2 therefore decreases as the relevant control handle on the transmitter is moved further towards either extreme, and is maximum when the handle is in the central position. The output of N_2 is integrated by A_1 to obtain an output voltage proportional to the pulse width. A_4 compares this output voltage with the triangular signal at the wiper of P_3, so that a variable duty factor signal is obtained for driving the power output stage comprised of T_4-T_5. Meanwhile, A_2 compares the proportional voltage from A_1 to the level set with P_2. When the output of A_1 is lower than the threshold, i.e., when the motor speed exceeds the preset level, T_2 activates Re_2. This causes the collector-emitter junction of series regulator T_5 to be bypassed by the relay contact, and so

213

enables the motor to run at full speed, because the forward drop across T_5 is eliminated.

The frequency of the triangular signal from A_3 is of the order of 2 kHz, which is suitable for most motors. Capacitor C_6 may be increased to lower the frequency for non-standard motors. Conversely, if the frequency is increased, care should be taken to observe the maximum switching speed of T_5, which is a commonly available, but relatively slow power transistor.

Presets P_4 and P_3 determine the limits of the inoperative range of the handle, and the point that corresponds to maximum motor speed, respectively. More specifically, P_3 sets the amplitude of the triangular signal, while P_4 sets the offset level, to enable A_4 to output the triangular wave undistorted and with the maximum possible voltage swing. Preset P_2 is used to define the point at which the

motor is switched to full speed. Some care should be taken in this setting to allow a sufficiently large control range for the handle, and also to avoid the risk of Re_2 clattering or being blocked.

Be sure to fit the 470n capacitor across the motor terminals, and the 47n capacitor between one of these and the motor body—see Fig. 2. The coil voltage of the relays should be equal to the voltage for the battery that powers the motor, while the contacts must be capable of handling the current demand of the motor. Transistors T_4 and T_5 should be fitted with a heatsink. Note that although the Type 2N3055 can handle currents up to 10 A, it may be a good idea to fit two in parallel with 0R1 emitter resistors for equal current distribution when heavy loads are to be controlled. The current rating of D_6 and D_7 must also be observed: for the stated 1N5401s, $I_{f(max)} = 3$ A, and two may have to be

1

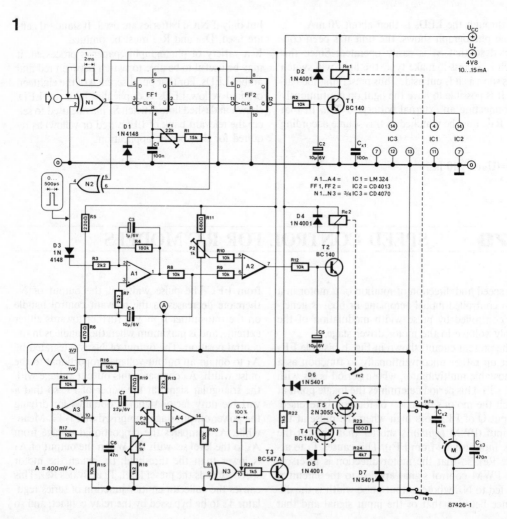

87426-1

214

connected in parallel when this current is approached. Finally, U+ is the model's battery voltage (4.8 V), and +Ucc is the supply voltage for the motor.

2

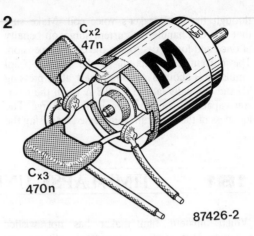

C_{x2}
47n

C_{x3}
470n

87426-2

180   STARTING-PISTOL SIMULATOR

In this circuit, a discarded power loudspeaker serves to simulate the loud bang from a starting-pistol. Power transistors T_1-T_2 and mains transformer TR_1 form a power oscillator, which can be started by pressing S_1. Zenerdiodes D_1-D_2 protect T_1-T_2 against inductive voltage surges. The operating frequency of the oscillator depends on the core material of Tr_1, and the current through its 240 V winding. While S_1 is kept actuated, the oscillation

frequency is lowered from several kHz to about 50 Hz as the charge voltage across flash capacitors C_2-C_3 rises. The charge current is limited by R_5, while D_3-D_4 form a voltage doubler, so that several hundred volts are available across the contact of Re_1. LED D_6 lights to indicate that the flash capacitors are fully charged, and that S_1 may be released. When the fire button, S_2, is pressed, Re_1 is energized, and a short pulse of 50-100 A_p is passed

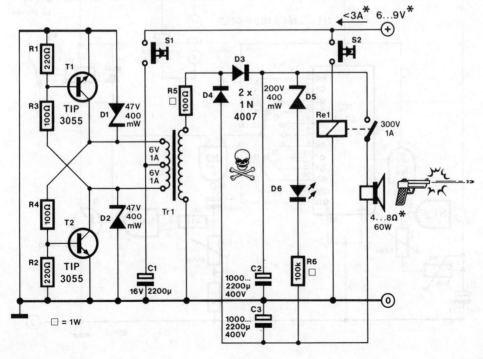

through the loudspeaker's voice coil. Make sure that this can handle the current surge, on penalty of once and for all destroying the cone suspension. The current consumption of the starting-pistol simulator is about 3 A immediately after pressing S1, and gradually falls to 0.5-0.8 A when the reservoir capacitors contain their nominal charge. The loudness of the bang can be increased by raising the supply voltage to a maximum of 12 V, provided the loudspeaker can handle a peak power of more than 1,000 W.

It is recommended to test the circuit at a supply voltage of 3 V. Finally, bear in mind that the generated high voltage is extremely dangerous, and requires due attention to be paid to proper insulation of all components in the high voltage section.

181 TIME-LAPSE UNIT

Which amateur film maker has not wished sometime that he could experiment with time exposures? Fortunately, it is now possible with a simple electronic circuit to see the grass grow without having to sacrifice a night's sleep.

The circuit consists of a clock oscillator, N1-N2, a 12-stage binary counter, IC2, and a monostable, N3-N4. Preset P1 is adjusted to make the highest oscillator frequency about 16 Hz. When switch S2 connects pin 4 of N2 to pin 8 of N3, the circuit works in "real time". Each successive step of S2 from this position doubles the time between exposures. At the minimum oscillator frequency of 0.5 Hz, and S2 connected to the Q11 output of IC2, intervals of up to two hours are possible between exposures.

As the signal at the wiper of S2 is a square wave, which is — by definition — logic 1 for half the time, it is essential that it is shaped in a monostable. The duration of the consequent pulses is determined by P3 Their width should, of course, not exceed the period of the clock oscillator.

Many film cameras are provided with a miniature socket via which they can be operated for single frame exposures and film transport. Contacts X and

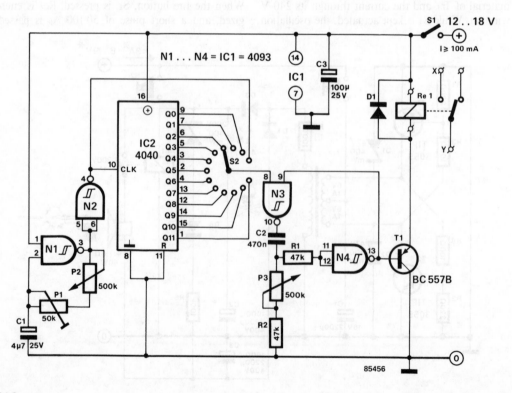

85456

Y of relay Re$_1$ should be connected to this socket via a suitable cable. If you have any trouble with this, or are not sure of the socket connections, it is best to seek advice from your local photographic dealers.

TIMER FOR FIXING BATH

When, after developing, photographs are immersed in the fixing bath at irregular intervals, it becomes difficult to observe the correct fixing time for each of these. This problem is solved by the present timer, which is capable of "remembering" up to 32 immersion times, and automatically provides a signal when a photograph is to be taken out of the bath. Any time a photograph is immersed in the fixer, the user presses the start key on the timer, which responds by lighting a LED. When the fixing interval has lapsed, the timer provides a short beep.

The circuit is composed of a 64-stage shift register which is loaded with zeroes on power up, because it lacks a reset input. Electronic switch ES$_1$ connects the frequency determining capacitor to the input of clock oscillator N$_1$. The logic level that exists at the D$_{in}$ terminal of IC$_3$ is shifted towards output Q at a speed that is defined by P$_1$, which enables defining fixing times between roughly 1 and 10 minutes, 9 minutes being a commonly used value. When the START button is pressed, S-R (set-reset) bistable N$_2$-N$_3$ toggles, and LED D$_1$ lights. A logic 1 is written into the shift register with the aid of a positive pulse transition applied to terminal CP. After 64 clock pulses from N$_1$, the logic high level is available at the output of the shift register, and enables oscillator N$_4$ to drive piezoelectric buzzer Bz$_1$. The LED is turned off shortly after the START button is pressed, because the bistable is reset by the CL. OUT pulse from IC$_3$.

The timer is conveniently fed from a 9 V battery, and should not consume more than about 10 mA.

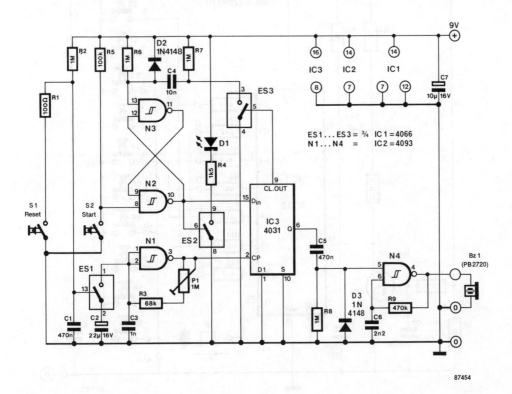

87454

217

183   7-DIGIT CODE LOCK

This code lock provides a high degree of security whilst being a very simple design. At the heart of the circuit is the Type 4022 octal counter. In the non-active state, C_2 is charged via R_5, so that the reset (R) input of the counter is kept logic high. This causes output Q_0 to be actuated, while all other outputs are logic low. When S_1 is pressed, T_1 is switched on via debouncing network R_2-C_1, and IC_1 receives a clock pulse. Also, C_2 is discharged via R_4-D_1, ending the reset state of the counter and enabling it to advance. The time required for R_5 to recharge C_2, i.e., to reset the counter, is the maximum time that can lapse before the next key is pressed. The above cycle is therefore repeated only when S_7 at the Q_1 output is pressed in time. When all keys have been pressed in time and in the correct order, Q_7 goes high for about 4 seconds to enable driving the unlock circuitry, e.g. a relay driver for an automatic door opener. The code for the lock shown in the circuit diagram is 1704570: this is but an example, however, and the combination code is readily altered by swapping connections between the counter outputs and the switches. When the 7-digit code is considered too simple to crack, the 4022 can be replaced by a 4017, which makes it possible to add two keys. This means that the number of combinations is 10^9 instead of 10^7.

The quiescent current consumption of the code lock is negligible at $0.5\ \mu A$, so that battery operation is feasible. The circuit works well from any supply between 6 and 15 V. The accompanying photograph shows that the code lock can be built as

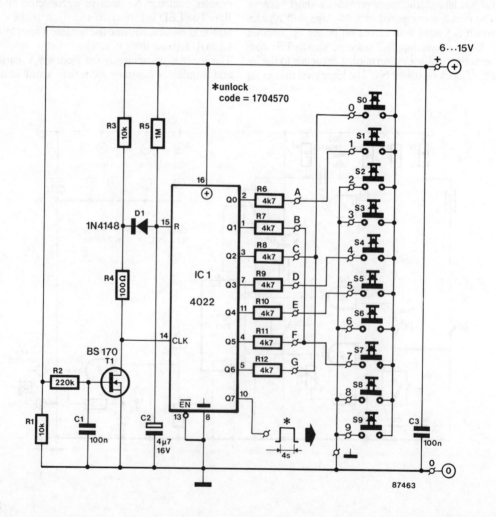

*unlock
code = 1704570

a very compact unit thanks to the use of a printed circuit board that holds the 10 keys also.

Parts list

Resistors ($\pm 5\%$):

$R_1;R_3 = 10K$
$R_2 = 220K$
$R_4 = 100R$
$R_5 = 1M0$
$R_6 \ldots R_{12}$ incl. $= 4K7$

Capacitors:

$C_1;C_3 = 100n$
$C_2 = 4\mu7$; 16 V; axial

Semiconductors:
$D_1 = 1N4148$
$IC_1 = 4022$
$T_1 = BS170$

Miscellaneous:

$S_0 \ldots S_9$ incl. = Digitast momentary action button (SE or S version, ITT Schadow).
PCB Type 87436

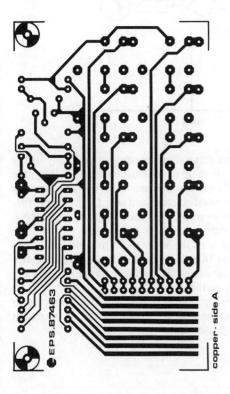

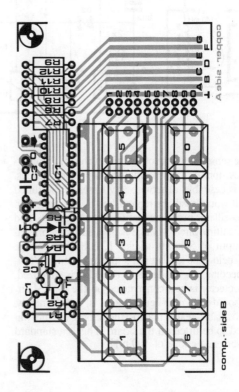

184   ABSORPTION-TYPE METAL DETECTOR

The action of the detector, which indicates the presence of ferrous as well as non-ferrous metals, depends on the absorption of magnetic energy. An inductor, which forms part of a tuned oscillator circuit, radiates a magnetic field. When a metal object is introduced into this field, enough magnetic energy is absorbed to cause the oscillator to stop working.

The Colpitt's oscillator in figure 1 operates at a frequency of around 70 kHz. Inductor L_1 also serves

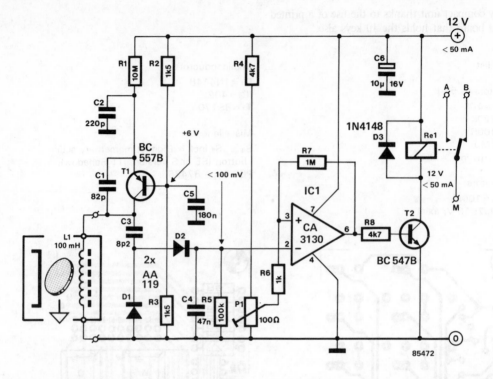

as the sensor. Because of the high value of the emitter resistor, R_1, the oscillator only just operates. This is desirable, otherwise any losses in the tuned circuit would easily be replenished by the transistor. The oscillator output is rectified by D_1 and D_2, and the resulting direct voltage is applied to the inverting input of Schmitt trigger IC_1. If that voltage drops below the level at pin 3 (preset by P_1), the output becomes logic high, and the relay is energized. The detector is best constructed on the printed circuit board shown in figure 2 (this is, unfortunately, not available ready made). Inductor L_1 is not intended to be fitted on the board. This is a standard non-screened choke of 100 mH.

If the oscillator does not readily start at any setting of P_1 the value of R_1 must be reduced. If, on the other hand, the oscillator does not stop working when a metal object is held near L_1, the value of R_1 must be increased. The stated value of R_1 has been found right when L_1 is a Toko type.

Starting with the wiper of P_1 to earth, adjust the preset so that the relay just does not operate. If a lower sensitivity is required, advance the wiper slightly further.

Current consumption is determined primarily by whether the relay is energized or not; in any case it is not greater than 50 mA.

---

185 ALTERNATING FLASHER

The proposed circuit is intended for use by modellers at railway crossings, work in progress, advertising boards, and many others. It can be built quite quickly from but a handful of components.

In the accompanying diagram, A_1 determines the flashing frequency, which may be altered by changing the values of R_2 and, particularly, R_3. The latter

may be replaced by a suitable preset if the frequency needs to be varied often.

Inverters A_2 and A_3 function as fixed delay elements, while A_4 inverts the drive to D_2. The alternately flashing LEDs may, of course, be of any colour suited to the application.

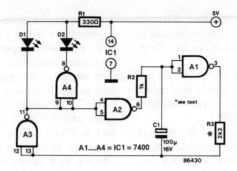

186   AUTOMATIC SLIDING DOOR

Nobody pays much attention to automatically opening and closing sliding doors nowadays. In view of the complex mechanics involved, not too many people have so far attempted to fit an automatic sliding door in their living room. If you are happy with a relatively slow movement, such a door can, however, easily be realized with the aid of a DC motor and a small electronic control unit.

A suitable length of stranded nylon wire is attached to the left- and right-hand sides of the door and strung across four nylon roller guides as shown. The wire is attached to the spindle of a DC motor, the rotational direction of which depends on its polarity. Such motors are available in variety in many model building shops or from electrical suppliers, and should be suitable for operation from 6...18 V.

It will be sufficient to loop the nylon wire a couple of times round the motor spindle. Correct tension is obtained by incorporating a tensile spring in the wire.

A small push button switch is fitted in the left- and right-hand door frames so that when the door is fully open or closed, a switch contact is closed.

You also need a light barrier or similar device that transmits a positive pulse of suitable length on the approach of a person. Such devices have been published in *Elektor Electronics* before, and there is also one elsewhere in this book.

The diagram in figure 1 contains a bridge circuit, consisting of transistors $T_1...T_4$ which, depending on the logic level at the bases of T_1-T_3 or T_2-T_4, determines whether the motor is at standstill,

1

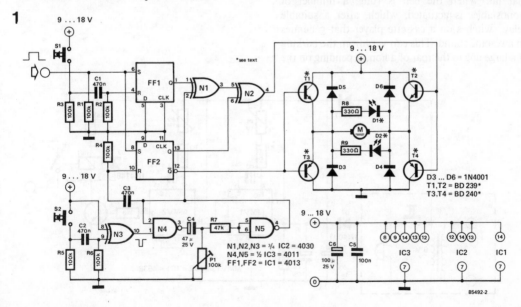

rotates clockwise, or turns anti-clockwise. When the circuit is being tested, the motor may be replaced by D_1 and D_2 (with limiting resistors R_8 and R_9 respectively).

The choice of transistors depends on the current drawn by the motor, which should not exceed 500 mA. T_1-T_3 and T_2-T_4 form complementary pairs, for instance, BD239-BD240.

A short pulse at pin 6 of bistable FF_1 sets the door in motion: the first time, it may be necessary to reverse the connections to the motor! When the door

is fully open, it touches switch S_2. It does not matter whether it is just a touch or whether the door keeps the switch depressed: the motor stands still for a short time, which is adjustable with P_1 and then rotates in the opposite direction so that the door closes. If, while the door is closing, the light barrier is actuated, the motor changes direction again, and the operation repeats itself. When the door is closed, switch S_1 provides a pulse which causes the motor to be switched off until the next time the light barrier is actuated.

187   BURGLAR DETERRENT

Most burglar deterrent systems are based on the same principle: once the presence of an unwanted or suspicious individual has been detected (by electronic or other means), some action ensues which makes it clear to passers-by or neighbours that something is amiss. It is often overlooked that the unwanted visitor first had to ascertain that there is nobody at home. The majority of burglars who operate by daylight just ring the bell. Once they have repeatedly rung without anyone answering the door, they go about their nefarious ways. Once inside, they may well set off a conventional alarm, but by then it is already too late. The circuit proposed here was designed to prevent the intruder getting that far. When the bell is rung, a number of monostables is actuated, which, after a suitable delay, switches on a cassette player that generates an awesome sound. This can vary from the barking of a large dog to the roar of a lion, depending on the

premises. Sometimes a simple "sorry, no canvassers" may be adequate.

The circuit consists basically of two monostables. The delay between the ringing of the bell and the cassette player being switched on is preset with P_1 between 0.22 and 2.4 seconds. The time the cassette player operates is set with P_2 between 47 s and 8 m 37 s. The cassette player is switched on via the relay contacts.

The circuit is powered by the bell transformer. In the circuit it is assumed that this is a 6 V type, and the relay is, therefore, also a 6 V type (which here draws a current of 50 mA).

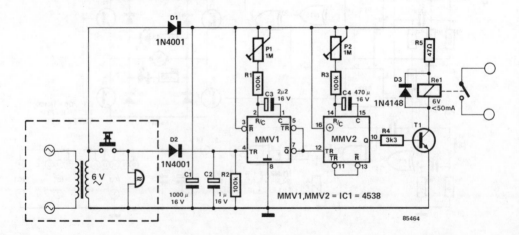

A telephone has the unfortunate disadvantage that you have to be near it to be able to make use of its communication possibilities. If you have a telephone answering unit, you know at least who has called and how many callers there were. If you cannot, or do not want to, hire or buy such a unit, the present low-budget one may be of interest. Low-budget involves the limitation, however, that the incoming calls are merely counted: who has called, or what the message was, can only be guessed. Moreover, to avoid problems with British Telecom (or whoever your PTT authority is), the unit is acoustically coupled to the telephone. Such a design

must, of course, have excellent pulse suppression, since extraneous sounds must not be interpreted as an incoming call. Finally, the counter's current consumption should be (very) low to enable its operation from a battery.

A small, inexpensive loudspeaker is used as the detector, the output of which is applied to window comparator A1-A2. In the absence of a signal from the detector, the output at interconnected pins 1 and 7 is logic high. When the loudspeaker picks up a sound from the telephone, the output consists of negative-going pulses. Monostable MMV1 is triggered by the leading edge of the first pulse, and sup-

1

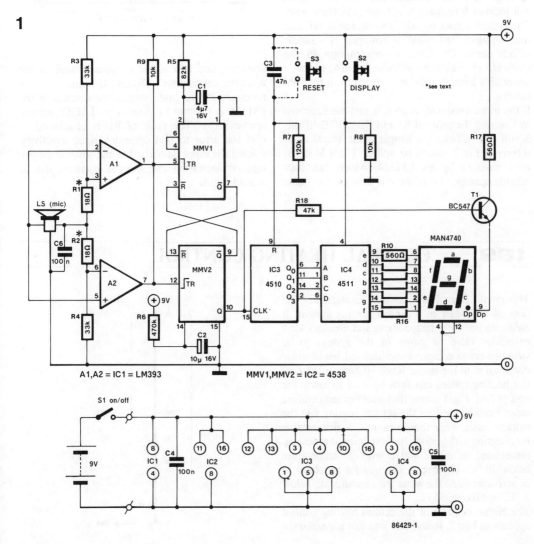

presses the pulse. Only after a time lapse of 0.4 s does MMV1 enable a second monostable, MMV2. If the sound is still being detected by the loudspeaker, MMV2 is then also triggered. This arrangement ensures that noise pulses of less than 0.4 s duration are effectively suppressed. Since MMV2 is retriggerable, and its mono time is about 5 seconds, the intermittent ringing of the telephone is converted into a single pulse.

The decimal point of the display is switched on via R_{18} and T_1 indicating that the circuit is in a triggered state.

The remainder of the circuit is straightforward: a decimal counter, IC_3, with switch-on reset (R_7 and C_3, and a BCD 7-segment decoder, IC_4. In the quiescent state, the display is not energized in order to keep the current consumption low. Pressing S_2 will indicate how many telephone calls there were. The circuit is reset by briefly switching it off, and then on again, but could be arranged by a simple switch across C_3. Current consumption in the quiescent state amounts to about 0.6 mA, so that a reasonably long life may be expected from the PP3 battery.

If the input sensitivity is poor, it may be improved by lowering the value of R_1 and R_2 to 10 Ω. If this is still not sufficient, a simple input amplifier as shown in Fig. 2 should be added. The LM393 is then replaced by an LM324, which has four suitable opamps. One of these is then used as input

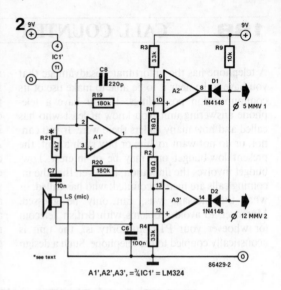

amplifier, and two of the remaining three as the window comparator. Diodes D_1 and D_2 are necessary in this case, because the outputs of the LM324, in contrast to those of the LM393, are not open-collector. The value of R_{21} is established by trial and error to find optimum input sensitivity. Adding the input amplifier has the small disadvantage of increasing the current consumption to around 1 mA.

189   CENTRAL HEATING CONTROL

This circuit is used for optimum regulation of the flow of hot water in a central heating system. It measures the water temperature, and arranges for a particular valve or pump in the system to be switched on to achieve a user-defined temperature distribution in the home. Residual heat in the central heating system can thus be used to lower the cost of fuel. Fig. 1 shows that water in temperature range I can be used for the central heating and the storage vessel, while that in range II is also suitable for directing to the boiler. In most cases, it is not recommended to re-use water with a temperature below 30 °C. The circuit arranges for an alarm to be activated when the water temperature falls below 5 °C, or exceeds 95 °C.

The circuit diagram of the central heating control appears in Fig. 2. Relays Re1 and Re5 are activated

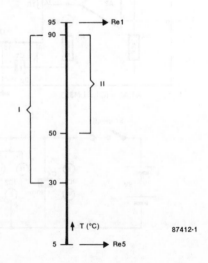

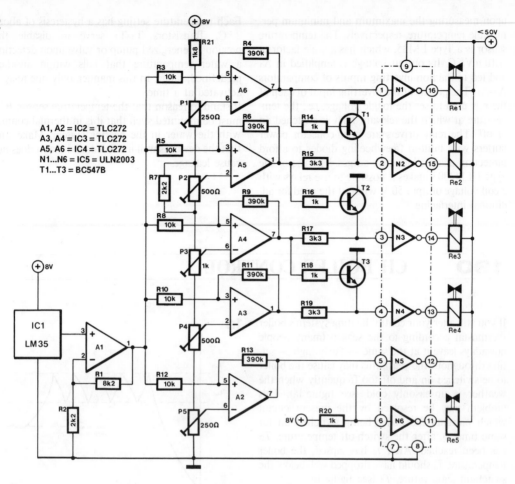

A1, A2 = IC2 = TLC272
A3, A4 = IC3 = TLC272
A5, A6 = IC4 = TLC272
N1...N6 = IC5 = ULN2003
T1...T3 = BC547B

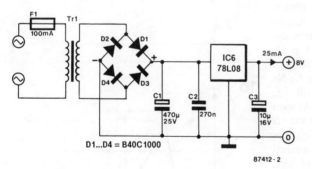

D1...D4 = B40C1000

87412-2

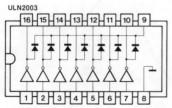

ULN2003

Relay	Preset	Temperature range
1	P₁	93-103 °C (upper limit alarm)
2	P₂	77-93 °C
3	P₃	33-77 °C
4	P₄	11-33 °C
5	P₅	5-17 °C (lower limit alarm)
(hysteresis on all toggle points: 2 °C).		

upon measuring the maximum and minimum permissible temperature, respectively. The temperature sensor is a Type LM35, which has a scale factor of +10 mV/°C. Its output voltage is amplified in A_1 and fed to the non-inverting inputs of comparators A_2-A_6. The presets at the inverting input of each of these is used to set the toggle voltage, i.e., the temperature at which the relevant relay is switched on or off. The relay drivers are open-collector power buffers with built-in freewheeling diodes to afford protection against inductive surges. The use of the Type ULN2003 makes it possible to use relays with a coil voltage of upto 50 V without the need for additional interfacing.

Each temperature setting has a hysteresis of about 2 °C. Transistors T_1-T_3 serve to disable the previously energized pump or valve upon detecting a water temperature that falls within another, predefined, range. In this manner, only one relay is activated at a time.

It stand to reason that the temperature sensor, IC_1, must be mounted such that it is in thermal contact with the water in the heating system. Make sure that the device is well-insulated, and that it does not cause leakage.

190   CH BOILER CONTROL

If you still alter your central heating system's boiler thermostat according to the season (many people nowadays leave it at the same — fairly high — setting throughout the year), this may cause the boiler to be switched on and off too frequently when the weather is unseasonly cold (see figure 1a). This problem may be resolved by the present circuit which prevents the boiler being switched on for some time, t_d, after the switch-off temperature, T_2, has been reached. After t_d has lapsed, the boiler temperature, T, should have dropped well below the switch-on temperature, T_1 (see figure 1b).

The circuit in figure 2 is an extension of the *central heating monitor* (*Elektor Electronics*, July/August 1984, p. 7-30) and formed part of the *electronic gas meter* (*Elektor Electronics*, November 1984, p. 11-59). The make contacts of a relay are inserted into the 24 V boiler circuit. The state of bistable N_2-N_3 determines whether transistor T_1 is on or off, i.e., whether the 24 V circuit is open or closed. As soon as the bistable is set, T_1 conducts and delay time t_d commences. At the same time, the reset of counter IC_2 is cancelled. After some time, IC_2 has reached maximum count: the consequent change of logic level at the output selected by S_1 causes the reset of the bistable via N_4. This is the end of t_d.

The set input of the bistable is connected to the collector of T_3 in the central heating monitor via N_1 and R_3-C_2 and R_2-C_1. That transistor drives the LED that indicates the interrupted heat request of the boiler thermostat.

Delay time t_d can be set within wide limits with P_1 and S_1. A period of 10 minutes is probably a good

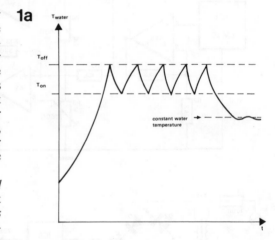

1a

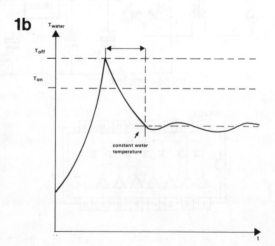

1b

2

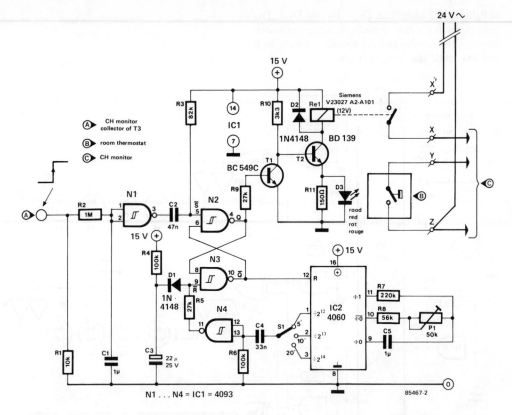

N1 ... N4 = IC1 = 4093

starting point. It is then impossible for the boiler to be switched on and off more than six times per hour. Based on the number of times the relevant LEDs in the central heating monitor light, you can alter the delay time with P_1 and S_1. Briefly connect

the junction of R_3-C_2 to earth: this causes the bistable to be set; D_3 goes out and the delay period starts. Adjust P_1 so that D3 lights again after 5, 10, or 20 minutes. It is also possible to use periods of 4, 8, or 16, or 6, 12, or 24 minutes.

191   COLOUR WHEEL

Coloured light effects enjoy a high popularity as ornaments, eye-characters, etc., and the present circuit proves how an apparently rotating colour effect may be obtained with a mere handful of commonly available components.

The colour wheel is composed of twelve bicolour LEDs, arranged in a circular form. First, a set of four red LEDs lights, followed by a green set, and, finally, amber. The colours are arranged to move in a clockwise direction, and at a speed that gives viewers the illusion that the motion is smooth and continuous.

The bicolour LEDs consist of anti-parallel connec-

ted green and red diodes in a single transparent case. When both light simultaneously, their composite colour, i.e. amber, is emitted.

Which group of LEDs lights depends on the duty factor of the drive signal from gates N_5, N_6 and N_7. Gate N_1 is a clock oscillator whose frequency is controlled by P_1 IC_1 has been connected to function as decade ring counter, which sequentially enables oscillators N_2, N_3 and N_4 by a logic high level at counter outputs Q_0, Q_1 and Q_2 respectively. If, for instance, N_2 is enabled, it oscillates at about 500 Hz with an output duty factor of 50%, causing both the green and red LEDs contained in $D_1 ... D_4$

to light. At the same time, $D_5 \ldots D_8$ and $D_9 \ldots D_{12}$ light as red and green, respectively, since the associated driver gates N_6 and N_7 provide a steady high and low level, again, respectively.

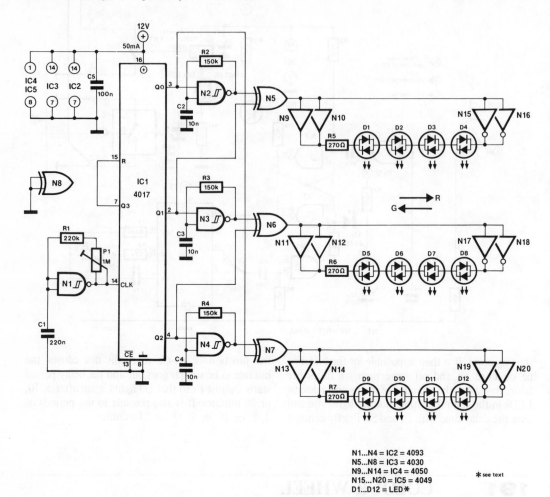

N1...N4 = IC2 = 4093
N5...N8 = IC3 = 4030
N9...N14 = IC4 = 4050
N15...N20 = IC5 = 4049
D1...D12 = LED *

* see text

86510

192   CURRENT MONITOR AND ALARM

These circuits are intended for remote monitoring of the current consumption on the domestic mains line.

The circuit in Fig. 1 lights the signal lamp upon detecting a mains current consumption of more than 5 mA, and handles currents of several amperes with appropriate diodes fitted in the D_1 and D_2 positions. Transistor T_1 is switched on when the drop across D_1-D_2 exceeds a certain level. Diodes from the well-known 1N400x series can be used for cur-

rents of up to 1 A, while 1N540x types are rated for up to 3 A. Fuse F_1 should, of course, be dimensioned to suit the particular application.

A number of possible transistor types have been stated for use in the T_1 position. Should you consider using a type not listed, be sure that it can cope with surges up to 700 V. As long as T_1 does not conduct, the gate of the triac is at mains potential via C_1, protective resistor R_2 and diode D_3, which keeps C_1 charged. When T_1 conducts, alternating

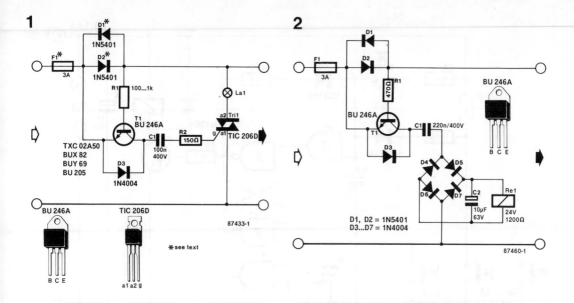

1

1N5401 D1*
D2* 1N5401
F1* 3A
R1 100...1k
La1
T1 BU 246A
TXC 02A50 BUX 82 BUY 69 BU 205
C1 100n 400V
R2 150Ω
a2 Tri1 a1 9 TIC 206D
D3 1N4004

BU 246A
B C E

TIC 206D
a1 a2 g

87433-1

*see text

2

D1
F1 3A
D2
R1 470Ω
BU 246A
T1
C1 220n/400V
D3
D4 D5
D6 D7
C2 10µF 63V
Re1 24V 1200Ω
BU 246A
B C E

D1, D2 = 1N5401
D3...D7 = 1N4004

87460-1

current can flow through the capacitor, and the triac is triggered, so that La$_1$ lights.

The circuit in Fig. 2 is a current triggered alarm. Rectifier bridge D$_4$-D$_7$ can only provide the coil voltage for Re$_1$ when the current through D$_1$-D$_2$ exceeds a certain level, because then series capacitor C$_1$ passes the alternating mains current. Capacitor C$_1$ may need to be dimensioned otherwise than shown to suit the sensitivity of the relay coil. This is readily effected by connecting capacitors in parallel until the coil voltage is high enough for the relay to operate reliably.

Finally, an important point:
Many points in these circuits are at mains potential and therefore extremely dangerous to touch.

193   DECEPTIVE LOCK

This circuit offers a means to fool all but the cleverest burglar, but, although it is a clever design, it has been kept simple, as a glance at the diagram will show. On the surface it looks like a simple operating panel with ten push buttons. However, anyone trying to open it illegally is in for a surprise! It is not just a matter of keying in the correct code, it is also necessary to keep one of the keys depressed for about 10 to 15 seconds.

The circuit is based on a single Type CD4093, which contains four NAND gates with Schmitt trigger inputs. Gates N$_1$ and N$_2$ form a bistable that contains the status of the lock.

Assuming that the circuit has been off for some time, switching it on causes network R$_1$-C$_2$ to set the bistable to the "lock" position, that is, the output of N$_2$ is logic low. Capacitor C$_3$ is discharged, and the only way the circuit can toggle is by

recharging this capacitor. This is done by pressing key S$_x$ long enough for the trigger threshold of N$_1$ to be reached. When that happens, the bistable is set to the "open" position, that is, the output of N$_2$ is logic high.

Capacitor C$_3$ remains charged via R$_4$-D$_2$, even after S$_x$ has been released. In other words, the bistable remains in the "open" position. The lock is closed again when one of the other keys is pressed, or, if required, by means of a special lock key. This causes C$_3$ to discharge rapidly via D$_1$-R$_3$, which returns the circuit to the "lock" condition.

When the lock is "open", relay Re will also be open in the present circuit. It is, however, possible to have the relay energized in this condition by connecting the remaining free gate in the 4093 in series with R$_5$ as an inverter.

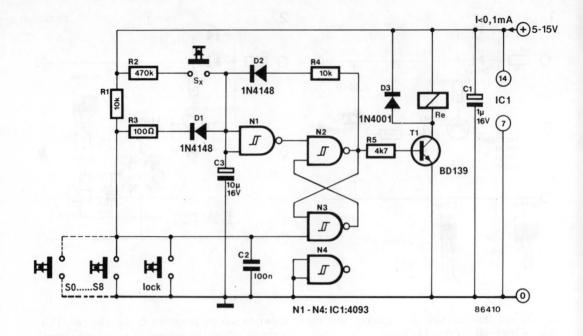

194   DESICCATOR

Many of the smaller working areas available to hobbyists suffer from humidity, which in no time causes a number of tools to be covered in a thin layer of rust. Humidity does not do most test equipment or books and the like any good either. The only solution to this is to try to keep the area drier by increasing the temperature.

A couple of 100 W light bulbs or a 100-200 W heating element work wonders in this respect, were it not for the increases in the electricity bill. And that is where the present circuit can help.

With reference to the diagram, the two HEF4001Bs, in conjunction with humidity sensor H, generate a voltage across R_5 that is directly pro-

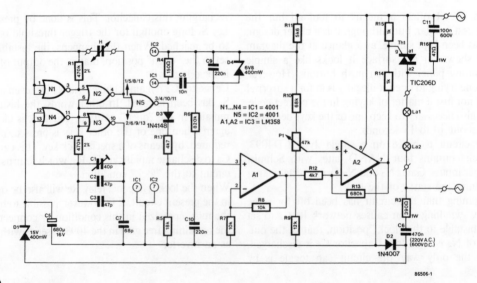

portional to the degree of humidity. The function of opamp A_1 is merely to present a high impedance to U_{R5}. The voltage is then applied to the inverting input of comparator A_2, which has an hysteresis of about 15 per cent. The reference voltage at the non-inverting input of A_2 can be set between 0.6 V and 3.0 V with P_1 which corresponds to a humidity between 20 per cent and 100 per cent. As soon as the ambient humidity exceeds the value set by P_1 the comparator toggles, the triac conducts and switches on the heating element. Current consumption of the circuit is a modest 13 mA.

If light bulbs are used, they should be shielded with a metal hood to prevent the likelihood of a fire. Calibration is carried out with the aid of a solution of cooking salt in some water; placed in a reasonably small, closed space, this will soon raise the humidity to 75 per cent. Adjust C_1 to obtain a potential difference across R_5 of 2.25 V. Next, adjust P_1 so that the triac just does not conduct. In practice, the circuit will then come on at a humidity of about 80 per cent.

For further details of this circuit, see also the April 1981 (p.19) and July & August 1981 (p.72) issues of Elektor Electronics.

---

195 ELECTRONIC BELL-PULL

The simplest circuit in this issue of *Elektor Electronics* consists of a single transistor and resistor, which, when put together as shown, constitute the electronic equivalent of an old fashioned, stylish bell-pull used in conjunction with a chime or bell circuit of any relative complexity offering whirling melodies, buzzing or ringing sounds, or chime imitations to prompt the houseowner to open the front door.

The bell-pull is made from a TO39-style NPN transistor which is taped or isolated by means of a length of heat shrink sleeving, after the emitter and collector leads have been fitted with wires for the electrical connection to the bell circuit. A small, conductive plate is secured onto the isolated transistor head, and the base lead is joined to this plate over a series resistor which is dimensioned accord-

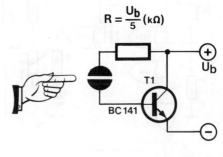

$$R = \frac{U_b}{5} (k\Omega)$$

BC 141

86446 - 1

ing to $R = U_b/5$ [kΩ]. The completed assembly may also be cast into epoxy resin to make a nice compact unit that can handle the treatment of even the roughest caller at the door!

---

196 ELECTRONIC DOG

To produce a faithful reproduction of the voice of man's best friend, we have borrowed several ideas from our music synthesizer. When push button switch S_2 is pressed, the frequency of voltage-controlled oscillator (VCO) A_1-A_2 changes in about an eigth of a second from almost 0 Hz to a presettable value of 100...1000 Hz. That signal is passed through band-pass filter A_5-A_6, the centre frequency of which corresponds with the highest VCO frequency. Voltage-controlled amplifier (VCA) T_1 ensures that the single pulse generated by the VCO when S_2 is open cannot be heard.

Gates N_1 and N_2 form a monostable relaxation os-

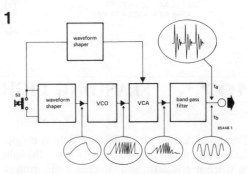

cillator. When S_2 is closed, a short pulse appears at the output of N_2 that charges capacitor C_2. Because of R_3, the pulse shape will be as shown in figure 1. This pulse controls the output frequency of the VCO as also shown in figure 1. Potentiometer P_1 determines the highest frequency: its setting depends on whether you want the sound of a yapping poodle or the deep bark of an alsatian.

The function of C_4 is similar to that of C_2: it shapes the pulse applied to the VCA. This transistor behaves as an electronic potentiometer, i.e., it operates as a voltage-controlled resistor. Adjusting potentiometer P_2 influences the manner in which the tone decays after the switch has been released.

Instantaneous dying of the tone would sound just as unreal as its lingering on. With a little care, and after some practice, it will be possible to create a variety of canine dialects.

The centre frequency of band-pass filter A_5-A_6 is set with P_3 Correct setting of this is important, but here again, trial and error is probably the best way. With the output connected to a power amplifier, the combination can be used as an alarm installation: even dyed-in-the-wool burglars think twice before they risk entering a house that is obviously guarded by a fierce dog!

2

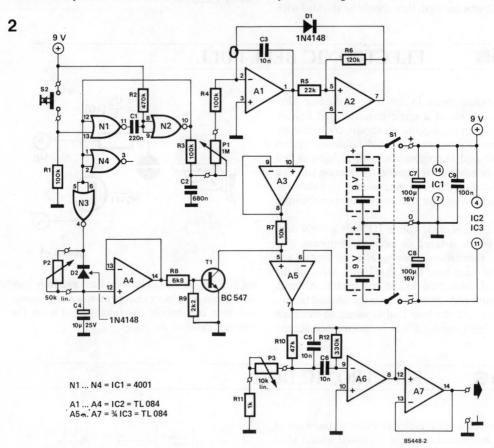

N1 ... N4 = IC1 = 4001

A1 ... A4 = IC2 = TL 084
A5 ... A7 = ¾ IC3 = TL 084

---

197   FLASHING LIGHT WITH TWILIGHT SWITCH

The special feature of this flashing light is the optical switch, which automatically switches the light on when it gets dark, and switches it off again at dawn. This makes the light ideal as a warning light near obstructions. It may also be used for educa-

tional purposes to show the operation of transistors in conjunction with optoelectronics.

Assuming that it is light, the LDR (light dependent resistor) has a low value so that there is sufficient base current through T_1 for the transistor to con-

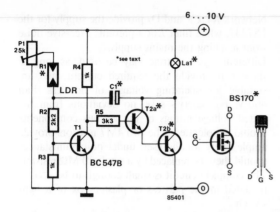

6 ... 10 V

85401

duct. Its collector voltage is then small, so that T₂, an n-p-n darlington, is off, and lamp L₁ stays out. When the ambient light reduces, the resistance of the LDR increases until the base current in T₁ becomes insufficient and the transistor switches off. Its collector voltage then rises, T₂ conducts, and L₁ lights. This process takes place quite quickly, because when the collector voltage of T₂ suddenly becomes nearly 0 V, this potential is immediately

applied to the base of T₁ via capacitor C₁, which really cuts off T₁. The capacitor then charges via P1 and the LDR that is now being illuminated by the lighted lamp. Owing to the optical feedback, the value of the LDR diminishes, the voltage across R₂ increases, and T₁ conducts again. The darlington switches off, and the lamp goes out: a new cycle has started.

The flashing frequency is primarily dependent on the value of C₁: with 47 μF, it is rather low; reducing the capacitance increases the frequency.

The BC 517 darlington may be replaced by two BC 547B transistors or a VN10KM MOSFET. The only thing that needs watching is the current through L₁: the maximum permissible with two BC 547Bs is 100 mA; with a BC 517 it is 400 mA; and with a VN10KM it is 500 mA. Current consumption of the circuit, with lamp L₁ out, is about 6 mA at 6 V and around 10 mA at 10 V.

The light-dependent resistor may be one of the usually available types: LDR 03, 05, 07. To ensure that the optical feedback works, the LDR must be fitted near lamp L₁. The onset of operation is set with P₁

198   FOUR POSITION TOUCH DIMMER

Any electric light may be adjusted with this dimmer to very low, low, medium and maximum, which in most cases will be sufficient. After all, it is all very well to be able to control an electric light over the

whole range of its brightness, but how often is that facility really used? Moreover, in everyday use, position control has practical advantages: setting, for instance, takes a second or two.

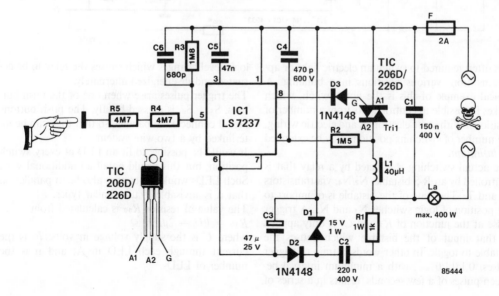

85444

The circuit is based on an LS7237 and some discrete components. The dimmer may also be used as an electronic on/off switch, in which case the mode select pin (7) must be connected to earth (pin 1). Such a switch does not produce sparks and consequent noise in nearby electronic equipment. Another possibility is leaving pin 2 open, whereby a three position dimmer ensues: low, medium, and maximum.

The LS7237 has all the necessary facilities to drive silicon-controlled rectifier (SCR) Tri_1. Resistor R_2 and capacitor C_4 filter a 50 Hz signal from the mains that serves to synchronize the on-chip phase locked loop.

Network R_1, C_2, and D_2 provide the supply for the LS7237, while filter L_1/C_1 prevents excessive noise from reaching the mains supply.

Different types of triac may be used, as long as these can provide the required current, and are suitable for operating voltages of not less than 400 V. For safety's sake, no deviations from the stated voltage ratings of the various components should be tolerated. The two 4M7 resistors provide ample safety for the user: under no circumstances should these be replaced by a single 10 MΩ resistor! The complete circuit is small enough to be accommodated in the pattress or plaster box of a light switch.

199   HOTEL SWITCH

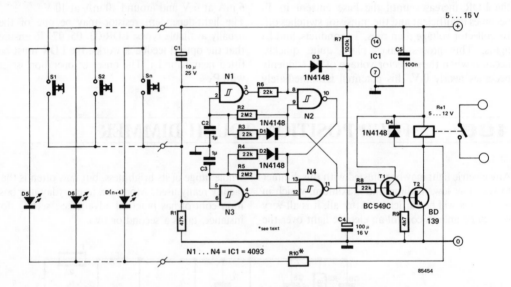

It is often required to switch an electric light or apparatus from various positions in a building. A typical example of this is the hotel switch, which makes it possible to control lights from a number of positions. With some electronics and electric wiring, the number of switching positions may be extended *ad infinitum*.

The actual switching is effected by a relay that is controlled by an R-S bistable, N_2/N_4, via transistors T_1 and T_2 The state of the bistable is of import to the position of logic switches N_1 and N_3. A trigger pulse at the junction of R_1 and C_1 is only applied to that input of the bistable which causes the bistable to toggle. In other words, a train of trigger pulses, 0;1;0;1;0..., with a minimum interval between pulses of a few seconds, results in a series of

logic level changes which causes the relay to be actuated and de-energized alternately.

The trigger pulses arise when one of the push buttons, $S_1...S_n$, is pressed briefly. The push buttons are all connected in parallel, so that they can be interlinked by a two-wire system.

It would be possible to fit an LED at every switch position, but this would entail an additional wire. Such LEDs would, of course, also be in parallel, so that it is advisable to use similar types.

The value of resistor R_{10} is calculated from
$$R_{10} = ((U - 2)/I_{Dn}) \ \Omega$$
where U is the supply voltage in volts; I_D is the current through each LED in A; and n is the number of LEDs.

Nowadays, most clocks and watches are quartz controlled and, therefore, accurate to within a few seconds a year. Older type electric clocks, particularly those used in large groups in warehouses, department stores, factories, railway stations, and so on, were centrally controlled and synchronized. This synchronization was effected by pulses derived from the mains and sent to each clock via a separate cable network. Many people have such a clock as a curiosity, but have not the means of driving it. The circuit described here will help. . .

With reference to the diagram, pulse shaper T_1 triggers monostable IC_2 at the mains frequency of 50 Hz. Counter IC_3 is reset automatically after every 3000 pulses by IC_4 and T_2. At the same time, bistable IC_5 toggles and causes the bridge circuit composed of $T_2 \ldots T_8$ to reverse the motor polarity every 60 seconds.

Depending on the type of clock you have, the transformer secondary voltage may have to be selected to supply about 0.7 times the normal operating voltage of the clock motor. Furthermore, the bridge circuit as shown should not be made to operate at voltages in excess of 30 V, while the maximum current is about 250 mA.

There is only one adjustment point in the circuit, namely P_1 which should be set to achieve maximum suppression of mains borne noise; if this can not be checked, the preset may be turned to its centre position. Should the clock be slow, P_1 may be adjusted to give a slightly lower resistance, but care should be taken to avoid setting a monostable time longer than 20 ms, as in that case only half the number of 50 Hz periods can reach the counter.

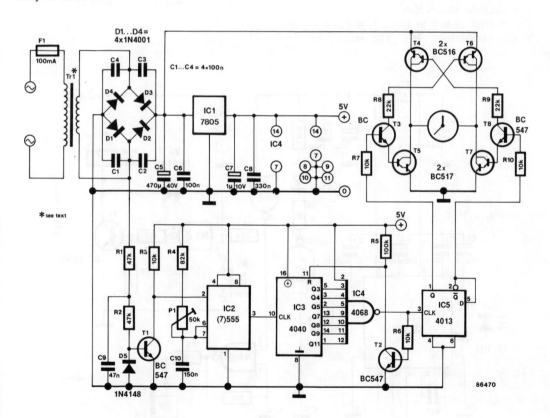

Infra-red light barriers enjoy great popularity as timing devices at sports venues, as detectors in alarm installations, as optoelectronic switches in counting equipment, and many others, because of their low cost and immunity to electrical interference.

The present light barrier consists of a transmitter and a receiver.

The transmitter, shown in figure 1, consists of an astable multivibrator (AMV), IC3. The output of the AMV, pin 3, consists of a pulse stream with a duty factor of about 30 per cent. The output is connected to a constant-current source, T2 This source provides infra-red transmit diodes D7 and D8 with a current of just over 20 mA, which pulsates in rhythm with the output signal of the AMV. The infra-red light is, therefore, transmitted in rhythm with the pulse stream also.

The receiver, shown in figure 2, is based on an SL486 demodulator, IC1. The output of the

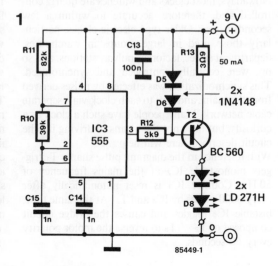

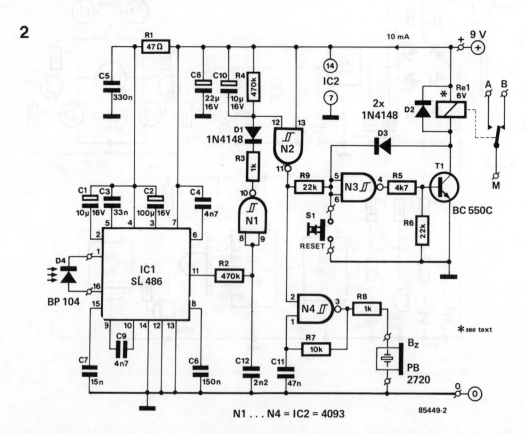

N1 ... N4 = IC2 = 4093   85449-2

Parts list (receiver)

Resistors:

$R_1 = 47\ \Omega$
$R_2, R_4 = 470\ k$
$R_3, R_8 = 1\ k$
$R_5 = 4k7$
$R_6, R_9 = 22\ k$
$R_7 = 10\ k$

Capacitors:

$C_1, C_{10} = 10\ \mu/16\ V$
$C_2 = 100\ \mu/16\ V$
$C_3 = 33\ n$
$C_4, C_9 = 4n7$
$C_5 = 330\ n$
$C_6 = 150\ n$
$C_7 = 15\ n$
$C_8 = 22\ \mu/16\ V$
$C_{11} = 47\ n$
$C_{12} = 2n2$

Semiconductors:

$D_1 \ldots D_3 = 1N4148$
$D_4 = BP104$
$T_1 = BC550C$
$IC_1 = SL486$ (Plessey)
$IC_2 = 4093$

Miscellaneous:

Re_1 = PCB type relay, 6 V
Bz = piezoelectric buzzer
  (Toko type PB2720 or equivalent)
S_1 = spring-loaded push-to-make switch

Parts list (transmitter)

Resistors:

$R_{10} = 39\ k$
$R_{11} = 82\ k$
$R_{12} = 3k9$
$R_{13} = 3\Omega9$

Capacitors:

$C_{13} = 100\ n$
$C_{14}, C_{15} = 1\ n$

Semiconductors:

$D_5, D_6 = 1N4148$
$D_7, D_8 = LD271H$
$T_1 = BC560$
$IC_1 = 555$

Miscellaneous:

Reflectors for D_7 and D_8 (optional)
PCB 85449

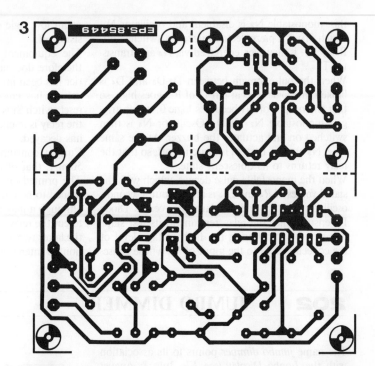

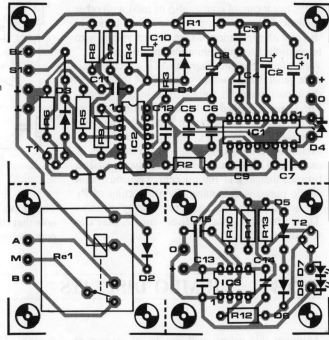

demodulator, pin 11, also consists of a 10 kHz pulse train with a duty factor of around 30 per cent. This pulse stream is applied to integrator R_2-C_{12}. The logic level at the input of N_1 remains low as long as D_4 receives the pulsating infra-red light. Because of

237

this, monostable N_2 is disabled, and oscillator N_4, which drives a piezoelectric buzzer, is switched off. Relay Re_1 is, however, energized via N_4 and transistor T_1.

When the pulse stream between D_7-D_8 and D_4 is broken, the logic level at pin 11 of IC_1 goes high, so that the output of N_1 becomes logic 0, which triggers monostable N_2 via D_1. Oscillator N_4 is then switched on and actuates the buzzer. At the same time, N_3 ensures that T_1 is switched off, so that the relay returns to its quiescent state.

When the monostable pulse decays, which with the stated values of R_4 and C_{10} is after about 5 seconds, oscillator N_4 stops and the alarm tone ceases. Diode D_3 ensures that the relay remains in its rest state, however, by transferring the high voltage level of the collector of T_1 to the input of N_3 whose consequent low logic output continues to hold the transistor off.

The equipment switched by the relay contacts, therefore, does not only indicate when the light barrier has been interrupted, but also when the supply voltage has failed. The relay is re-energized when reset switch S_1 is operated. If D_3 and S_1 are omitted, the relay is re-energized when the monostable pulse has decayed.

Current consumption of the transmitter is about 50 mA; that of the receiver around 10 mA.

The printed circuit board shown in figure 3 is intended to be cut into three along the dashed lines, although it may not be necessary in some situations to cut the relay section from the receiver section. If the latter two are separated, they should on completion be interconnected by a suitable cable.

202   JUMBO DIMMER

The name *jumbo dimmer* points to its association with the *Jumbo Display* (see *EE*, July & August 1985), but it can, of course, also be used with other appliances such as lamps, pumps, ventilators: in short for all applications where a direct voltage is to be controlled by pulse duration modulation.

With reference to the diagram, A_1 is a rectangular-wave generator: a useful by-product of this stage is the (quasi) triangular voltage at its inverting input. This signal is applied to the non-inverting input of comparator A_2. The reference voltage for this stage is derived from preset P_1. The output of the comparator is a rectangular voltage with a frequency of around 200 Hz and a pulse duration that is variable between nought and 100 per cent. The onset point of the pulses is determined by the setting of P_1. The actual control function is provided by transistor T_1, which switches the relatively large display current of up to 5 A.

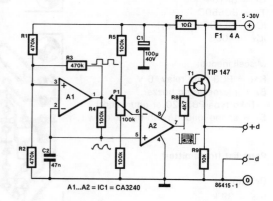

The supply voltage must lie between 5 V and 30 V: note that the efficiency of the circuit is directly proportional to the supply voltage.

203   JUMBO DISPLAYS

Although this project will not be of interest to everybody, it has many possible applications. The name refers to the respectable dimensions of the seven-segment displays: 280×140 mm. These sizes immediately indicate that the displays are intended to make alphanumeric information legible at a distance. This is of import, for instance, for score boards, speed indicators, lap counters, digital church clocks, etc.

These displays have a number of advantages:
■ they are entirely solid state, which prevents segment failure since the life of LEDs is much

1a

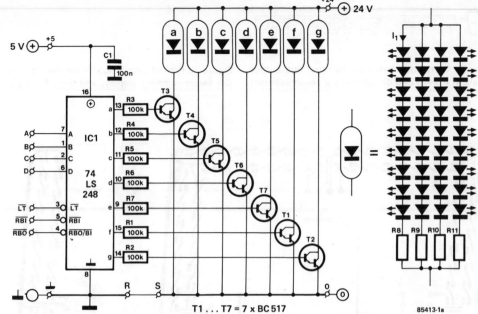

Figure 1. Circuits for the control of (a) a seven-segment display; (b) a "1" display, and (c) a ":" display.

b

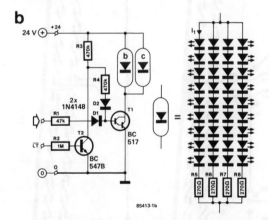

c

longer than, for instance, that of incandescent lamps;

■ they do not need intricate reflector constructions;

■ if any one LED fails, they remain fully legible by
virtue of the special segment construction;

■ they are easily arranged in a variety of colours —
red, green, blue, yellow, orange;

■ they work from 24 V with relative high efficiency, which keeps heat dissipation low.

It may be said that the large number of LEDs required is a disadvantage, but, in our opinion, this is
largely negated by the advantages.

The seven-segment display, shown in figure 1a, is
based on a type 74LS248 decoder, which has the
same features as the well-known type 74LS47/247,
but has in addition internal pull-up resistors and in-

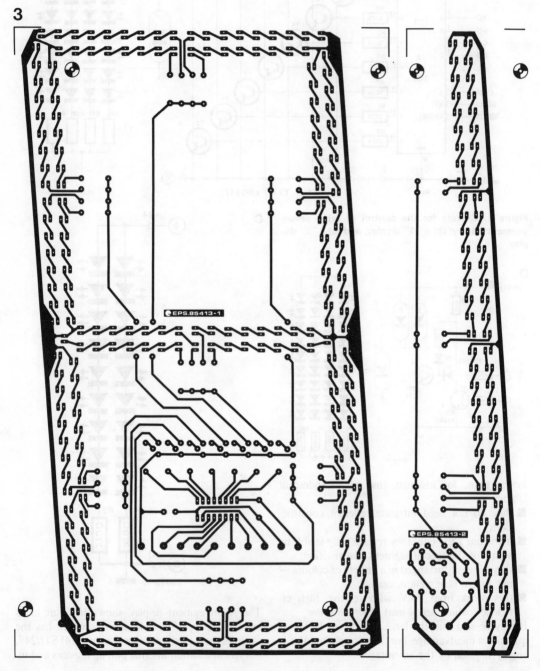

Figure 2. Correlation between the input and output signals of a 74LS248 decoder and a seven-segment display.

Figure 3. Printed circuit boards for the ":" display; the seven-segment display; and the "1" display.

85413-2

EPS.85413-1

EPS.85413-2

verted output signals, so that external transistors can be used to cope with the large currents drawn by the segments. The inputs and outputs to the decoder, the read-outs, and the additional functions are correlated in figure 2.

All input and output controls have been arranged external to the decoder, so that they can be used in the same way as with normal displays. Wire link R-

S serves to interconnect the earths of the +5 V and +24 V supplies.

At the output of the decoder there is a switching stage for each segment that switches the relevant segment on or off.

Each segment consists of four parallel groups of eight or nine LEDs in series with a current limiting resistor.

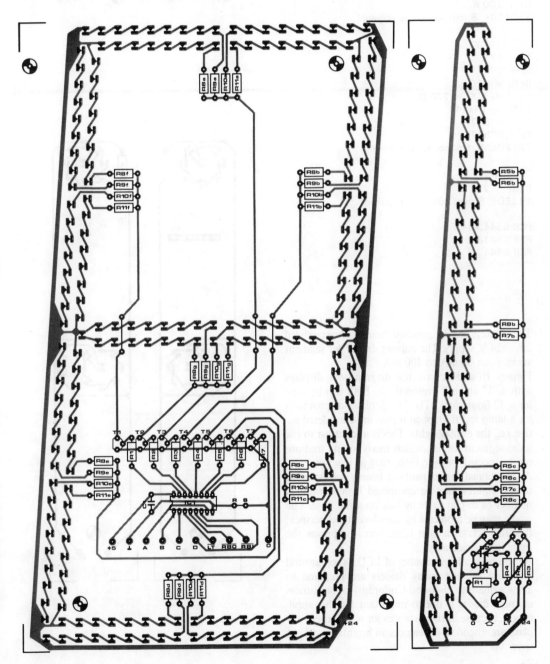

Parts list

Seven-segment display:

$R_1 \ldots R_7 = 100\ k$
$R_8 \ldots R_{11}$ (7X) = 270 Ω (with 9 LEDs)
                      = 330 Ω (with 8 red LEDs)
                      = 390 Ω (with 8 green LEDs)
$IC_1 = 74LS248$
$T_1 \ldots T_7 = BC517$
$C_1 = 100\ n$
232 LEDs, 5 mm, colour as required

"1" display:

$R_1 = 47\ k$
$R_2 = 1\ M$
$R_3, R_4 = 470\ k$
$R_5 \ldots R_8$ (2X) = 270 Ω
$D_1, D_2 = 1N4148$
$T_1 = BC517$
$T_2 = BC547B$
72 LEDs, 5 mm, colour as required

":" display:

$R_1, R_2 = 270$ Ω
18 LEDs, 5 mm, colour as required

PCB 85413-1
PCB 85413-2
PCB 85413-3

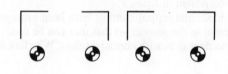

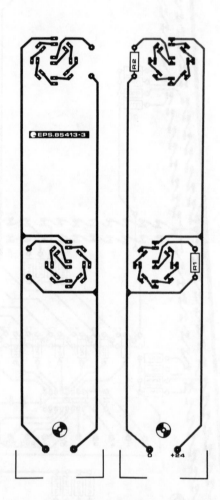

The displays can be powered from a non-stabilized 20...24 V supply. The current drawn per segment varies from 50 mA to 100 mA.

Figures 1b and 1c give the diagrams for displays with a "1" and a ":" respectively. Both can be used for a 12-hour clock. The "1" display has provision for a lamp test (LT); open inputs are considered active, i.e., the display lights. This is in contrast to the seven-segment display which treats inputs that are not connected as logic high, that is, inactive.

As mentioned earlier, read-out boards consisting of several figures may be composed by mounting a number of displays side by side on a flat base. The whole may be protected by translucent red perspex: this also acts as a light filter, which improves the legibility considerably.

As you need a large number of LEDs, shop around for these because many dealers are prepared to allow a quantity discount. Uniformity of brightness of these diodes is not so important for this application, because at the distances for which these displays are intended, differences in brightness do not show up.

An LED indicator with a difference: three alternately lighting LEDs indicate a direction, for instance, in a model railway, or to an emergency exit, or to a door on badly lit stairways, and so on.

When the supply voltage is switched on, the inputs of gates $N_4 \ldots N_6$ are logic 1, their outputs logic 0, and all LEDs light. One of the RC networks $(R_1 + P_1/C_1; R_2/C_2; R_3/C_3)$ will reach the trigger threshold first. Let us assume it is $R_1 + P_1/C_1$. The output of N_1 then goes low, the output of N_4 goes high, and D_1 goes out. There is then no voltage for R_2/C_2, the output of N_2 remains logic high, and N_5 remains logic low: D_2 then lights. Subsequently, the output of N_3 goes low, the output of N_6 becomes 1, and D_3 goes out. The logic 0 of N_3 is, after a delay in $R_1 + P_1/C_1$, again at the input of N_1. The output of N_1 goes high, that of N_4 goes low, and D_1 lights. This process repeats itself, so that first one, then two, and then one LED again lights. At every step, the light pattern shifts one place to give the impression of a running, flashing light. The running speed is set with P_1

It does not really matter whether you use inverting gates (4049) or non-inverting ones (4050) in the IC_2 position, as long as you connect the unused gates to the positive or negative supply rail. The RC networks may also be modified to taste or if special effects are desired.

If you want to make the circuit even smaller, forget IC_2 and use the three remaining inverters in IC_1 as LED drivers, provided you are using a type 40106. The LED currents are then only $5 \ldots 10$ mA, so you have to use high output LEDs (that are bright at low currents).

The current consumption of the circuit without LEDs and operating from 15 V is about 100 μA. With LEDs, it depends very much on the LEDs and the supply voltage: with standard LEDs and at 15 V, each LED draws up to 30 mA.

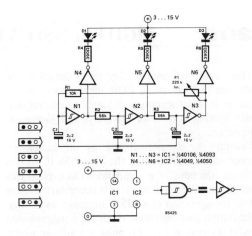

This switch is energized by light and can, therefore, be used, for instance, to switch on the aquarium lighting in the morning. Both the sensitivity and the hysteresis of the circuit can be preset; Re is energized in the presence of sufficient light.

The sensor is an n-p-n phototransistor Type TIL81 or BP103, which conducts when light falls upon it. The consequent current is divided between T2 and

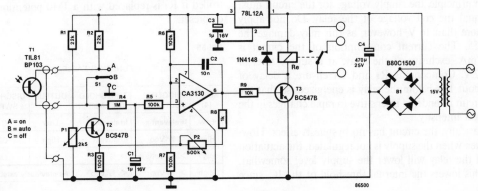

R_4-C_1. Since T_2 is connected as a current source, no current will, however, flow through R_4-C_1 as long as the current in T_1 is smaller than that through T_2 as determined by P_1 When the current in T_1 is large enough, some will flow through R_4 and charge C_1. As soon as the resulting potential across C_1 is greater than half the supply voltage, the CA3130 toggles. A current then flows through R_8, P_2, and R_3, which will cause a small reduction in the current through T_2. This means that even if the current in T_1 drops slightly, the circuit will not revert to its original state. The magnitude of this hysteresis is dependent on the setting of P_2. Note that the hysteresis prevents the circuit oscillating around the starting level.

The sensor may also be a photodiode or light-dependent resistor (LDR), but a phototransistor gives better performance, particularly when the difference between the on and off states of the circuit is small.

Resistor R_4 and capacitor C_1 could be omitted, but they augment the hysteresis by delaying the input signal from reaching the CA3130.

The current consumption of the circuit is determined primarily by the requirements of the relay. Ignoring the relay, the circuit consumes about 10 mA, which makes it possible to use a Type 78L12 as voltage regulator.

206   LIGHT-SENSITIVE TRIGGER

This circuit activates a relay upon detecting the absence of light on an LDR (light dependent resistor). It is particularly well suited to control outside lighting as used for driveways and garage entrances.

Contrary to its normal use as an astable or monostable multivibrator, the Type 555 IC in this circuit functions as a comparator. To explain this rather unusual application, it is neccessary to note that the operation of a 555 is normally as follows: the output goes high upon receipt of a trigger (start) pulse on input pin 2. This pulse is a voltage whose level is lower than $\frac{1}{3}$ of the supply voltage. The output goes low again when the voltage at the second input, pin 6, has briefly exceeded $\frac{2}{3}$ of the supply level. In the present design, the second input is not used, but the output of the chip can none the less revert to the low state, since pin 6 is connected direct to the positive supply rail. This set-up is accounted for by the accompanying Table, taken from the 555's data sheets.

In principle, the supply voltage for the circuit must equal the coil voltage of the relay. Do not apply more than 16 V, however, as this may damage the 555. The current consumption of the circuit is 4 mA, exclusive of the relay, at a supply level of 12 V. Components R_2 and C_1 ensure a delay of about 10 s before the relay is energized, so that the circuit is rendered insensitive to rapid changes in the light intensity.

Basically, the circuit has no hysteresis effect. However, when the supply is not regulated, the actuation of the relay will lower the supply level somewhat. This lowers the internal threshold of the IC, since

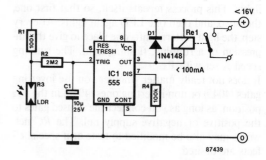

87439

the trigger point is defined as $\frac{2}{3}$ of the supply level (pin 2). Therefore, the hysteresis of the circuit can be dimensioned as required by fitting a resistor in series with the supply. It is also possible to fit a resistor between pins 5 and 7 of the 555, as shown in the circuit diagram. The amount of hysteresis is inversely proportional to the value of the resistor, and 100K is a reasonable starting point for experiments.

The sensitivity of the trigger circuit can be controlled if R_1 is replaced with a 1M0 potentiometer or preset.

NE555

FUNCTION TABLE

RESET (4)	TRIGGER VOLTAGE (2)	THRESHOLD VOLTAGE (6)	OUTPUT (3)	DISCHARGE SWITCH
Low	Irrelevant	Irrelevant	Low	On
High	$< \frac{1}{3}$ V_{DD}	Irrelevant	High	Off
High	$> \frac{1}{3}$ V_{DD}	$> \frac{2}{3}$ V_{DD}	Low	On
High	$> \frac{1}{3}$ V_{DD}	$< \frac{2}{3}$ V_{DD}	As previously established	

This low-cost timer circuit can offer switching intervals up to about 24 hours and may, therefore, be useful for a variety of domestic as well as electronic applications.

Depression of S_1 causes Re_1 to be energized and the timer to be started; the position of P_1 determines the duration of the timing interval — the given value for C_2 allows a maximum of 12 hours. Doubling the capacitance of C_2 lengthens the timing interval accordingly; the timer may thus be employed to control a NiCd battery charger. Depressing S_1 at any time during the interval causes the timer to be reset and Re_1 to be deactivated.

The funtion of FF_1 is that of a debouncer circuit for S_1 which, when actuated, causes FF_1 to apply a logic high pulse to the clock input of FF_2, which toggles. IC_2 starts counting, since its reset condition is ended. At the same time, T_1 is driven with a positive logic level, and Re_1 is energized. After the timing interval has lapsed, i.e. when counter output Q_{13} goes high, FF_2 is reset and Re_1 deactivated in consequence.

Setting the exact duration of the timing interval is readily accomplished by temporarily using counter output Q_3 rather than Q_{13} to reset FF_2; with the component values as indicated, the interval should be adjustable between 3 and 45 seconds. Divide the desired relay-on time by 1024 and set P_1 accordingly; connect the FF_2 R input to Q_{13} again, depress S_1 and have Re_1 power the relevant equipment for as long as set.

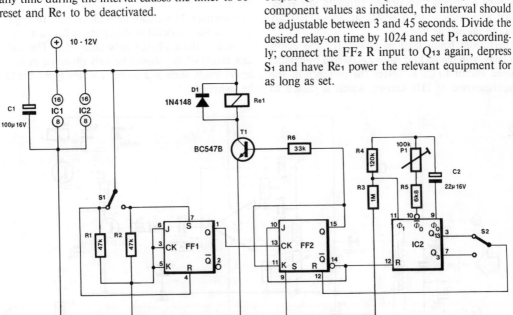

This combination of transmitter and receiver is based upon the use of the mains network in the home for remote control of mains-operated domestic appliances.

Figure 1 shows the transmitter, which merely superimposes a 36 kHz signal on the 50 Hz mains voltage if S_1 is operated. It is noted that IC_1 is fed direct off the mains voltage by means of a rectifier

circuit composed of D_1, D_2, zener diodes D_3, D_4, and smoothing capacitor C_4; the proposed configuration is to supply $+20$ V with respect to the mains neutral (0) line. The 36 kHz output signal of the opamp is fed to the mains by means of coupling capacitor C_3. R_2 is a bleeder resistor to discharge C_1 and C_2 after the circuit has been unplugged from the mains outlet.

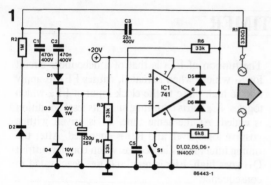

1

The receiver, shown in Fig. 2, is fed with an inexpensive door bell transformer, although any other type supplying 6 to 8 V AC at about 300 mA should do just as well.

Apart from being used to power Tr1, the mains voltage with the 36 kHz carrier is filtered by parallel tuned circuit L1-C6 to detect the presence of the superimposed 36 kHz carrier, which is passed to

amplifier IC1 via R7. Subsequent rectification by D9 enables the relay driver circuit composed of T1 and T2 to energize Re1. Preset P1 is adjusted to find the right compromise between receiver sensitivity and noise immunity. R14 should be dimensioned to suit the relay coil current.

As to the construction of the receiver and transmitter, it should be made quite clear that **the presence of the mains voltage necessitates the use of sound and safe con-ABS enclosures to prevent accidental contact with the live wires**. Do not take any risk in this respect, neither while experimenting with the circuits as shown nor while setting up and testing. The transmitter, then, is readily fitted in a salvaged mains adaptor case with a small hole drilled into it for S1.

The receiver ABS enclosure is likely to be of larger size if a mains socket is incorporated for easy connection to the appliance to be controlled. The contact rating of Re1 should be duly observed in case heavy loads, such as a coffee machine (4 A), are to be switched.

2

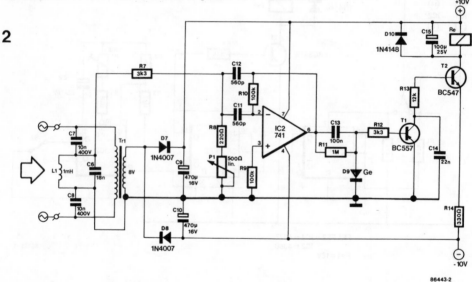

209   MAINS FAILURE ALARM

This circuit was originally developed to detect and signal interruptions of the mains supply to artificial respiration systems. The signalling is done in two ways: a buzzer is sounded, and a small lamp is quenched.

The supply current to the monitored equipment induces a variable flux in a small transformer that serves to keep the relays actuated, so that La1 lights

and Bz is off when the mains voltage is available. When a mains failure occurs, apparatus X no longer draws current, so that both Re1 and Re2 are de-actuated, resulting in the lamp being turned off, and the battery-operated buzzer being activated.

Transformer Tr2 is a modified 3 VA mains type which functions as a current transducer: the original primary winding functions in this appli-

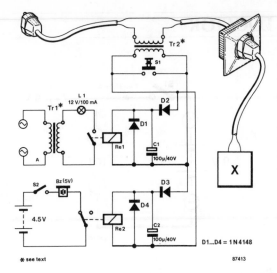

cation as the secondary, while the original secondary winding is replaced by about 7 turns of 20SWG (∅ 1 mm) enamelled copper wire. Every precaution should be taken to ensure that the new winding is capable of safely handling the current demand of X. Thanks to the so created high turns ratio in the transformer, a relatively small current suffices to keep the relays actuated and the smoothing capacitors C_1-C_2 charged. Push-button S_1 makes it possible to test the alarm by simulating the absence of induced current. Tr_1 can be a small bell type, or one salvaged from a mains adapter for a pocket calculator. Switch S_2, finally, is used to turn off the buzzer when apparatus X is disconnected or switched off.

210   MAINS VOLTAGE MONITOR

It is often desirable to know at a glance whether the mains voltage is at the low side; for instance, when you are about to work on a computer program. The danger is, of course, that when it is already low, further loads may cause the mains to drop below an acceptable level.

The supply for the present circuit is taken direct from the mains, which exists across R_1 and P_1. The 15 V stabilized voltage produced by R_2, C_1, C_2, D_1, and D_2 provides two reference voltages. These voltages are compared in A_1 and A_2 with a fixed proportion of the mains. If the mains is below 210 V, D_7 lights, and when it is higher than 250 V, D_8 lights.

When neither D_7 nor D_8 lights, T_1 switches on and causes D_4 to light, indicating that the mains voltage is within acceptable limits. The mains voltage limits are set with P_1 with the aid of a multimeter and a variac; where perfectionism is not required, the preset may be set to roughly the centre of its travel. Remember that this circuit is not isolated from the mains and it must, therefore, be housed in a man-made fibre case.

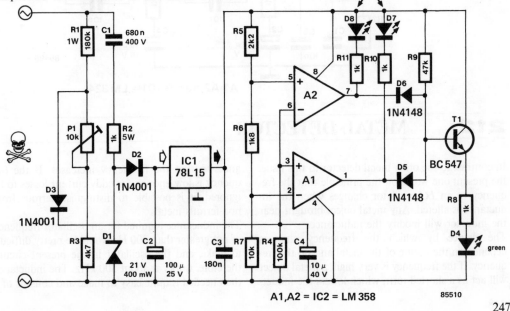

A1,A2 = IC2 = LM 358   85510

211 MAINS WIRING LOCATOR

The accompanying circuit shows a simple means of locating current-carrying conductors. The detector coil is a telephone pick-up with suction pad. The magnetic field of a current-carrying conductor induces a very small voltage in L_1 that is amplified in opamps A_1 and A_2. Capacitors $C_2 \ldots C_5$ have a value which ensures maximum amplification in A_1 and A_2 of signals around 50 Hz. Diode D_1 will light during positive halve-waves of the mains current.

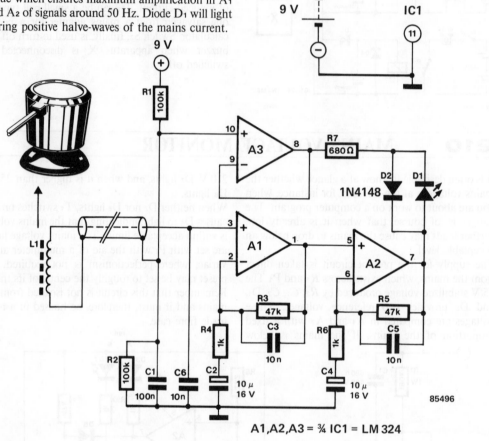

A1,A2,A3 = ¾ IC1 = LM 324

212 METAL DETECTOR

In contrast to the other metal detector in this issue, the present one works on the principle that the frequency of an *LC* oscillator changes when the inductance is altered. Any metal object brought near the inductor will modify the inductance.

The degree by which the frequency changes depends on the nature of the metal and on the frequency. If the frequency is very high, a metal object will act as a shorted turn, which lowers the induct-

ance, so that the frequency increases. If the frequency is low enough for eddy-current losses to be ignored, it is possible to distinguish ferrous from non-ferrous metals.

The inductance required for an oscillator frequency of not greater than 200 Hz would be pretty difficult to make, and the oscillator in the present circuit, therefore, works at about 300 kHz. The inductance then needed is quite easy to make and consists of a single turn of coaxial cable as shown in the accompanying diagram.

The circuit consists of oscillator T_1, frequency-to-voltage converter IC_1, and BiMOS operational amplifier IC_2. With a detector coil diameter of c. 440 mm, the values of capacitors C_1 and C_2 ensure an oscillator frequency of around 300 kHz. Smaller diameter coils need more turns.

The level of the oscillator signal should be at least 500 mV$\pi\pi$ to be able to drive the 4046B satisfactorily. At that level, the phase comparator ensures that the internal phase-locked loop always locks. The source follower output at pin 10 is fed to a CA3130 where it is amplified substantially.

The centre frequency of the phase-locked loop, and,

therefore, the zero of the centre-zero microammeter, is set with P_1; fine adjustment with P_2 may be necessary if the sensitivity of the opamp is high. That sensitivity is set with P_3 which is connected in the negative feedback loop to the inverting input. There is also positive feedback via the microammeter and R_{10} to the non-inverting input. If, therefore, a meter with a different resistance is used, it may be necessary to alter the values of R_9, R_{10}, and R_{11} accordingly.

Note that in treasure hunts the size of the objects sought should have some relation to the diameter of the detector coil: looking for coins with a 440 mm (17.5 in) diameter coil is a fruitless task!

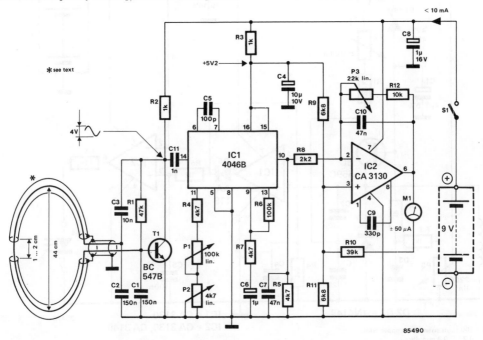

85490

213   METAL PIPE DETECTOR

Water and gas pipes, as well as electrical conduit, embedded in walls are not easy to trace, although this is essential when work is to be carried out to the wall. This handy little unit will be a godsend at such times.

The principle of the detector is based on the property of metals of absorbing magnetic energy when they are brought into a magnetic field.

Transistor T_1 in figure 1 is a simple LC oscillator, of which the sensor, L_1, forms a part. The oscillator

frequency is around 15 kHz. When energy is withdrawn from the magnetic field around L_1 by a metal object, the alternating voltage across the LC circuit will diminish. By rectifying that voltage in IC_1, and applying the resultant direct voltage to a differential amplifier, IC_2, which compares it with a voltage preset with P_3 an on/off indication is obtained. When L_1 is brought in the vicinity of metal, D_4 goes out. The sensitivity of the detector is set with P_1 and P_3

The unit is powered by a 9 V battery (PP3). To calibrate the detector, adjust P1 for maximum resistance and connect an oscilloscope to the collector of T1. Adjust the peak value of the oscillator signal with P2 so that the oscillator just does not stop working. This is checked by adjusting P3 so that the LED just lights. If then a coin is held near the ferrite rod, the LED should go out, indicating that the

oscillator has ceased working.

At the start of the search, use the smallest peak value of the oscillator signal (P1 at maximum resistance), combined with the lowest trigger level (wiper of P3 to earth). After the location of the pipes has been ascertained roughly, the peak value of the oscillator signal and the trigger level can be increased until the required accuracy is obtained.

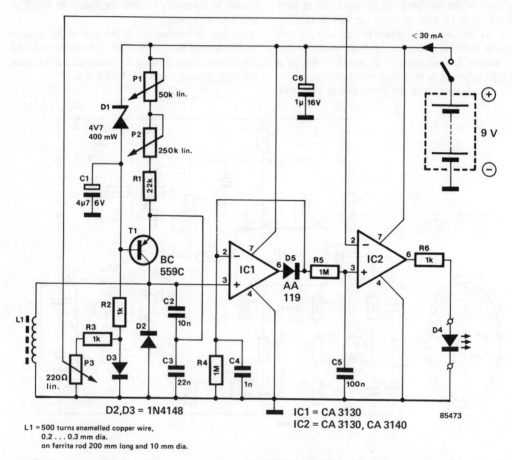

L1 = 500 turns enamelled copper wire,
0.2 . . . 0.3 mm dia.
on ferrite rod 200 mm long and 10 mm dia.

D2,D3 = 1N4148

IC1 = CA 3130
IC2 = CA 3130, CA 3140

85473

214   MINIATURE RUNNING LIGHTS

The type UAA170 integrated circuit is normally used to drive up to sixteen LEDs, and the present circuit is no exception, as can be seen from figure 1. The 555 is used as an astable multivibrator, but note that its output is not connected to the UAA170. Instead, the driver is fed from the junction of an RC network with a triangular voltage, the period of which is set with P1 It is advisable to use

a tantalum capacitor in the C_1 position to keep the leakage current down.

The voltage at the input of IC2 must not exceed 6 V. To ensure that the triangular voltage remains below that value, the supply voltage of IC1 is limited to 9.1 V by D17. If necessary, this zener diode may be replaced by an 8.2 V or even 6.8 V type. The voltages on pins 12 and 13 determine the

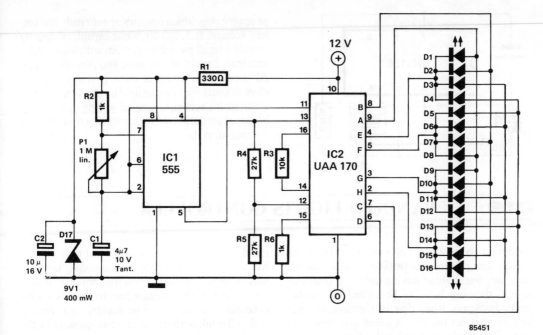

85451

voltage range swept by the LEDs.

The reference voltage for D_{16} is provided via pin 5 of IC_1 and amounts to about ⅔ of the supply voltage to the 555. The reference voltage for D_1 is determined by the potentional at the junction of R_4-R_5 (= pin 12 of IC_2), which with values shown amounts to about 3 V.

Current consumption is around 30 mA, so that battery supply is only possible with two PP3s in series and a 12 V regulator.

215   MUSICAL GREETING CARDS

The designer of this circuit will readily admit that it is literally not much to make a song or dance about, since what is shown as the circuit diagram speaks (sings) for itself.

Available in about 30 different song versions, the Type UM3166-xx is a fully autonomous melody

Table

TYPE	MELODY	TYPE	MELODY
UM3166- 1	JINGLE BELLS + SANTA CLAUS IS COMING TO TOWN + WE WISH YOU A MERRY X'MAS	UM3166-16	TOMORROW
		UM3166-17	WE WISH YOU A MERRY X'MAS + SILENT NIGHT
UM3166- 2	JINGLE BELLS	UM3166-18	WEDDING MARCH (WAGNER)
UM3166- 3	SILENT NIGHT	UM3166-19	FOR ELISE
UM3166- 4	JINGLE BELLS + RUDOLPH, THE RED-NOSED REINDEER + JOY TO THE WORLD	UM3166-20	WHEN THE SAINTS GO MARCHING IN
		UM3166-21	CONGRATULATION + HAPPY BIRTHDAY
UM3166- 5	HOME SWEET HOME	UM3166-22	JINGLE BELLS (NEW VERSION)
UM3166- 6	LET ME CALL YOU SWEET HEART	UM3166-23	IF YOU LOVE ME
UM3166- 7	CONGRATULATIONS	UM3166-24	TWINKLE TWINKLE LITTLE STAR
UM3166- 8	HAPPY BIRTHDAY TO YOU	UM3166-25	MARCH OF TOY SOLDIER
UM3166- 9	WEDDING MARCH (MENDELSSOHN)	UM3166-26	ROCKABYE BABY
UM3166-10	I WILL FOLLOW HIM	UM3166-27	CHORAL SYMPHONY (BEETHOVEN SYMPHONY NO. 9)
UM3166-11	LOVE ME TENDER, LOVE ME TRUE		
UM3166-12	SUCH A WONDERFUL DAY	UM3166-28	HAPPY BIRTHDAY TO YOU (NEW VERSION)
UM3166-13	EASTER PARADE		
UM3166-14	GRADUATION MARCH	UM3166-29	BLUE BELLS OF SCOTLAND
UM3166-15	ALOHA OE	UM3166-31	LULLABY (SCHUBERT)

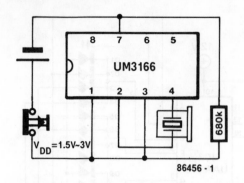

generator chip which operates at extremely low battery voltages (1.3...3 V), while capable of directly driving a small piezo-buzzer from antiphase output terminals 2 and 4. If you wish, you may connect an AF amplifier to either of these pins in order that more listeners may be captured by the melody selected from the accompanying table. The melody may be played continuously by connecting terminal 3 to 7 rather than 1.   (St)

216   RANDOM LIGHTS CONTROLLER

Unfortunately, we are all well aware that the annual holiday season is an anxious time for many people, since they worry about leaving the home unattended and therefore liable to be visited by burglars and/or hooligans. Right now is, therefore, an ideal time to construct this circuit before you leave your home and all of your highly-valued property.

It goes without saying that simulating one's presence in the home may be accomplished by having some electronic or mechanical timer device switch on a number of lights when it grows dark,

merely keeping them on until a fixed time interval has lapsed. The potential housebreaker, however, may soon detect the regular pattern that occurs every evening, encouraging him to embark on his nefarious activities, since he realizes he is dealing with a harmless timer rather than persons in the home.

This circuit, while also being a timer, offers a better simulation of human activity, since it automatically arranges for a number of lights to be switched on and off in an apparently random manner, which

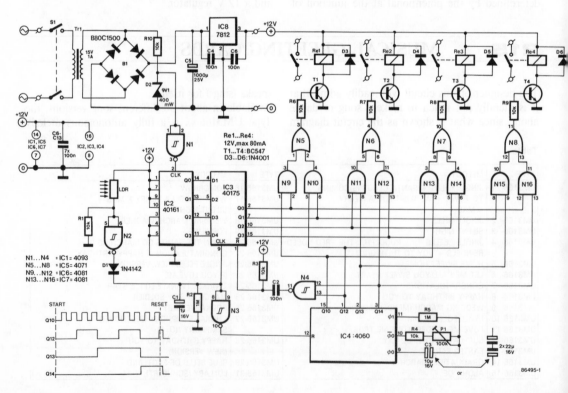

gives the burglar the impression that there are people at home. In actual fact, the lights pattern is pseudo-random, but 16 possible configurations are bound to ensure sufficient diversity to keep your mind at ease and that of the attentive burglar quite puzzled for at least a few weeks.

And now for the operational principles of this easy-to-build circuit. The evening's specific lights configuration is determined by the four-bit logic code supplied by counter IC_2 at the moment it becomes dark. Since this never happens at precisely the same time every evening, IC_2 may be considered as a four-bit (1 of 16) random code generator. Whenever the LDR fails to detect the presence of daylight, the output of N_2 goes high, and D_1 charges C_1. Meanwhile, N_1 constantly applies 100 Hz pulses to the input of counter IC_2. When the voltage across C_1 and R_2 has risen to a level, sufficiently high to be recognized as a logic one by the clock input of quad latch IC_3, the four-bit counter code is latched and transferred to the $Q_0 \ldots Q_3$ outputs of IC_3. In addition, N_3 simultaneously enables IC_4 to start counting and dividing its on-chip generated clock signal.

The latch (IC_3) and counter (IC_4) outputs are combined in AND gates $N_9 \ldots N_{16}$. The oscillator parts to IC_4 R_4-P_1-R_5-C_3 (the latter is a bipolar type which may be substituted by two series-connected electrolytic capacitors) have been dimensioned such that output Q_{10} produces 15-minute long, 50% duty factor pulses; this interval may be set accurately by means of P_1. Since IC_4 is a binary (2^n) divider, outputs Q_{12}, Q_{13} and Q_{14} provide pulse period times of 60, 120 and 240 minutes respectively. Whether or not these pulses can appear at the outputs of $N_9 \ldots N_{16}$ depends on the current logic level of each of the associated latch outputs $Q_0 \ldots Q_3$. The AND gate outputs have been paired in four OR gates $N_5 \ldots N_8$; therefore N_5 and N_7 may supply either 15, 60, or 75-minute intervals, while N_6 and N_8 cater for relay-on times of either 60, 120, or 180 minutes; longer times (e.g. 360 minutes) are not feasible since N_4 resets IC_3, five hours (Q_{12} AND Q_{14} = 60 + 240 = 300 min.) after it fell dark at the LDR mounting position.

It is seen that Re_1 and Re_3 are therefore best used for those lights that can be expected to go on and off for relatively short periods during the evening, while Re_2 and Re_4 are energized for longer times at later hours that same night.

Finally, the inset timing diagram illustrates the pulse sequence relevant to the four relay outputs.

217 REMOTE CONTROL FOR LIGHT SWITCHES — PART 1

We all sometimes wish that some of the switches around the home were just a little easier to locate and operate, notably so in the dark and with less frequently used light switches, such as those for the cellar or garage light. For the physically handicapped, some switch locations present a real hindrance to their mobility in the home; for them, it would be very convenient to be able to operate the switch from a distance.

The proposed wireless control system differs from, say, an IR-based set-up in that it requires no line-of-sight path between transmitter and relevant receiver, while the practicable operating range is of the order of a few metres.

The circuit diagram of the control transmitter shows an oscillator composed of T_1, T_3 and T_2, the latter transistor merely functioning as a switching device. The oscillator frequency is set at about 30 kHz by means of C_5, C_6 and L_1: the latter consists of about 200 turns of 36 SWG ($\varnothing$ 0.2 mm) enamelled copper wire on a paxolin former to suit the diameter of 10 to 20 cm long ferrite rod, which may be salvaged from a discarded MW/LW pocket radio. The tap on the coil is made at 20 turns from the earth connection.

In order to compensate for the relatively low radiation efficiency of the proposed transmitter aerial, the peak pulse voltage across C_6 amounts to some 150 V_{pp} when the oscillator is turned on for 8 ms by T_2, which is driven with an 18 Hz signal from IC_1.

The pulsed mode operation of the oscillator ensures a relatively low mean power consumption of the battery-operated transmitter when a receiver unit is to be activated.

Testing the transmitter is readily done with a scope; observe the pulsed 30 kHz carrier, which should look as indicated by the inset signal waveform drawing; the pulse-on time of 8 ms is determined by C_4-R_4, and their values had better not be changed, since they are the optimum compromise between transmitter current consumption and output power.

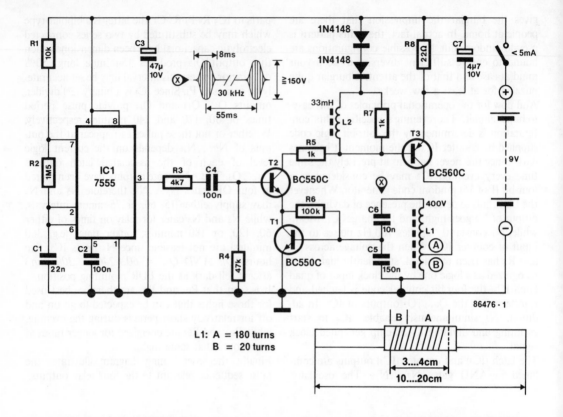

L1: A = 180 turns
    B = 20 turns

3....4cm
10....20cm

86476 - 1

218   REMOTE CONTROL FOR LIGHT SWITCHES — PART 2

Just like the associated hand-held transmitter (see previous article), the receiver is simple to construct. As can be seen from the circuit diagram, parallel tuned circuit L_1-C_1 receives the transmitter signal, which is first buffered by means of a dual gate MOSFET — T_1 — in order to prevent excessive loading of the tuned circuit. Further amplification is performed by T_2, before rectifier circuit D_1-C_6 can provide a pulsating voltage to T_3, which drives PLL detector IC_1 with a sawtooth-like signal. The lock output—pin 8—of IC_1 controls Re_1 via relay driver circuit T_4-T_5.

As to a few details concerning the receiver circuit, the PLL chip signals the lock condition by pulling pin 8 low; C_{14} is charged and functions as a buffer device in case the PLL input voltage disappears because of the fact that the transmitter coil is no longer held steady for optimum reception (directive effect of the ferrite rod). At the receiver input, R_1 should be mounted direct at the relevant MOSFET

gate so as to prevent possible oscillation tendency of T_1.

Like the transmitter coil, L_1 is wound on a 4 cm long paxolin former, which can be slid over the ferrite rod to find the position that gives optimum reception. Use 210 turns of 36 SWG (∅ 0.2 mm) enamelled copper wire; the coil length should be about 3 cm. L_1 and L_2 should be separated from each other with a metal screen to preclude stray coupling.

The receiver is readily tested and adjusted by placing an operative transmitter at a distance of about 4 metres. The optimum position of the coil on the ferrite rod can now be found by connecting a scope to the drain of T_1 and sliding L_1 for maximum received signal. In the absence of an oscilloscope, the signal at the PLL input (pin 3) may be connected to a loudspeaker to position L_1 for maximum voice coil movement at 18 Hz. After it has been positioned correctly, L1 may be glued into place on the rod.

Adjusting the PLL is done with P1, which should be turned carefully across its travel to establish the points at which the PLL fails to lock on the incoming signal (Re1 is deactivated and the lock indication LED, if fitted, goes out). Now set P1 to the position in between the no-lock points. Carefully manoeuvre the transmitter to a place where reception is worse, i.e. where Re1 is observed to go off. Careful adjustment of P1 and further trial and error will enable the user to establish the preset position that corresponds to optimum receiver sensitivity and reliability under less than favourable circumstances.

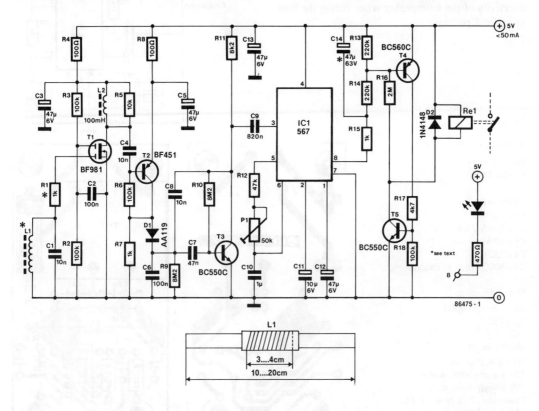

219   RODENTS DETERRENT

There are a number of well-founded arguments against the use of poison to get rid of mice, rats and other rodents in and around the home. From an ecological point of view, the undesirable side effects are mainly the disturbance of the natural food chain of animals we do not wish any harm whatsoever; most poisonous substances devised to exterminate mice are, unfortunately, quite difficult to break down compounds, which may, in the end, become manifest as dangerous to our own health. The ecologically accepted method of getting rid of a population of mice is, therefore, based on the controlled introduction of such predators as cats and owls, causing a high degree of stress on part of the mice, which are then quite quick to leave the relevant premises or area.

Another method of bringing about a high degree of stress is to produce a high-pitch, frequency-swept signal just above the audible range for human beings. The signal is swept rather than of constant frequency in order to prevent mice from becoming immune to the sound.

The proposed rodents deterrent is based upon the Type 555 timer chip, which is configured to produce a 20 to 40 kHz output signal, swept at a 50 Hz rate. The latter frequency is obtained from the mains by means of C4 and R3, which pass the modulating signal to input pin 5. The output of the swept oscillator is connected direct to a high-efficiency piezo-ceramic horn tweeter, which ensures a sufficiently high sound pressure level to keep rodents out of reasonably sized areas, such as attics and garages. The completed rodents deterrent circuit, along with the tweeter, may be mounted in a simple ABS enclosure, but care should be taken to observe the directivity of the loudspeaker when fitting the unit in its final position.

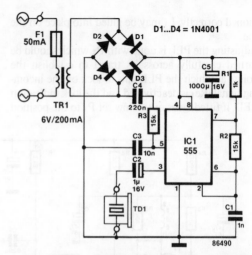

Parts list

Resistors:
R1 = 1 k
R2;R3 = 15 k

Capacitors:
C1 = 1 n
C2 = 1μ;16 V electrolytic
C3 = 10 n
C4 = 220 n
C5 = 1000μ;16 V electrolytic

Semiconductors:
D1 . . . D4 = 1N4001
IC1 = 555

Miscellaneous:
Tr1 = 6 V;200 mA.
TD1 = piezo horn tweeter.
F1 = 50 mA, fuse, slow.
Fuseholder, PCB type, for F1.
PCB Type 86490
ABS enclosure for wall mounting.

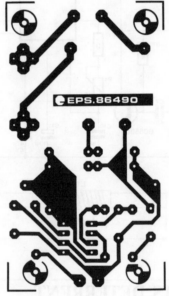

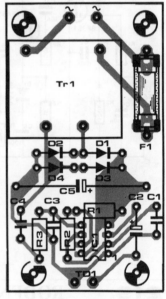

220   SET POINTER

Aneroid barometers invariably have two pointers: one that is operated by the mechanics, and one that is set manually. The manually set pointer is really nothing but a mechanical memory that enables variations in barometric pressure to be ascertained. The set pointer can, of course, be made electronic, for which a slide potentiometer is ideal. Such a pointer is not restricted to a barometer: it can also be used with a thermometer, a hygrometer, a battery that needs to be monitored; in short, with any sensor that delivers a slowly varying voltage.

The circuit consists of an amplifier, IC1, and a display stage, IC2. The display consists of between 3 and 9 LEDs, the centre one of which, D5, is yellow and represents the point of origin. Potentiometer P1 can be adjusted to make this LED light. When the input voltage rises slightly, D6 (the colour of which depends on the application) lights; when it drops, D4 (again, the colour depends on the application, but it should be different from D6...D9) lights. Greater variations in input signal cause D7...D9 or D3...D0 respectively to light. It is at all times possible to adjust P_1 in a manner which causes the centre LED to light.

The potentiometer could be provided with a graduated scale to enable the input voltage to be read direct. It is not difficult to produce such a scale. Apply voltages of 0.1 V, 0.2 V, and so on in steps of 0.1 V, and for each voltage turn P_1 till the centre LED lights. At each of the positions of P_1 so found, draw a thin line.

The sensitivity of the circuit is of some import, because about 1 V is necessary at pin 5 of IC_2 to make D_1 and D_9 light. As the amplification of IC_1 is unity (R_4/R_3), about 1 V is, therefore, also needed at the input of the circuit for these LEDs to operate. Opamp IC_1 deducts the voltage at the wiper of P_1 from the input signal, and adds the potential at the junction of R_5 and R_6 to the result.

Since P_1 is connected to the reference voltage (1.28 V), only this voltage can be compensated for. Strictly speaking, there is no reason why P_1 should not be connected to the positive supply line in series with a suitable resistor. In that case, the display is only stable if the supply line is well regulated.

If the input sensitivity is too low, the values of R_4 and R_2 may be increased; note, however, that these values should always be the same.

Current consumption is determined primarily by the current through the LEDs, and that in itself is about ten times the current through R_5 and R_6. The latter current is equal to the on-chip reference

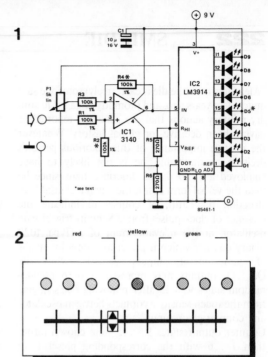

voltage of 1.28 V divided by the total resistance of $R_5 + R_6$. The maximum current through the LEDs is about 40 mA (the current via pin 7 must not exceed 4 mA!) so that the total current does not exceed 50 mA.

---

221   SIREN

In spite of its modest configuration, the circuit shown here is capable of generating quite a sound. This is made possible by the n-channel MOSFET, T_1, which drives the loudspeaker.

Such a MOSFET can be driven direct by CMOS logic circuits, and the type chosen here has an output (=drain-source) resistance of only three ohms. Moreover, its drain current can be as high as 1.7 A, while the maximum drain-source voltage is 40 V. These parameters are independent of the polarity of the applied voltage, since the device has internal diode protection.

Since the MOSFET is virtually indestructible, it is perfectly all right to load it with just a loudspeaker. The circuit can be controlled simply from a computer, and is operated by making the ENABLE input logic high (which can also be done with a simple switch instead of a computer). When the input at pin 5 of gate N_2 is high, the pulses from

Schmitt trigger N_1 cause N_2 to oscillate. The output of N_2 is applied to the MOSFET via buffer N_3. The frequency of N_2 can be adjusted with P_1

As to applications, this siren is particularly suitable for use in alarm installations.

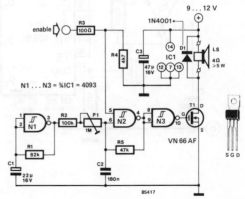

"Alea iacta est" (the die is cast, freely) someone said quite a few years ago, and promptly engaged in sundry military actions that are generally reported as having been decisive for global history. Whatever the relative importance of this notorious person's decision at that time, he is not likely to have employed a SMD die as described here, since he used the verbal form *cast* rather than a clausal construction (in Latin, of course) to indicate the presence of clock pulses from a Schmitt-trigger gate oscillator, at the relevant input of a Type 4029 binary counter which is preset to state 9 by means of jam (preset) inputs $J_0 \ldots J_3$ while its $Q_0 \ldots Q_2$ outputs may represent 1 of 6 pseudo-random states $9 \ldots 15$ after removing one's fingers from the touch-sensitive contacts between oscillator and counter clock input.

Counter output states $9 \ldots 15$ were chosen rather than $1 \ldots 6$ with the corresponding preset 1, in order that the $\overline{CO}$ (carry out) could be connected to PE (preset enable) via inverter N_2. This arrangement causes the binary value at the $Q_0 \ldots Q_2$ outputs to vary between 1 and 6, since Q_3 is left unused. $\overline{CO}$ goes low any time the counter reaches output state 16, which can not be represented by means of the four binary outputs to the IC ($2^4 = 16$).

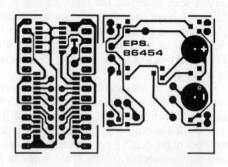

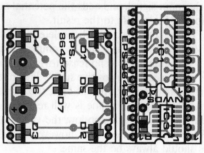

Consequently, the counter loads the preset value 1 (9), since PE goes high.

LEDs $D_1 \ldots D_7$ are arranged in the form as usual

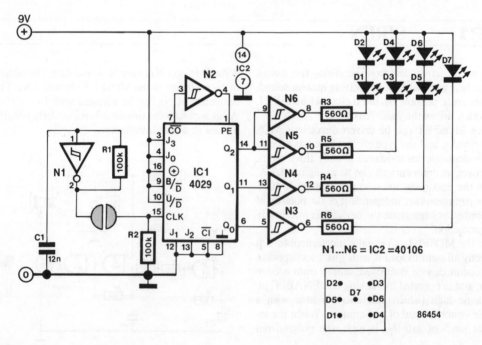

Parts list (all parts SMD)

Resistors:
$R_1; R_2 = 100 k$
$R_3 \ldots R_6 = 560 \, \Omega$

Capacitor:
$C_1 = 12 n$

Semiconductors:
$D_1 \ldots D_7 =$ LED Type CQV231 or LSS210D0
  (Siemens)
$IC_1 = 4029$
$IC_2 = 40106$

Miscellaneous:
battery clips for PCB mounting
PCB Type 86454
9 V battery PP3

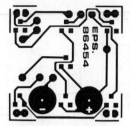
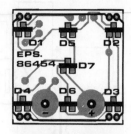

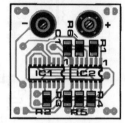

on the "six" face of a die, and the random number is, of course, displayed as an imitation of the spot(s) seen on the cube faces.

As to the construction of the SMD die, the tiny parts are fitted onto ready-made, through plated PCB Type 86454, which comes together with the Type 86452 (sideway RAM for BBC and Electron, also a SMD project in this issue).

It is noted that the 9 V battery is clipped direct onto the circuit board to make a compact unit with the LEDs facing up. The "cast" contacts are four lengths of stripped wire at the LED side of the PCB, mounted at all four sides. Placing your fingers onto either two of these wires facing one another causes all seven LEDs to light, while on release a pseudo-random value is displayed.

223   SMOKE AND GAS DETECTOR

This circuit is intended for use as a preventive device. We all know about accidents that occur through the accumulation of gas or of people overcome by smoke. The preventive character manifests itself by timely warnings in case of high gas concentrations in a manner that does not cause the gas to explode.

The circuit is based on sensor type TGS109 which is sensitive to gases enumerated in the accompanying table.

Power is provided by an 8-volt bell transformer which is tapped at 5 V. The voltage developed across the 5 V winding is rectified by D_3, smoothed by C_1, and regulated by R_2, D_4, and C_2. The resulting direct voltage of about 5.6 V is used to supply IC_1. The 3 V alternating voltage is used to operate the sensor, which needs 1 V at about 0.5 A. Resistor R_1 provides the necessary voltage drop.

The mutual inductance between the two windings of the sensor increases with rising gas concentra-

Table	Hydrocarbons:	iso-butane $CH_3CH(CH_5)CH_3$ n-butane $CH_3CH_2CH_2CH_3$ ethane CH_3CH_3 propane CH_3H_8, $CH_3CH_2CH_3$ methane CH_4
	Inorganic gases:	hydrogen H ammonia NH_3 carbon monoxide CO
	Organic solvents:	ethanol CH_3CH_2OH acetone C_3H_6O, CH_3COCH_3 n-hexane $CH_3(CH_2)_4CH_3$ benzene C_6H_6

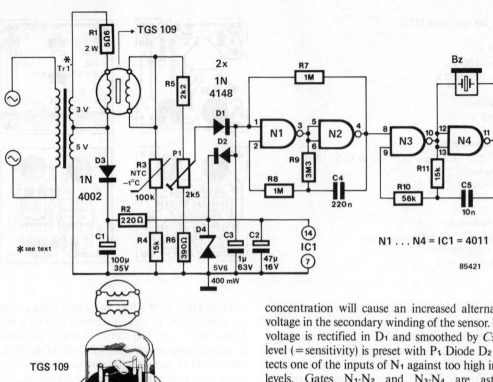

TGS 109

*see text

TGS 109

tions. Note that there is no difference in the two windings: the sensor may therefore be inserted into the socket in any way it fits. In practice, a rising gas concentration will cause an increased alternating voltage in the secondary winding of the sensor. This voltage is rectified in D_1 and smoothed by C_3; its level (=sensitivity) is preset with P_1 Diode D_2 protects one of the inputs of N_1 against too high input levels. Gates N_1-N_2 and N_3-N_4 are astable multivibrators which cause the buzzer to operate when there is too high a concentration of gas.

Resistor R_3 serves to counteract changes in sensitivity caused by temperature variations.

The detector can be built into a small case, but bear in mind the heat dissipation in R_1.

Finally, in case of an alarm, be careful in the inspection of the relevant room or space for which the alarm is sounded.

224   STAIRCASE LIGHT CONTROLLER

This circuit has been designed to function as an automatic switch-off facility on the lines of the well-known hotel switch circuit, i.e. the combination of two switches and a single light. While not exactly a replacement of any of the two changeover switches at the top and the bottom of the stairs, the proposed controller may be fitted into one of the relevant junction boxes in which a live mains line is available.

The circuit diagram shows that the controller is fed direct off the mains. C_3 and R_{21} create a suitable series impedance which charges C_4 to 6.8 V by means of rectifier D_6 and zener diode D_7. Set-reset bistable T_3-T_4 keeps track of the position of S_2, which determines which of the two triacs is to be driven so as to turn the light on. Any time S_2 is operated, timer IC_1 is started by means of C_1-R_{17}, C_2-R_{18}, N_1, N_2 and N_3; the output of the latter goes high in this condition, resetting IC_1 and causing it to pull all of its counter outputs low. Note that the reset condition can also be forced by depressing S_1. FET T_5 is turned off at reset, and 50 Hz clock pulses are applied to the Φ_I (clock input) terminal of IC_1. Any one of the five timer outpus $Q_8 \ldots Q_{13}$

260

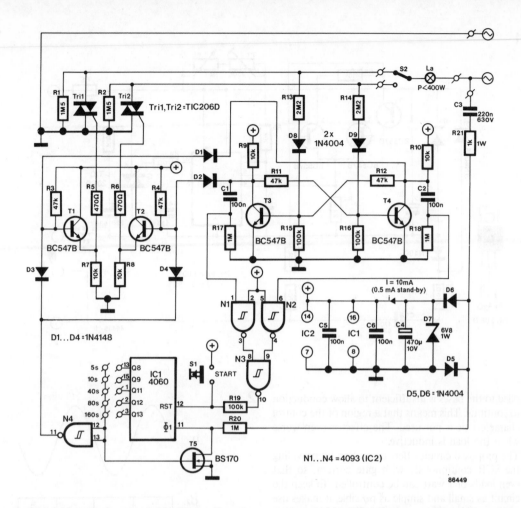

Tri1,Tri2 = TIC206D

D1...D4 = 1N4148

I = 10mA
(0.5 mA stand-by)

D5,D6 = 1N4004

N1...N4 = 4093 (IC2)

86449

may be wired to the inputs of gate N4 to select the desired on-time for the light; longer intervals may be realized by adding a further counter.

When the selected light-on interval has lapsed, T5 conducts and disables IC1 from receiving clock pulses; the counter state is thus frozen until a reset pulse is applied at terminal 12. Finally, T1 and T2 provide DC control of the relevant triac, while AND gate simulators D1-D3-R3 and D2-D4-R4 ensure the correct selection of Tri1 or Tri2 to power the bulb.

The circuit is readily constructed on a piece of veroboard and fitted into an ABS mains wiring junction box, as a replacement of one of the switches in the hotel circuit.

As many points in the circuit are at mains potential, due precautions should be taken in the construction and wiring of the controller. Note that S1 should be rated at 240 V AC, in view of the necessary isolation with respect to the mains voltage.

Tri1 and Tri2 require no heatsinks if the bulb is rated at 100 W or less, while the maximum power rating for the triacs is about 400 W.

225   SUPER DIMMER

Most dimmers use a silicon-controlled rectifier (triac or thyristor) which is triggered at a fixed phase angle and then conducts until the next zero crossing of the mains voltage. This method is simple, but at the same time it gives problems in controlling small or inductive loads (hysteresis; flickering). The cause of these problems lies in the fact that owing to the small load the current sup-

1

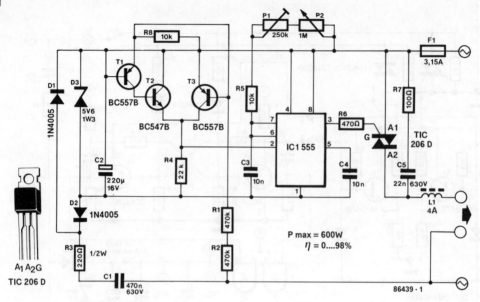

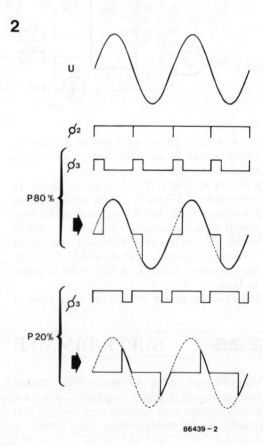

plied to the bases is insufficient to allow conduction to continue. This means that a region of the control characteristic is not used. The effect is even worse when the load is inductive.

The proposed circuit offers a solution by providing the SCR continuously with gate current, so that even loads of 1 watt can be controlled. To keep the circuit as small and simple as possible, it makes use of the well-known timer-buffer Type 555.

The output of the 555, which is normally active high, is made active low with the aid of a negative supply voltage. The supply is provided by network C_1-R_3, rectifier D_1-D_2, and stabilizer D_3-C_2. Transistors T_1 to T_3 provide a start pulse at the trigger input of the 555 during the zero crossings of the mains. For a period determined by the setting of P_1 and P_2, the output of the timer is high, and there is, therefore, virtually no potential difference between pins 3 and 8, i.e. the SCR is turned off. When the set period has lapsed, pin 3 goes low and the SCR is triggered. For the remainder of the half period, a gate current flows which keeps the SCR in conduction. The minimum position at which, for instance, a light bulb should just not light, is set with P_1.

Filter R_7-C_5-L_1 provides the requisite decoupling of the SCR.

Finally, note that the maximum power that can be controlled is of the order of 600 watts.

This circuit is intended for use in a small private telephone installation. The ringing tone sequence is 400 ms on, 200 ms off, 400 ms on, 2 s off.

In the accompanying diagram, N_1 and N_2 form an oscillator that operates at a frequency of 5 Hz, which gives a period of 200 ms. The oscillator signal is fed to two decade scalers, which are connected in such a manner (by N_3 and N_4) that the input signal is divided by 15.

The second input of N_4 may be used to switch the divider on and off by logic levels. If this facility is not used, the two inputs of N_4 should be interconnected.

Resistors R_3 to R_6 incl. form an OR gate that controls a relay via T_1 and T_2 which are connected in a darlington circuit.

Outputs 5 to 9 of IC_2 go high sequentially, so that the relay is energized for 400 ms (when 5 and 6 are high), then off for 200 ms (output 7 is not connected), and then energized again for 400 ms (when 8 and 9 are high). After that, the relay is off for 10 periods = 2 s, and then the cycle repeats itself.

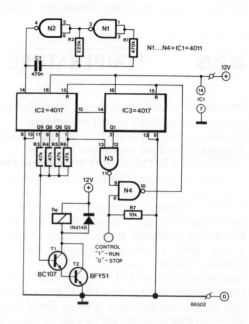

TEMPERATURE REGULATOR WITH ZERO CROSSING SWITCH

227

This temperature regulator can be built without special ICs and may be used with powers up to 3.5 kVA.

The circuit is based on a two-point regulator with a thermistor as the temperature sensor. As the load current is switched only during zero crossing of the mains, no additional interference suppression is necessary.

The series combination R_1C_1 serves to lower the mains voltage to a level suitable as supply voltage for trigger T_1. As R_1 is small compared with the reactance of C_1, the current leads the voltage by nearly 90°.

If the ambient temperature is higher than a given value, determined by potentiometer P_1 the resistance of R_{th} is low enough to cause T_1 to conduct. Silicon controlled rectifier Th_1 is supplied with gate current and switches on during the negative half cycle of the mains, because the current through R_1C_1 leads the voltage. When Th_1 is on, thyristors

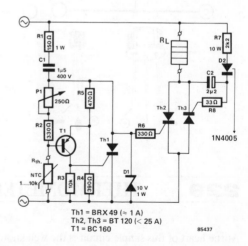

Th_2 and Th_3 remain in the blocked state, so that no current flows through heating element R_L.

When the temperature drops below the value determined by P_1 transistor T_1 and thyristor Th_1 remain off, so that Th_2 conducts. As the voltage across zener diode D_1 leads the mains voltage, Th_2 switches on when the remains crosses zero. At the

onset of the negative half cycle, Th_3 switches on. During the positive half cycle, C_2 is charged via R_7 and D_2, and so provides the gate current to switch on Th_3 at the onset of the negative half cycle.

228   TEMPERATURE SENSOR

The LM35 is a temperature sensor which provides an output voltage that is directly proportional to the temperature being measured in degrees Celsius. This means that if the temperature is 0 °C, the output voltage is 0 V. The output voltage increases by 10 mV for every degree Celsius, i.e., at 19.8 °C, the output voltage is 0.198 V.

This is an important advantage over other temperature sensors that are calibrated in kelvin. Using such sensors to measure in degrees Celsius requires a very stable reference voltage that must be deducted from the reading.

Another advantage of the LM35 is its very low current consumption of less than 60 μA. This means a long battery life and small internal power dissipation, so that errors caused by internal heat are

minimal: 0.1 °C with a battery voltage of 4 V.

The sensor can be connected direct to an analogue or digital multimeter, or, more interestingly, to a computer which can then process and store the information. A suitable interface for this purpose is described in *direct reading digitizer* elsewhere in this issue.

The accuracy of the LM35/LM35C is typically 0.4 °C at 25 °C.

To keep the self-heat minimal, the load should be not smaller than 5 kΩ.

If a long screened cable is used between the sensor and indicator, an *RC* network (10 Ω in series with 1 μF) should be connected between the output of the sensor and earth to prevent any oscillations.

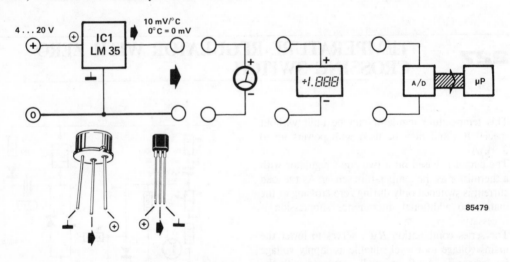

85479

229   THERMOMETER

At the heart of this simple circuit is the well-known Type KTY10 temperature sensor from Siemens. This silicon sensor is essentially a temperature-dependent resistor, which is connected as one arm in a bridge circuit here. Preset P_1 functions to balance

the bridge at 0°C. At that temperature, moving coil meter M_1 should not deflect, i.e., the needle is in the centre position. Temperature variations cause the bridge to be unbalanced, and hence produce a proportional indication on the meter. Calibration at,

say, 20°C is carried out with the aid of P2.
The bridge is fed from a stabilized 5.1 V supply,
based on a temperature-compensated zenerdiode. It
is also possible to feed the thermometer from a 9 V
battery, provided D1-D3, R1 and C1 are replaced
with a Type 78L05 voltage regulator, because this is
more economic as regards current consumption.

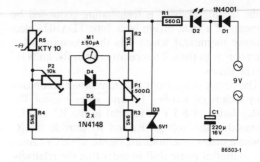

1

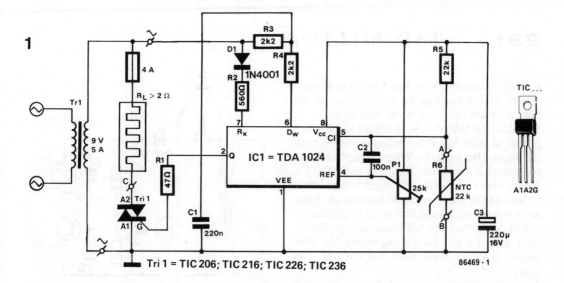

Tri 1 = TIC 206; TIC 216; TIC 226; TIC 236

86469 - 1

Many people with a keen interest in growing plants
insist on the fact that many of the more exotic
species, such as certain species of orchid and fungi,
will only thrive in warm soil and relatively high
humidity.
Whether or not this is a correct assumption, this circuit offers the possibility to keep the soil tempera-

ture in a miniature hot-house at a constant, adjustable level.
The heating element is made of several loops of
plastic covered steel wire, such as used in gardening.
The wire used in the prototype had a diameter of
1 mm and a resistivity of about 0.2 Ω per metre.
The circuit diagram of the soil heater shows that

2

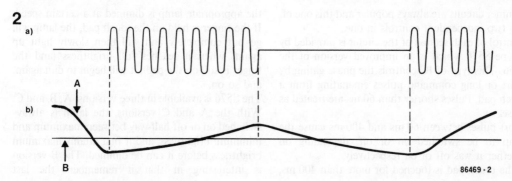

a)

b)

A

B

86469 - 2

the heating element is temperature controlled by means of a triac, driven by a Type TDA1024 electronic thermostat which gets the necessary information as to the soil temperature from R_6, an NTC type sensor.

The circuit is fed from the transformer secondary by means of rectifier D_1 and series resistor R_2. Regulation at 6.5 V is internal to the IC, and C_3 smoothes this voltage. R_3 and R_4 provide the IC with a mains synchronizing signal, while C_1 causes a controlled phase shift in order that the relatively low operating voltage can still ensure the correct zero-crossing synchronization.

The temperature sensor circuit is composed of R_5, R_6, and P_1 The sensor proper, R_6, must be placed into the soil at a suitable position, electrically well isolated, of course. The optimum soil temperature, which should be established by trial and error, is adjustable with preset P_1; Fig. 2 shows the correlation between soil temperature, heating element voltage, and preset temperature.

If necessary, a more powerful heating element may be dug into the soil, but the ratings of the fuse, Tr_1 and Tri_1 should then be changed accordingly. The transformer secondary voltage, however, should remain at 9 V. With the components as indicated in the circuit diagram, the heating energy is about 40 joules.

231   TWIN BELL-PUSH

It is often desirable for a single doorbell to be operated by two bell-pushes. for instance, one at the front door and the other at the back-door.

The additional bell-push, S_2, in series with the break contact of relay Re_1, is connected in parallel with the original bell-push, S_1. When S_2 is pressed, the bell voltage is rectified by D_1 and smoothed by C_1. After a time $\tau = R_1R_2C_2$, the direct voltage across C_2 has risen to a level where T_1 switches on. Relay Re_1 is then energized and its contact breaks the circuit of S_2, so that the bell stops ringing. After a short time, C_1 and C_2 are discharged, the relay returns to its quiescent state, and the bell rings again.

In this way, S_1 will cause the bell to ring continuously, while S_2 makes it ring in short bursts, so that it is immediately clear which bell-push is operated.

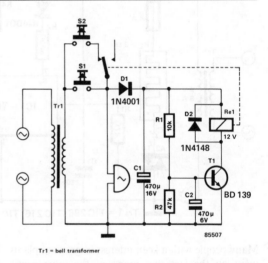

Tr1 = bell transformer

232   TWIN DIMMER

Dimmer circuits are always popular and this one offers two independent controls in one.

Control of each section of the circuit is provided by a type S576 which is an improved version of the S566. This type of IC controls the phase gating by short or long command pulses emanating from a touch pad. Pulses shorter than 60 ms are treated as noise.

Short pulses between 60 ms and 400 ms cause the lamp to be switched on or off, depending on whether it was off or on respectively.

If the touch pad is touched for more than 400 ms,

the appropriate lamp is dimmed at a certain speed. If the finger is held on the touch pad, the lamp will go out completely and will then slowly light up again: when it reaches full brightness (and the finger is still on the pad), it will begin to dim again, and so on.

The S576 is available in three versions: A, B, and C. With the A and C versions, the lamp is always switched on or off half-way between maximum and minimum brightness, and it first attains maximum brightness before it can be dimmed. The B version is interesting in that it remembers the last

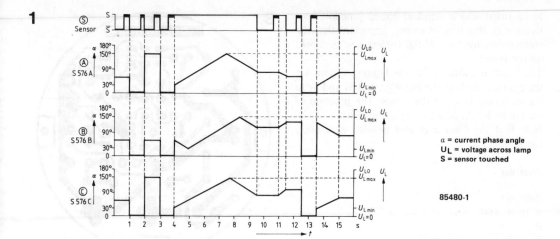

1

Sensor S $\overline{S}$

(A) S 576 A
α 180° 150° 90° 30° 0
U_{LO} U_{Lmax} U_L
U_{Lmin} $U_L = 0$

(B) S 576 B
α 180° 150° 90° 30° 0
U_{LO} U_{Lmax} U_L
U_{Lmin} $U_l = 0$

(C) S 576 C
α 180° 150° 90° 30° 0
U_{LO} U_{Lmax} U_L
U_{Lmin} $U_L = 0$

1 2 3 4 5 6 7 8 9 10 11 12 13 14 15 s
t

a = current phase angle
U_L = voltage across lamp
S = sensor touched

85480-1

brightness level, so that the lamp is always switched on or off at the last brightness setting. These various possibilities are summarized in figure 1. The circuit of the twin dimmer is shown in figure 2. Power for the ICs is provided via R_2, C_4, D_1, and D3. The supply is smoothed by C_1. Capacitors C_3 and C_6 determine the speed with which the lamps dim or get brighter.

The twin dimmer is best built onto the printed circuit board shown in figure 3. This board is intended

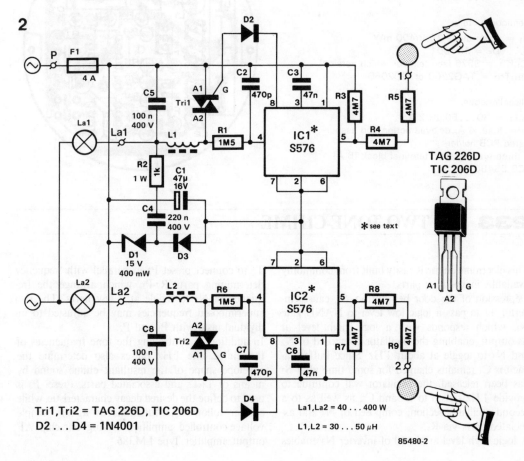

2

P F1 4 A

C5 100 n 400 V
Tri1 A1 G A2
La1 La1 L1
R2 1k 1 W
C1 47μ 16V
C4 220 n 400 V
D1 15 V 400 mW
D3

D2

C2 470p 8 C3 47n 3 1 R3 4M7 R5 4M7

R1 1M5 4 IC1* S576 5 R4 4M7

7 2 6

TAG 226D TIC 206D

* see text

La2 La2 L2
C8 100 n 400 V
Tri2 A2 A1 G

7 2 6

R6 1M5 4 IC2* S576 5 R8 4M7
C7 470p 8 C6 47n 3 1 R7 4M7 R9 4M7

A1 G A2

1

2

D4

Tri1,Tri2 = TAG 226D, TIC 206D
D2 ... D4 = 1N4001

La1,La2 = 40 ... 400 W
L1,L2 = 30 ... 50 μH

85480-2

267

to be fitted into a standard round junction box. Because of this, it is, of course, important that the components used are of the correct size as shown on the board.

The board is connected to the lighting system via three terminals: L to the live wire, and S_1 and S_2 to the switching wires of the lamps. The junction of the lamps is (already) connected to neutral.

Note that the dimmer cannot be used with neon tubes.

Parts list

Resistors:
R_1, R_6 = 1M5
R_2 = 1 k/1 W
$R_3 \ldots R_5, R_7 \ldots R_9$ = 4M7

Capacitors:
C_1 = 47 µ/16 V
C_2, C_7 = 470 p
C_3, C_6 = 47 n ceramic
C_4 = 220 n/400 V
C_5, C_8 = 100 n/400 V

Semiconductors:
D_1 = zener diode 15 V/400 mW
$D_2 \ldots D_4$ = 1N4001
IC_1, IC_2 = S576 (see text for which version)
Tri_1, Tri_2 = TAG226D or TIC206D

Miscellaneous:
L_1, L_2 = 30 ... 50 µH/2 A
F_1 = fuse, 4 A, delayed action and associated PCB holder
1 three-way ceramic terminal block (5 A)
PCB 85480

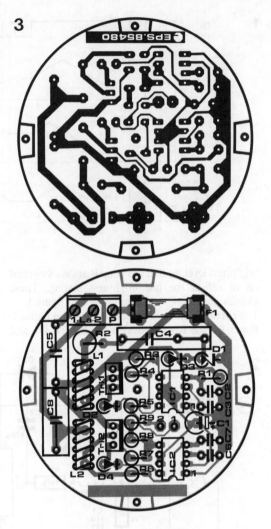

3

---

233   TWO-TONE-CHIME

This electronic chime is easily built from commonly available, inexpensive parts.

Depression of the door bell button, S_2, causes inverter T_1 to pass a logic low level to NAND gate N_1, which responds with a logic high level at its output, enabling the oscillator composed of N_2 and N_3 to toggle at about 1 Hz. Since buffer capacitor C_1 remains charged for some time after S_2 has been released, the oscillator will continue to provide 1 Hz pulses to C_4 and C_5, as well as to a second oscillator section, composed of N_4 and associated parts via R_6.

A logic high level at pin 10 of inverter N_3 enables

T_2 to connect preset P_2 in parallel with frequency determining parts R_7-P_1, which arrange the frequency of N_4 to toggle at a few hertz. The two superimposed frequencies may be adjusted to individual taste with P_1 and P_2.

In addition to controlling the tone frequencies of the chime, the 1 Hz pulses also determine the envelope shape of the resultant chime sound by means of T_4-T_5 and associated parts. Preset P_3 is used to define the desired decay characteristic, while emitter follower T_6 functions as a very simple voltage-controlled amplifier, driving one-chip AF output amplifier Type LM386.

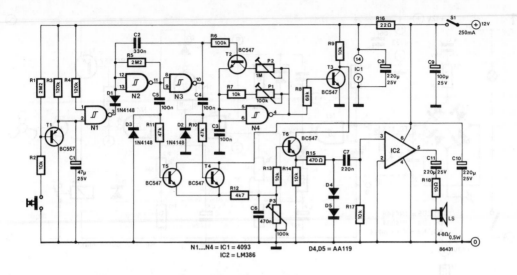

234   VENTILATOR CONTROL

Many toilets have a ventilator, which is energized along with the toilet light. However, since not every visit of the toilet requires the ventilator to start turning, this circuit offers an improved control method, which is still based upon the use of the light switch.

The circuit configuration marked **I** in Fig. 1 may be used in case the toilet ventilator is powered from the same mains lines as the light. Bridge rectifier B_1 and opto-coupler Type TIL113 serve to detect whether or not the toilet light is on. The ventilator is arranged to start turning after the light switch has been operated twice. If this is the case, the output of N_1 will go high twice; the first time, C_4 is charged, the second time will cause pin 6 of N_2 to be logic high, while the output of this NAND Schmitt trigger gate will supply a logic low pulse to N_3 when the voltage at point 3 reaches the logic one level (see timing diagram Fig. 2). N_3, then, charges C_5 which, along with P_2 and R_9, determines the ventilator "on" interval, while P_1, C_4 and R_8 establish the maximum interval between the reception of first and second trigger pulse.

The circuit option with T_2 may be used if it is less desirable to run an additional wire to the light for the purpose of obtaining the trigger pulses; the LDR should be located as close as possible to the bulb in order to preclude erroneous triggering due to the presence of daylight. The use of the LDR does not change the basic operation of the circuit, of course, and the indirect method of triggering is in

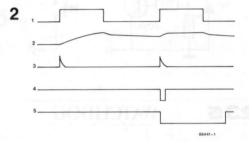

fact to be preferred in view of the risk associated with direct mains connection in the case of the first mentioned circuit option.

Another interesting use of the circuit option which incorporates S_1, T_3 and T_4 is a semi-intelligent door bell arrangement; bell 1 will sound any time S_1 is depressed, while bell 2 will only do so if the button is operated twice within the given interval; it is not difficult to come up with a number of useful applications for this circuit when used in and around the home. However, note that the timer parts C_4, P_1 and R_8 will have to change places with C_5, P_2 and R_9 respectively, if the second bell is to be kept from sounding for about 50 seconds after S_1 has been operated twice.

The power supply for the circuit may be of conventional design, incorporating the ubiquitous 78xx type of regulator. Current consumption of the circuit is mainly dependent on the type of relay, but 50 to 180 mA would appear to be a typical value.

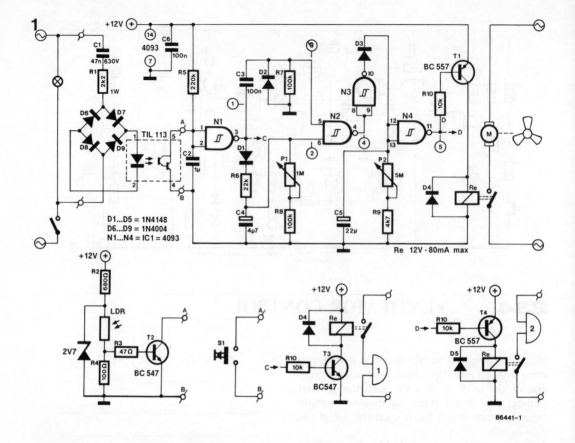

Re 12V · 80mA max

86441-1

D1...D5 = 1N4148
D6...D9 = 1N4004
N1...N4 = IC1 = 4093

235   WATCHDOG

This timer automatically switches off equipment left operating unattended for more than about thirty minutes.

The circuit operation is readily understood by following its power-on and time-out functions. Almost immediately after S4 has been depressed, relay contact rela closes to power Tr1 and the equipment connected to the mains outlet. This happens because the initial presence of the +12 V supply voltage in the circuit causes counter-oscillator IC1 and set/reset (S/R) bistable N1-N2 to be reset by means of a short, logic high pulse at the junction of R1 and C1. The outputs of N1 and N3 go high and low respectively and T4 can energize Re1. So far for the power-on automatic hold function of contact rela.

After being reset, IC1 starts counting down its on-chip generated clock pulses which have a frequency of about 2 Hz. LED D1 flashes at this rate to indicate the countdown condition. Note that S2 has

been provided to reset, i.e. disable the timer permanently, in which case D1 lights steadily. The LED, therefore, has a threefold indicator function in the present circuit: timer on (flashing), timer and equipment off (off) and timer off while the equipment is on (steady light).

As long as counter output Q12 remains at logic low level, the voltage at the collector of Q5 inverter T2 can not cause the relay coil current to be interrupted by T4. If, however, some 34 minutes $(T(Q_{12}) = \frac{1}{2} \times 2^{12} = 2048\ s)$ have lapsed since IC1 and N1-N2 were reset, Q12 goes high, causing the two-gate bistable to toggle; the output of N1 goes low, but Re1 remains energized by T4, since the other input of NOR gate N3 is still high, i.e. counter output Q5 has not been set as yet. The selfoscillating buzzer starts sounding at a 2 Hz rate, however, since T3 is driven by NOR gate N4 which receives two logic low levels at its inputs. The user is thus notified that the has another

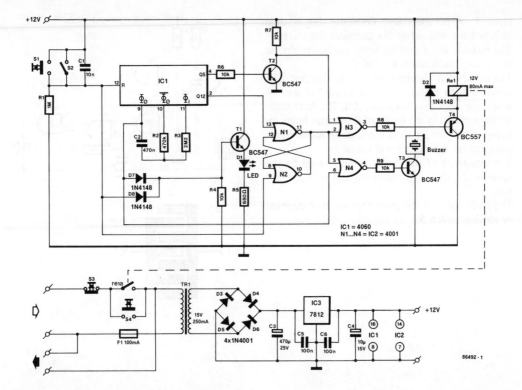

15 seconds or so left to depress S_1 for another 34-minute interval. If no such action is taken to reset the timer before Q_5 goes high, N_3 disables the relay driver transistor, and contact rela consequently cuts the mains voltage to Tr_1 and the connected equipment.

The foregoing outline of the circuit operation makes clear that depressing S_1 or switching on S_2 is the only way to keep the buzzer from sounding and the mains relay from switching off both equipment and timer circuit. If desired, push-to-break switch S_3 may be operated to break the mains supply within the half hour interval, and without the annoying sound of the buzzer.

Finally, the indicated timing intervals may be changed to suit individual requirements by using other counter outputs and/or another clock frequency for IC_1 (adapt the values of R_2-C_2).

236   WATER-DIVINER

This little unit may be used to give an audible alarm when, for instance, a washing machine hose has burst, or when it starts to rain so you can get the washing in, or it can call you to the bathroom to turn the bathwater off. No doubt you will be able to think of some more uses.

The circuit may be powered from a 9 V battery which, since the current consumption is very low, will last for at least a year. After a year it should be replaced because it will then become unreliable owing to its self-discharge.

Basically, the unit consists of a sensor, an R-S bistable, an oscillator, and a driver stage for the alarm buzzer.

The sensor consists of a waste piece of wiring board, about 40×20 mm. Connect all odd and all even tracks together with wire links, that is, 1 to 3 to 5, and 2 to 4 to 6. Tin the tracks to protect them against corrosion. When the board is dry, the resistance between the two sets of tracks is high, but when it is wet, the resistance drops sharply.

The sensor is in series with resistor R_2 and the two together, therefore, form a humidity-dependent voltage divider, which resets the R-S bistable when

input 1 of N2 goes low. Oscillator N3 is then
switched on, and driver N4 energizes the buzzer.
The bistable is set automatically on power up via
the series combination R_1 and C_1.

The circuit can also be used as a lie-detector. The
sensor is then replaced by two lengths of wire of
which the ends have been stripped. The bare wires
are then placed in the hands of the person being in-
terrogated. If the lies (which causes his hands to become damp) the buzzer will sound.

The sensitivity of the circuit is determined by the
value of R_2: some experimenting may be necessary
here.

The oscillator (and, therefore, the buzzer) is disabled
by closing switch S_1.

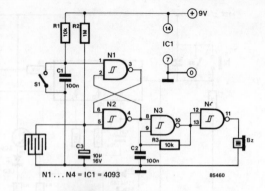

N1 ... N4 = IC1 = 4093

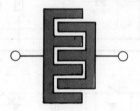

237   12-VOLT NICD BATTERY CHARGER

If you attempt to charge a 12 V NiCd battery from a 12 V lead-acid car battery, you will soon find that that is not really possible: the charging voltage should be somewhat higher than the nominal battery voltage. A 12 V battery should be charged from a source of about 14 V.

The present circuit is, therefore, a voltage doubler based on the well-known 555 IC. The IC oscillates, which means that output 3 is connected alternately with earth and the +12 V supply voltage.

When pin 3 is logic low, C_3 is charged via D_2 and D_3 to almost 12 V. When pin 3 is logic high, the voltage at the junction of C_3 and D_3 becomes almost 24 V, because the negative terminal of C_3 is at +12 V and the capacitor itself is charged to about 12 V. Diode D_3 is then reverse biased, but D_4 conducts, so that C_4 is charged to just over 20 V, which is ample for our purposes.

The 78L05 in the IC_2 position functions as a current source, which tends to keep its output voltage, U_η, appearing across R_3, at 5 V. The output current, I_η, is therefore easily calculated from
$$I_\eta = U_\eta/R_3 = 5/680 = 7.4 \text{ mA.}$$

The 78L05 itself also draws current: the central terminal (normally earthed) delivers about 3 mA. The total load current is, therefore, of the order of 10 mA, which is a good value for continuously charging NiCd batteries. The LED has been incorporated to indicate that charging current flows.

The characteristic of the charging current versus battery voltage in figure 2 shows that the circuit is not perfect: a 12 V battery will be charged with a current of only about 5 mA. There are several causes for this:

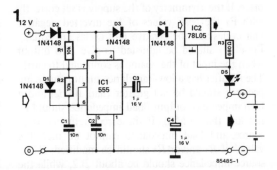

- the output voltage of the circuit tends to drop with increasing current;
- the voltage drop across the 78L05 is about 5 V to which must be added the 2.5 V the IC needs to operate correctly;
- there is a voltage drop of about 1.5 V across the LED.

None the less, a 12 V NiCd battery with a rated capacity of 500 mAh can be charged continuously with a current of 5 mA, which is 1 per cent of its capacity.

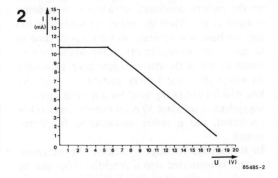

238   ACTIVE RECTIFIER WITHOUT DIODES

The active rectifier proposed here is based on the property of an operational amplifier that its output cannot become negative if its power supply is asymmetrical. We have used an RCA type CA 3130 opamp which is eminently suitable, because it can cope with input voltages down to 0 V, and has a CMOS output stage that can also work down to 0 V.

With a supply voltage of 15 V, the maximum input level is about 1.2 V_{rms}. The frequency range, for not more than 1 dB change in output, extends from DC to just over 25 kHz.

Negative half cycles at the input of the opamp are inverted and amplified by a factor R_2/R_1. Positive half cycles are also inverted, but, as stated, the output of the opamp cannot become negative, and it therefore remains at 0 V. The positive half cycles are also applied to the output of the opamp via a resistive divider, R_1-R_2-R_3-P_2 The result of all this is that only positive half cycles are present at the output, just as if full-wave rectification had taken place. If the asymmetry of the supply is set correctly with P_2 the peak values of the inverted negative half cycles and the positive half cycles are equal. Preset P_1 should be adjusted to give zero output when the input of the opamp is connected to earth. The rectifier has a low-impedance input (source impedance should be not greater than 100 Ω) and a high-impedance output (load impedance should be not less than 1 MΩ). If these requirements as to source and load impedance cannot be met, the values of R_1 and/or R_3 should be modified: R_1 + source impedance should be about 2k2, while the parallel combination of R_3 and the load must be around 10 kΩ.

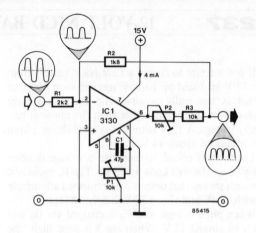

239   BATTERY CHARGE/DISCHARGE INDICATOR

Many of today's cars and motor cycles are equipped with a meter for monitoring the battery voltage. However, this meter does not provide information on the battery condition, or whether it is being charged at all. When the voltmeter reading is too low, the battery is generally in such a poor state as to necessitate switching off heavy loads to save power for use of the starter engine later. Especially on motorcycles, the battery capacity is relatively low, which justifies the need for a reliable monitoring system. A standard 30 A ammeter offers too low resolution, and is rather awkward to fit permanently.

In this charge/discharge indicator, the measured current is converted into a potential difference by R*, which is either two 1R0 5 W resistors, a fuse,

or a few turns of copper wire. The direction of the current through R* is detected by comparator IC1, which then indicates whether the battery is being charged or discharged by lighting the relevant LED. The 100R preset enables shifting the indication threshold somewhat. Input terminal + on the indicator unit is best connected to a point behind (that is, electrically behind) the contact switch, although it is also possible to fit the circuit with a separate on/off switch. Finally, the circuit is only suitable for use in or on vehicles having a 12 V battery.

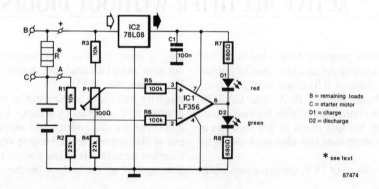

Sealed 6 V or 12 V lead-acid batteries, under normal charging conditions, are charged at a constant voltage of 2.3 V per cell. The charging current reduces during the charging: when it reaches a value of 10 mA, the battery is deemed fully charged. To check this, you do not need an expensive ammeter. The present circuit uses an LED (light-emitting diode) to indicate when the battery is fully charged.

The green indicator LED is connected in the collector circuit of a p-n-p transistor. As soon as the transistor conducts, the LED lights. This happens when the voltage drop across resistor R_1 reaches the forward bias threshold of the base emitter junction (about 0.6 V). When this resistor has a value of 56 Ω, a charging current of around 10 mA will cause this drop. To ensure that the charging current can exceed 10 mA, R_1 is shunted by diode D_1 which limits the voltage drop across the resistor to about 0.7 V. The maximum charging current depends on the diode used and lies between 1 and 3 A.

The LED does not light when the charging current is less than about 10 mA, i.e., when the battery is fully charged, when the battery is connected with wrong polarity, or when the output is short-circuited. The red LED will light when the battery is connected with reverse polarity.

The indicator should be connected between the charger and the battery. It may either be built into the charger housing, or be constructed in a small case that can conveniently become part of the charging cable.

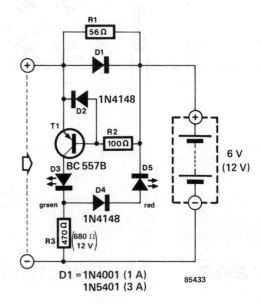

D1 = 1N4001 (1 A)
      1N5401 (3 A)

85433

---

241   BATTERY FITNESS CENTRE

This circuit is designed primarily for maintaining lead-acid batteries that are often not used for long periods in good working order. It charges the battery, after which the battery discharges slowly through its internal resistance and the present circuit. When the state of charge reaches a predetermined level, the charger is switched on again, the battery charges, and so the cycle repeats itself.

The circuit is based on Schmitt trigger T_1/T_2. Zener diode D_7 determines the state of charge at which the charger is switched off. Resistor R_2 provides the required hysteresis. With the mains disconnected and no battery connected to the battery terminals, check with voltages (from a regulated power supply) of 13.6 V and 12.5 V applied across the battery terminals that the relay switches off and on respectively. The "on" threshold may be corrected by, for

instance, connecting a 1N4148 (cathode to + line!) in series with D_7. The "off" threshold is corrected by altering the value of R_2, for example, by replacing this component with a 100 Ω preset.

It is, of course, possible to replace the mains transformer and bridge rectifier by a battery charger (see, for instance, *Elektor Electronics*, June 1984, p. 6-45), in which case the rest of the circuit can be fitted inside the charger.

It is not possible to connect a full discharged battery to the circuit, because the relay would not be energized. Such a battery should first be charged to above 10 V, but it is also possible to fit a switch in parallel with the relay contact and switch on the mains with that.

It is possible, of course, to maintain two 12 V batteries in condition by doubling the secondary voltage of the mains transformer, the zener voltage of D_7, the hysteresis, the rated coil voltage, and connecting the batteries in series across the terminals. Fuse F_1 is necessary to provide protection against short circuits. The transformer primary circuit may

also be protected by a fuse (like F_1 a delayed action type) rated at 1 A.

The circuit does not need a smoothing capacitor because that function is carried out by the battery.

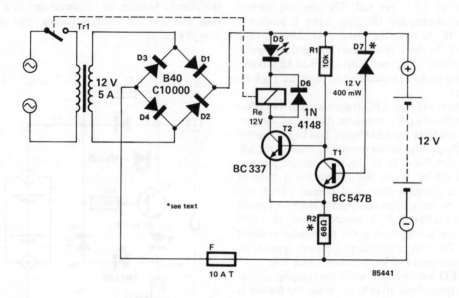

242   BATTERY GUARD

This protective circuit is readily incorporated in battery-powered equipment which is typically intended to operate for less than about a minute; possible applications that come to mind include IR remote control units, calculators, etc. Forgetting to switch off such devices irrevocably causes the built-in batteries to be exhausted after a while, however "low" the standby current.

The proposed battery guard automatically switches off the supply current to the circuit, either after about one minute has lapsed after power-on, or when the battery voltage has fallen below the acceptable level for normal operation.

Series regulator FET T_1 can pass a maximum current of 150 mA in the circuit as shown, and it is advisable to use a more powerful type than the BS250 in case more than about 100 mA is expected to be consumed by the equipment connected to the output terminals. The Type BS250 FET drops about 0.5 V at a drain current of 100 mA, and 0.8 V at 150 mA, whence the foregoing consideration.

As T_1 is a p-channel FET, it conducts and powers the equipment when the output of Schmitt trigger

NAND gate N_3 is low, i.e. when both gate inputs are high. This is so at power-up, since C_2 is still discharged and the inputs of N_4 are kept at logic low level via R_6. Consequently T_1 is enabled and causes C_2 to be charged via R_3. After about one minute (R-C time), the voltage across R_3 is low enough for N_3 to recognize a logic low level at pin 1, thereby turning off T_1. N_2 provides a hold function of this state, since otherwise N_3 might oscillate owing to the slowly varying voltage across R_3.

At power-on, the output of N_2 is pulsed high by means of R-C network R_1-R_2-C_1, whereby any residual charge in C_2 is cleared; the circuit may, therefore, be switched on with S_2-S_1 immediately after automatic power down.

Battery voltage monitoring is accomplished by D_3, R_5, R_6 and N_4. The latter's trigger threshold level is, as with all Schmitt trigger gates, in direct proportion with the supply voltage level to the IC. As long as the supply (i.e. battery) voltage is sufficiently high, N_4 will recognize a logic low level at junction R_5-R_6-N_4. However, if the battery voltage falls, D_3 keeps the input voltage to N_4 at a fixed level, caus-

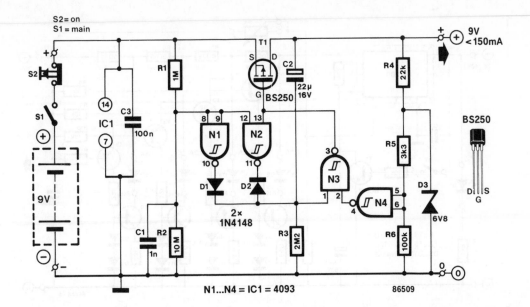

S2= on
S1 = main

N1...N4 = IC1 = 4093   86509

ing the gate to supply a logic low level to N3, which consequently turns off the series regulator FET.

It should be noted that the exact values of R3, C2, R5 and R6 may have to be adapted to suit operation with certain makes of the Type 4093. Also note that the interval time of one minute may be changed to individual requirements by suitable redimensioning of timing elements R3-C2.

Adjustment of the battery guard is carried out by temporarily exchanging R5 and R6 with a 100 k preset to determine the correct resistor values for a given switch-off level. Current consumption of the proposed circuit is mainly determined by the zener diode, which has been biased to pass only 1 mA. After automatic power-down, the guard circuit draws a (negligible) current of less than 1 μA.

EPS. 86509

243   CURRENT INDICATOR

Who has not sometimes wished that the power supply he was using had a voltmeter AND an ammeter? Unfortunately, the high cost of such units prohibits their use in many situations. The proposed circuit, which does not include the input section of the power supply, can be built from standard components, except for the low-value 5-watt resistors.

We shall not dwell on the well-known Type L200 voltage regulator, but shall confine ourselves to the current indicator section.

Fig. 1 shows that the circuit contains five LEDs: one (D1) to show whether the supply is switched on, and the other four to indicate the current consumption in steps of 0.5 A; 0.8 A; 1.3 A; and 1.8 A. As

may be deduced from these figures, the unit is capable of providing up to 2 A at an output voltage anywhere between 3 V and 30 V. The colour of the LEDs is immaterial, although it would be useful if the final one would be red to show that maximum current is being drawn.

The non-standard resistors, R4 to R7 incl., "measure" the actual current consumption. Between point A and the positive output terminal there exists a potential difference. When this p.d. reaches a value of 0.6 V, T2, and consequently T6, switch on and this causes D2 to light. In the same way, when the p.d. between points B, C, and D respectively, and the positive output terminal reaches

1

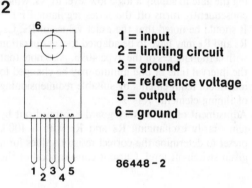

about 0.6 V, transistor pairs T_3-T_7; T_4-T_8; and T_5-T_9 switch on, and the associated LED will light.

Resistor R_2 and capacitor C_2 provide a soft start facility at switch-on. Transistor T_1 provides an emergency switch-off facility, which in practice has proved very useful.

The input section (not shown) should consist of a mains transformer with 24 V; 2.8 A secondary; a bridge rectifier (e.g. B80C2200/3300); and a 4700 μF; 40 V smoothing capacitor.

The L200 regulator should be mounted on a suitable heat sink. This device has internal short-circuit and overload protection; its pin assignment is given in Fig. 2.

2

1 = input
2 = limiting circuit
3 = ground
4 = reference voltage
5 = output
6 = ground

86448-2

---

244   CURRENT INDICATOR FOR 723

Although the Type 723 voltage regulator has been with us for quite a few years, it is still a favourite component for making simple and good quality power supplies. The 723 possesses excellent characteristics, including a highly stable output voltage, adjustable current control, and short-circuit protection, but it lacks an output for signalling the activity of the built-in current limiter.

The current limiter in the 723 consists of only one transistor, whose base and emitter are brought out to chip pins 2 and 3 respectively. When the voltage across these pins exceeds 0.5 to 0.6 V, the transistor is turned on and cuts the drive to the output tran-

sistors. In most applications, the voltage drop for the B-E junction of the current sense transistor is developed across an externally fitted resistor. In the the supply proposed here, this is either R_6, R_6//R_8, or R_6//R_9. A difficulty arises if it is intended to provide an overcurrent indication for the shutdown circuit with the aid of an external transistor fitted in parallel onto pins 2 and 3, since the external and internal transistor are highly unlikely to have precisely the same characteristics. When the internal transistor has the low B-E voltage of the two, the indication will not work, while in the other case the external transistor takes away the base current for

278

the internal transistor, so that the current limiter is rendered ineffective.

In this design of a power supply, a current overload indication was realized by fitting the external transistor with a high value base resistor, R7, to ensure that the current limiter in the 723 is not disabled. A further transistor, T3, has been added to keep the base current for T2 as low as possible. Since the base-emitter junction then has a diode characteristic, the associated voltage drop is always lower than that of the transistor internal to the 723.

The three output voltages from this supply are probably the most commonly used for testing asymmetrically fed designs: 5 volt for many TTL and CMOS circuits, 9 volt for battery operated equipment or logic circuits equipped with a 7805 regulator (this requires an input of at least 8.5 V), and 12 volt for RS232 drivers, and miscellaneous opamp or transistor based circuits. The current limiter can be set to 10 mA, 100 mA, or 1 A for safely powering experimental circuits. Power regulator T1 should be fitted with a heat sink sized at least 10 × 10 cm. LEDs D7 (green) and D8 (red) are the power on and current overload indicator, respectively.

The output voltages of the supply may not be as accurate as required, and this is mainly due to the use of resistors from the E12 series. Close tolerance is especially important in the 5 V range, since the value shown for R3 gives a theoretical output of 4.9 V. This can be increased readily by fitting a resistor in parallel with R3, until the output voltage is 5.0 V precisely. Switches S1 and S2 are preferably SPDT types with a centre position, but three-way rotary switches should also do if in both cases the centre contact is not used.

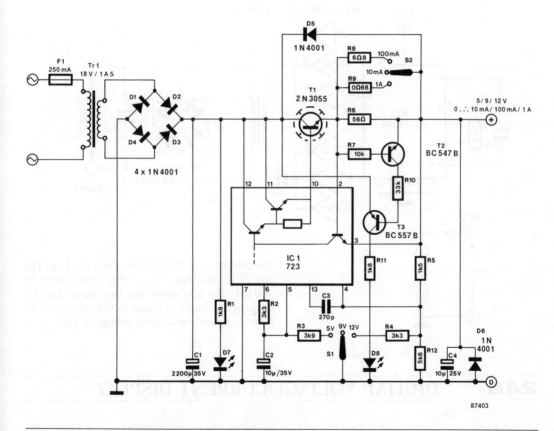

87403

245 DC/DC CONVERTER

In circuits where two signal paths must be electrically isolated, use is often made of an optocoupler. Unfortunately, these devices require two power supplies: one for the sender, and the other for the receiver. In industrial and professional undertakings this requirement is met by a proprietary

DC/DC converter. As these are by and large very expensive, they are not of very much interest to the average hobbyist. However, the do-it-yourself converter presented here is much less expensive and, moreover, easy to build.

The circuit diagram in figure 1 shows that the converter consists of an oscillator, IC1, and a driver, IC2, on the primary side, and of a rectifier, D1...D4, and buffer capacitor, C3, at the secondary.

In our prototype, operating from a 12 V battery at the maximum 74 per cent efficiency, we measured a secondary output voltage of 10.64 V, and a secondary output current of 9 mA (the corresponding primary current amounted to 10.8 mA). The secondary current should not exceed 10 mA, because the secondary output voltage then drops below

10 V and the efficiency deteriorates. That applies also to low-load conditions: when the secondary is open-circuit, the output voltage is 14 V, but the efficiency is, of course, 0 per cent! In other words: the circuit works optimally at a secondary load current of 9 mA.

Oscillator IC1 operates at a frequency of around 100 kHz. Its two output signals are each amplified in three parallel-connected buffers contained in IC2, and then applied to the primary of the isolating transformer. The voltage induced in the secondary winding is rectified and smoothed by C3. The stated value of that capacitor is more than adequate for the relatively high secondary frequency of 200 kHz. The isolating transformer is a DIY item: it is wound on a pot core of 22 mm dia. and 13 mm high with 0.35 mm dia. enamelled copper wire — 80 turns for

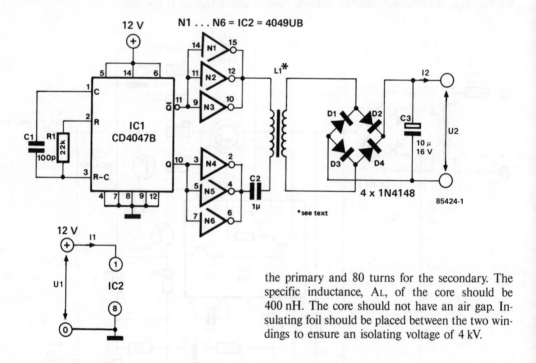

the primary and 80 turns for the secondary. The specific inductance, A_L, of the core should be 400 nH. The core should not have an air gap. Insulating foil should be placed between the two windings to ensure an isolating voltage of 4 kV.

---

246   DIGITAL VOLTAGE/CURRENT DISPLAY

This V/I display module is eminently suitable for building into an existing DC power supply, where it gives a precise indication of the set voltage or the current consumption of the load.

The circuit diagram appears in Fig. 1. The 3-digit readout is based on A/D converter Type CA3162

and BCD-to-7 segment decoder Type CA3161, both from RCA. The common anode connections of LED displays LD1-LD3 are successively connected to the positive supply line via T1-T3.

Provision has been made to select the correct position of the decimal point. In the voltage range, the

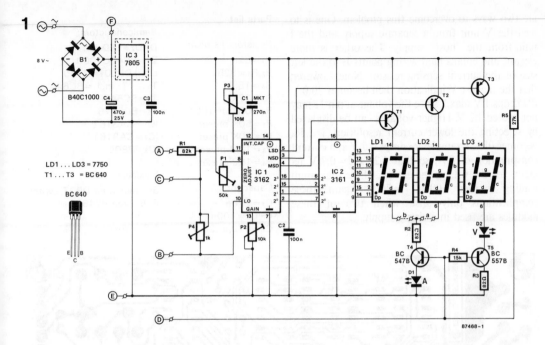

1

decimal point lights on LD₃, and the resolution is therefore 100 mV. Two current ranges are possible: 0-9.99 A (link a) or 0-0.999 (.999) A (link b). The current sensing resistor is therefore either 0R1 or 1R0—see Fig. 2. It is important that R₆ does not affect the output voltage of the supply in question. It must, therefore, be fitted ahead of the voltage divider that controls the output voltage. DPDT switch S₁ selects between voltage and current readings. When voltage measurement is selected, P₄-R₁ attenuates the input voltage by a factor 100. Also, point D is pulled low so that the decimal point on the LS display, and the "V" LED, are illuminated. When current measurement is selected, the drop across the sensing resistor is applied direct to the HI-LO inputs of DAC IC₁. The sensing resistor has such a low value as to render the voltage divider ineffective.

There are four adjustment points in the module:

P₁: current range nulling;
P₂: full-scale current calibration;
P₃: voltage range nulling;
P₄: full-scale voltage calibration.

These points should be adjusted in the above order. Two presets, P₁ and P₃, are required to ensure correct nulling of the module. P₁ compensates for the quiescent current consumption of the regulator circuit in the supply. The resulting small negative deviation in the voltage range is compensated by P₃. The V/I display module is conveniently fed from

the unregulated voltage available in the supply (max. 35 V)—see points E and F in Fig. 2; bridge rectifier B₁ may then be omitted. The minimum input voltage for IC₃ is 8 V, and this regulator should be fitted with a heat-sink if the input voltage is greater than 12 V. It is, of course, also possible to power the module from a separate 8 V; 200 mA mains transformer.

The unit can be constructed as a double to obtain simultaneous V and I readings. It should be noted, however, that the current sensing resistor is short-circuited via the ground connections when both modules are fed from the same supply. There

2

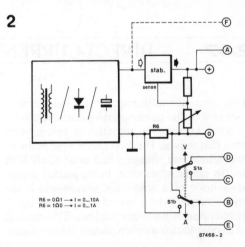

R6 = 0Ω1 → I = 0...10A
R6 = 1Ω0 → I = 0...1A

87468-2

281

are two ways to overcome this problem. One is to feed the V unit from a separate supply, and the I unit from the "host" supply. The other is more elegant and entails hard wiring points E to the left side of the current sensing resistor. Note, however, that the highest V indication then becomes 20.0 V (R_6 drops 1 V max.), since the voltage at pin 11 may not exceed 1.2 V. Higher voltages can be displayed by selecting the lower current resolution, i.e., R_6 becomes 0R1. Example: R_6 drops 0.5 V at a current consumption of 5 A, so that $1.2-0.5=0.7$ V remains for the voltage indication, whose maximum reading is then $100 \times 0.7 = 70$ V. Again, these complications only arise when two of these modules are used in a single supply.

Parts list

Resistors ($\pm 5\%$):
$R_1 = 82K$
$R_2;R_3 = 82R$
$R_4 = 15K$
$R_5 = 27K$
$R_6 = 0R1$ or $1R0^*$
$P_1 = 50K$ preset
$P_2 = 10K$ preset
$P_3 = 10M$ preset
$P_4 = 1K0$ preset

Capacitors:
$C_1 = 270n$
$C_2;C_3 = 100n$
$C_4 = 470 \mu$;25 V

Semiconductors:
$D_1;D_2 = LED$ red
$B_1 = BC40C1000$
$LD_1;LD_2;LD_3 = 7750$
$T_1 \ldots T_3$ incl. $= BC640$
$T_4 = BC547B$
$T_5 = BC557B$
$IC_1 = CA3162$
$IC_2 = CA3161$
$IC_3 = 7805$

Miscellaneous:
$S_1 =$ miniature DPDT switch.
PCB Type 87468

* See text.

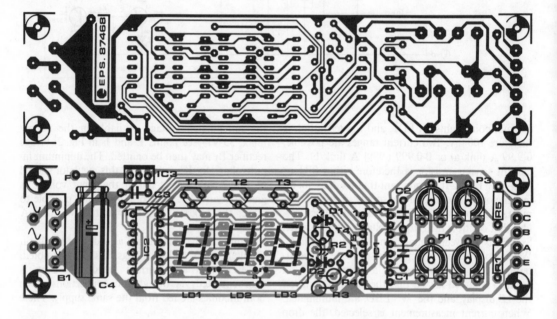

247   DIRECT-CURRENT MONITOR

Many direct-current monitor circuits use a resistor in series with the current-carrying wires, and actuate some indicator by the ensuing voltage drop across that resistor. The drop causes a reduction in the available load voltage, which at relatively high currents can be appreciable. In the present circuit, use is made of a reed relay, around which the current-carrying wire is wound a number of times. The consequent losses are minimal. This method has a bonus in that a switch contact is immediately

available for a number of applications.
One possible application is that of a low loss lamp monitor. As long as the lamp (here represented by R_L) is on, the LED lights. The number of turns depends on the relay used and the load current. As a guide, most reed relays operate at 50 ampere-turns, so that in the case of, say, a car headlight (60 W at 12 V gives a current of 5 A) about 10 turns are required.
The more complex circuit diagram shows an elec-

tronic fuse, which also offers overvoltage protection. The state of the circuit is indicated by two LEDs. When the supply is switched on, the thyristor is off, and relay Re will be energized via the 150-ohm resistor. The load will then be connected and the green LED lights.

If the load current becomes too high, the reed relay will close and trigger the thyristor via the 470-ohm resistor. The thyristor then short-circuits relay Re, which causes the load to be disconnected. At the same time, the green LED will go out and the red one will light. The circuit may be reset with S_2, which breaks the current through the thyristor and causes it to switch off.

Overvoltage protection is provided by the zener diode across the reed relay. When the input voltage becomes greater than the zener voltage and the thyristor trigger voltage, the thyristor will be triggered and switch on the protection circuit.

These two applications are primarily of use in cars, but, no doubt, ingenious readers will think of others.

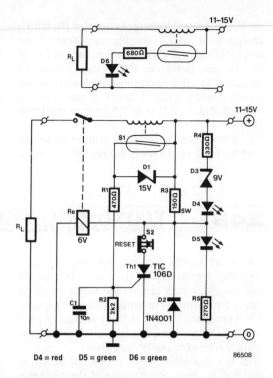

D4 = red   D5 = green   D6 = green   86508

248   DIRECT-VOLTAGE DOUBLER

A direct-voltage doubler is particularly useful when from an available supply voltage a higher one has to be derived. As the current in most such cases is pretty small, the cost of a suitable circuit can be kept down.

Astable multivibrator IC_1 is a rectangular-wave gen-

erator operating at about 8.5 kHz whose output drives transistors T_1 and T_2. When the level at pin 3 of IC_1 is low, T_1 is off and T_2 conducts. As the negative terminal of C_3 is then connected to earth, the capacitor charges via diode D_1. When the output of IC_1 is high, T_2 is off and T_1 conducts. Ca-

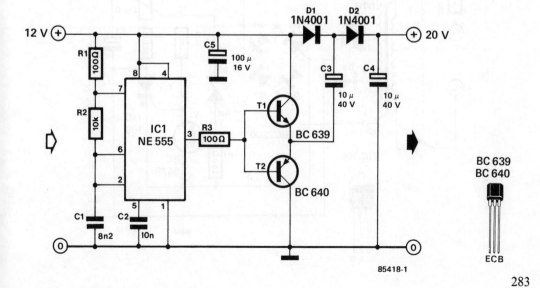

85418-1

283

pacitor C_3 cannot discharge because of D_1, but C_4 charges to a voltage roughly equivalent to the supply voltage of $+12$ V and the p.d. across C_3 and D_1. In our prototype, this voltage across C_4 amounted to 20 V approximately. The maximum current should not exceed 70 mA: at that value, the output voltage is 18 V, at an efficiency of thirty-two per cent.

We have not tested the circuit with other supply voltages, but it can be safely assumed that it can be used over the whole supply voltage range of the NE 555.

Construction is possible on a small piece of prototyping board, after which the doubler can be fitted inside the power supply unit.

If a regulated output is required, it is possible to connect an appropriate voltage regulator, for instance, in the 78LXX series, but in that case the power requirements of the regulator must, of course, be taken into consideration when the maximum load current is calculated.

249   ECONOMICAL POWER SUPPLY

The power supply described here uses a silicon-controlled rectifier (SCR) that, depending on the load current, selects taps on the secondary of the mains transformer. The output voltage of around 9 V is eminently suitable as input voltage for a 5 V regulator, which consequently works with the absolutely minimum power dissipation.

With low to medium load currents, the SCR is in the blocking state. Rectification of the secondary transformer voltage then takes place in D_1, D_2, D_5, and D_6 only. The load current flows during the positive half cycle via D_1, load, and D_5; during the negative half wave it flows through D_2, load, and

D_6. The tapped secondary voltage amounts to 8 V in either case, while a 2 V section remains unused. With increasing load current, the output voltage drops until no current flows any more through the zener diode. Transistor T_7 switches off which removes the short circuit from the gate of the SCR, which then conducts. As soon as that happens, the full secondary transformer voltage is rectified by $D_1 \ldots D_4$, while diodes D_5 and D_6 are reverse biased.

As the voltage across the zener diode is always lowest during the zero crossing of the secondary voltage, the SCR always switches on at or near that

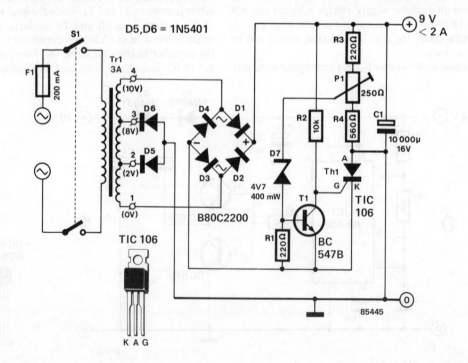

instant. This prevents high current pulses and other noise often associated with SCR switching: no further suppressors are therefore necessary.

To build this supply, you need a mains transformer with a 12 V secondary that has taps at 2 V steps: 2-4-6-8-10-12 V. For load currents up to 1.5 A, a 2 A transformer will suffice; an output current of up to 2 A requires a 3 A transformer.

250   LEAD-ACID BATTERY CHARGER

Although in electronics more NiCd than PbH_2SO_4 batteries are used (or so we're told), there is still a healthy demand for good chargers for the lead-acid types. The present one enables 6- or 12-volt types to be charged rapidly; switches itself off automatically; and is protected against thermal overload, short circuits, and polarity reversal of the battery.

If you are not fully acquainted with modern sealed lead-acid batteries, here are some of its more important properties. It may be used in any position, even upside down. The charging voltage should be 2.3 V per cell (2.45 V for fast charging): i.e., 6.9 V for a 6 V battery and 13.8 V for 12 V types. The charging current need not be limited to 0.1...1 C (=capacity in Ah — the actual figure depends on the manufacturer). The battery is charged when the charging current has dropped to 1 per cent of the capacity. Some manufacturers state that it is preferable that their batteries are charged in a horizontal position. Never charge these batteries with a NiCd battery charger!!

The circuit of the suggested charger is based on a type L200 voltage regulator which ensures a constant charging voltage. The actual level of the charging voltage is set with P_1 in the absence of a battery. Resistors R_1 and R_2 provide current limiting, but R_2 is only necessary if a charging current above 0.5 A is required or to enable the output current more precisely. The current is limited to

$[0.45(R_1+R_2)/R_1R_2]$ A; its actual value is indicated by M_1.

The L200 may be mounted on a small heat sink, but this is not strictly necessary since the device has internal thermal protection.

Normally, the battery charger works from the mains, but it can also operate from a 12 V (car) battery.

All possible situations, some of which are highly undesirable, are enumerated in table 1. The one exception is that when the battery is really flat, the table does not apply. The battery must then be seen to be connected correctly to the charging terminals.

Table 1.

condition			LED	meter
polarity correct	voltage at input		lights	400 mA
	no voltage at input		out	0 mA
polarity reversed	voltage at input		out	400 mA (!)
	no voltage at input		out	0 mA
battery not connec-ted	voltage at input		lights	0 mA
	no voltage at input		out	0 mA

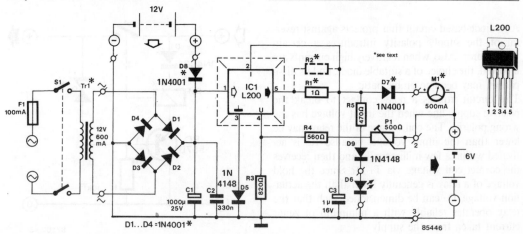

Also, the LED indication will then initially not work.

Table 2 gives some examples of 6 V batteries and circuit variations required for the different types. The charging currents here are limited to 1/10 of the battery capacity in Ah (ampere-hours): this is a safe value which is permissible under all circumstances). If the charger is required for 12 V batteries, the mains transformer must have a secondary voltage of at least 18 V, and capacitor C_1 must become a 35 V type. Furthermore, resistor R_4 should be increased to 1k8 and preset P_1 to 1 kΩ.

Table 2.

battery type	Tr_1	$D_1...D_4$ D_7,D_8	R_1	R_2	M_1
6 V 4 Ah	12 V; 0.6 A	1N4001	1 Ω	∞	0.5 A
6 V 6 Ah	12 V; 1.0 A	1N4001	1 Ω	2 Ω	1.0 A
6 V 8 Ah	12 V; 1.2 A	1N5401	1 Ω	1 Ω	1.0 A
6 V 10 Ah	12 V; 1.5 A	1N5401	0.82 Ω	0.82 Ω	1.0 A

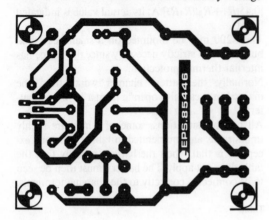

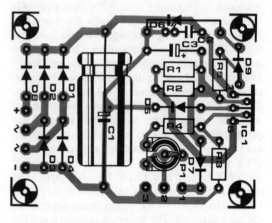

Parts list

Resistors:
R_1 = 1 Ω
R_2 = see text
R_3 = 820 Ω
R_4 = 560 Ω (see text)
R_5 = 470 Ω
P_1 = 500 Ω preset (see text)

Capacitors:
C_1 = 1000 μ/25 V (see text)
C_2 = 330 n
C_3 = 1 μ/16 V

Semiconductors:
$D_1...D_4,D_7,D_8$ = 1N4001
   (see table 2)
D_5,D_9 = 1N4148
D_6 = LED
IC_1 = L200

Miscellaneous:
M_1 = moving coil meter, 500 mA
   f.s.d.
Tr_1 = mains transformer, secondary
   12 V, 600 mA (see text)
S_1 = DPST mains on/off switch
F_1 = fuse, 100 mA, delayed action
heat sink for IC_1 (optional — see text)
PCB 85446

251   LOSS-FREE SUPPLY PROTECTOR

Any diode-based circuit that protects against reversal of the supply polarity introduces a certain voltage drop. Also, when relatively high currents are involved, the choice of a suitable diode, and its dissipation, may become problematic.

This circuit utilizes a relay contact to break the positive supply line when the input voltage has the wrong polarity. The coil voltage of the relay may be lower than the input voltage, because Re is activated within a few milliseconds, and then receives the correct coil voltage via T_1-D_1. Since the hold voltage of a relay is generally lower than the actuation voltage, D_2 can be dimensioned such that the relay operates reliably with a minimum of zener current taken from the supply.

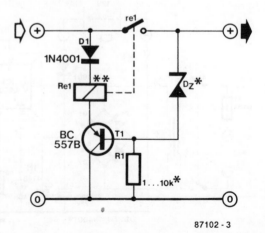

87102-3

Integrated 3-pin voltage regulators are not suitable for use where the input and output voltages are nearly equal. In fact, with most such regulators, the input voltage is typically 3 V higher than the output potential. To cater for situations where the two voltages are nearly equal, it is necessary to use discrete components. The series transistor is then connected in a common emitter circuit, so that the output voltage is lower than the input voltage only by the saturation voltage of the transistor. However, it is then difficult to provide short-circuit protection as is the case in integrated regulators. But, where there is a will, there is a way.

In Fig. 1, the series transistor obtains its base current from T_2, which together with T_1 forms a differential amplifier. This arrangement ensures that the junction of voltage divider R_4-R_5 has the same potential as the cathode of zener D_2. The crux of the circuit is that T_3 has a certain current amplification, but T_2 can only provide it with as much base current as R_2 allows. The potential difference across R_2 has a maximum value of the zener voltage minus the base-emitter voltage, U_{BE}, of T_2, which in practice is about 4 V. The maximum current through R_2 is, therefore, about 11 mA, so that, assuming that T_3 has a current amplification of 50, the maximum output current is 0.55 A. If a higher current is drawn, the output voltage will drop. If it drops below the zener voltage of D_2, the p.d. across R_2 will drop also. The result is that the output current will behave as shown by the fold-back characteristic in Fig. 2. It is clear, therefore, that the series transistor is protected against high (short-circuit) currents.

Diode D_1 and resistor R_1 provide a soft start, because the voltage across the diode, which is connected to the output of the regulator, is nought at switch-on. Since the circuit, because of the high gain, has a tendency to oscillate, capacitor C_1 is included to improve the stability.

The output voltage level, U_o, can be freely selected, within the limits of the series transistor, by D_2, R_3, and R_4, and is determined from
$U_o = U_Z(R_5 + R_4)/R_5$.

Resistor R_2 must be matched with the actual current amplification of the transistor used. The maximum dissipation of a well-cooled BD140 is of the order of 5 W. If a noise-free output is required, an additional 10 μF electrolytic capacitor should be connected in parallel with D_2. The circuit will then have a real soft start: there will be no output for about 0.2 s after switch-on.

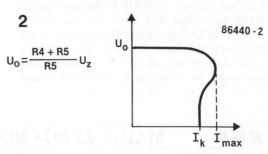

1

2

$$U_o = \frac{R4 + R5}{R5} U_z$$

86440 - 1

The unusual circuit shown in figure 1 has an unusual efficiency: according to SGS, this amounts to no less than 37 per cent at an output voltage of 3 V and output current of 2 A. With traditional secondary regulation, an efficiency of about 8 per cent would have been normal. The output voltage can be varied over the range 1.2...25 V, and the output current can be 1.5 A at any of these voltages, provided IC$_2$ is mounted on a suitable heat sink.

Another advantage of primary regulation is that the power supply is protected against variations in the mains supply. This aspect is normally ignored

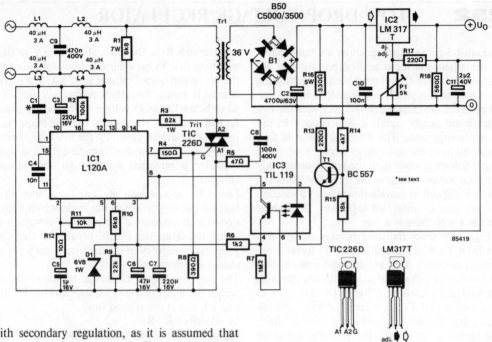

with secondary regulation, as it is assumed that primary fluctuations have no effect on the secondary regulation. The present circuit is, therefore, of particular importance for use where the mains supply is subject to large variations.

The regulation functions so that the voltage drop across voltage regulator IC_2 is held constant. This voltage drop is transferred by current source T_1 into a current through the LED in the opto-coupler. When the voltage drop diminishes, the current through the LED is smaller. The transistor in the opto-coupler gets less drive, and the voltage at pin 3 of IC_1 drops. Voltage regulator IC_1 contains a complete circuit for phase gating control with silicon-controlled rectifier Tri_1. The gating angle of this triac depends on the comparison between the direct voltage at pin 3 and an on-chip generated sawtooth signal, the frequency of which is determined by capacitor C_1 (= 100 n). In our example, the triac switches the mains voltage earlier so that buffer capacitor C_2 receives more energy.

Noise caused by the phase gating circuit must be prevented of entering the mains supply by a mains noise filter as shown.

SGS application

---

254   MAINS ZERO-CROSSING DETECTOR

Both safe and remarkably simple to construct, this circuit detects the zero crossing moments of the mains voltage, in order to provide other circuitry with timing information about the correct instant for switching mains-connected loads; in other words, when the least possible switching dissipation is involved, and, therefore, least interference is induced on the mains lines.

The proposed circuit operates direct off the mains, while comprising no more than two opto-couplers and two resistors. It is seen that photodiodes D_1 and D_2 are connected in antiparallel while being fed with the mains voltage via a resistor, which limits the current through the relevant diode to about 2 mA as it conducts (i.e. lights) during the negative or the positive half wave (D_2 or D_1 respectively) of the mains sinewave; in either case, the circuit output voltage is low, since the associated phototransistor conducts and draws current from $+ Ub$ via R_2.

However, at the moment of zero crossing, neither one of the diodes conducts, and the voltage at the circuit output rises to near +Ub level, whence the 100 Hz pulse train.

The value of R_2 may be adapted to suit the level of +Ub and the manufacturer-specified typical collector current through the phototransistor. For the Type TIL111, the current should not exceed about 50 mA. The type of optocoupler used in the circuit should not be very critical, but the value of R_1 had best be left at the indicated 100 k so as not to run into excessive diode dissipation.

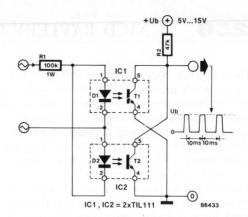

IC1, IC2 = 2×TIL111

86433

---

255   NEGATIVE SUPPLY CONVERTER

It is sometimes required in certain circuits that are powered from just one battery to derive a negative supply voltage from the positive battery potential. As the loading of such negative lines is normally pretty minimal, it is possible to use a TL 497A IC to provide the negative voltage. This saves a transformer, rectifier, and a smoothing capacitor.

The TL 497A is a switch-mode IC from Texas Instruments, that may be used as an upwards/downwards transformer, but also as a negative supply converter.

Inductor L makes it all possible, because when the on-chip transistor is switched off, a fairly large back-e.m.f. is generated across L, which causes a negative potential at the emitter of the transistor. The diode then conducts, and capacitor C_F charges. The output voltage, U_o, is determined by

$$U_o = [-U_b t_i / t_o] V$$

where U_b is the supply voltage; t_i is the time the transistor is switched on; t_o is the time the transistor is switched off. Period t_i is determined by the value of C_T.

The output voltage is devided across $R1$ and $R2$ and applied to the inverting input of an on-chip comparator, whose +input is a 1.2 V reference voltage. When the actual value of U_o lies below the wanted value, the comparator toggles and switches on the oscillator, which in turn drives the transistor. The TL 497A also contains a current limiting circuit which ensures that the coil cannot be saturated and that that transistor is not affected by voltage spikes.

Coil L may be any fixed inductor with a value of 100...500 μH.

The output voltage is calculated from

$$U_o = -[N + 1.2] V$$

where N is the numerical value of $R2$ in kilohms. The output current should not exceed 50 mA.

Texas Instruments Application

289

Quite arguably, Nickel Cadmium (NiCd) batteries are frequently used as replacements for disposable types of battery; this is possible because they can be inserted readily in the existing battery compartment and supply the same voltage as disposable batteries. The fact that one need not go out to purchase (relatively expensive) batteries puts the rechargeable cells in an advantageous position.

However, one drawback of the use of rechargeable batteries is the need to remove them from the equipment any time their charge is exhausted. It would, therefore, be convenient to leave them where they are, i.e. in the battery compartment, as they receive the charge current.

Two circuits are suggested for the incorporation in existing battery-operated equipment. Figure 1 shows the absolute minimum in the form of a simple current source. The reference voltage is obtained from the forward drop across LED D_1 (about 1.5 V for a red LED). R_2 fixes the current through the LED, and the voltage at the base of T_1 is therefore about 1.5 V lower than the positive supply rail. The voltage across R_1 is about 0.85 V, and this value may be used to determine the charge current for the battery, since $I_B=0.85R_1$, independent of the circuit supply voltage.

The value of R_1 is thus readily calculated if it is known that most NiCd batteries are preferably charged with a current of one tenth their capacity in amperes per hour (Ah). A number of the more popular battery types and associated values for R_1 have been listed in Table 1.

A noteworthy aspect of the circuit is the fact that LED D_1 will go out in the absence of a battery, since the voltage across R_1 inevitably drops; the

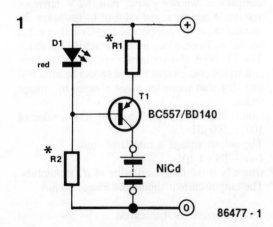

1

86477 - 1

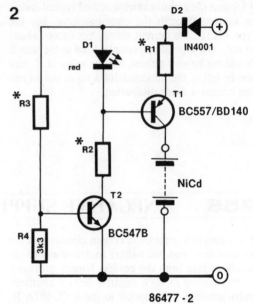

2

86477 - 2

Table 1.

battery type		size	capacity [mAh]	charge current [mA]	R_1 [Ω]
9 V block			110	11	82
lady	R1	N	180	18	47
micro	RO3	AAA	180	18	47
penlight (mignon)	R6	AA	500	50	15
baby	R14	C	1200	120	6.8
			1800	180	4.7
mono	R20	D	4000	400	2.2

Table 2.

number of cells	V_{in} (min.)	R_2 [Ω]	R_3 [Ω]
2	5	270	22
3	6	330	27
4	7.5	470	39
5	9	560	47
6	10	680	56
7	12	820	68

LED current which used to flow through R_2 will now pass through R_1 and the base-emitter junction of T_1.

The elaborated version of the NiCd charger, shown in Fig. 2, includes a diode to protect the circuit from being damaged by input voltages having the wrong polarity. R_3, R_4 and T_2 have been incorporated to disable the charger in the absence of a sufficiently high input voltage; Table 2 lists the relevant values for R_2 and R_3, given the number of 1.2 V cells contained in the NiCd battery.

Almost any type of silicon PNP transistor in the BC series should work satisfactorily in the T_1 position if the charge current does not exceed about 100 mA. Higher input voltages and/or charge currents are, however, better handled by a medium-power transistor from the BD series.

The input voltage to the charger need not be elaborately regulated or smoothed; in fact, any type of inexpensive adapter providing the necessary direct output voltage and current may be used. Depending on the number of cells contained in the NiCd battery, the charge current may also be obtained from the 12 V car battery.

The circuits as shown are readily fitted on a small piece of veroboard to suit incorporation in the relevant equipment; the input voltage to the charger is conveniently connected to a small plug or socket fitted onto the cabinet.

257 ONE-CHIP DC CONVERTER

This DC step-up circuit may prove useful for the incorporation in equipment that requires the presence of a supply voltage in excess of the normal circuit supply rail of, for instance, $+5$ V. Ideal therefore for generating the necessary $+8\ldots12$ V voltage to feed RS232 transmitter devices, or the $+25$ V programming voltage for EPROMs, the Type L497 DC converter requires very few additional passive parts to produce any of the output voltages listed in the table below.

As to the components in support of the converter chip, note L_1, which is a small coil, readily made by winding about 85 turns of 34 SWG (ϕ 0.2 mm) enamelled copper wire on a small (11 × 7 mm) pot core having an Al rating of 160, e.g. the Siemens Type 6531-L160-A48. The total inductance of L_1 should be of the order of 100 μH. Resistor R_1 must be dimensioned as indicated in the table for any of the no-load output voltages. Note that the voltage across R_2 is fixed at 1.2 V, and that the value of R_1 may therefore be computed from $R_1 = (V_{out} - 1.2)$ $<k\Omega>$.

Finally, the output current may, of course, be boosted by means of a medium power transistor in a suitable configuration at the V_0 output.

V_i	V_o*	I_i (max)	R_1▼
5	10	125	8.8
5	15	80	13.8
5	20	60	18.8
5	25	50	23.8
$<V>$	$<V>$	$<mA>$	$<k\Omega>$

* Specifies no-load output voltage.
▼ Theoretical value; select nearest E12 or E24 value.

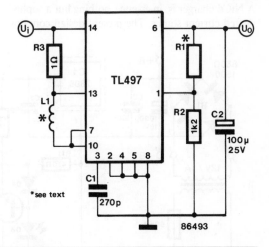

258 PRECISION RECTIFIER

This precision rectifier operates from an asymmetrical supply, handles input signals up to 3 V_{pp} and has a frequency range that extends from DC to about 2 kHz. Its amplification is unity, and depends mainly on the ratio R_4/R_3. Opamp A_1 is connected as a voltage amplifier ($A_0 = 1$), A_2 as an inverting amplifier ($A_0 = -1$). Opamp A_2, transistor T_1 and

diode D_2 ensure that the output voltage, U_2, is identical to the positive excursions of the input voltage, U_1. When U_1 is positive, the output of A_1 is held low at about 0.25 V, so that T_2 is disabled and can not affect the rectified output signal.

Components R_2 and D_1 protect the pnp input stage in A_2 against negative voltages, which are effectively limited to —0.6 V. For negative excursions of the input signal, the function of A1, T2 and D2 is similar to the previously mentioned components. The peak output voltage of the rectifier circuit is determined mainly by the maximum output swing of the opamps and the voltage drop across the transistors plus D2: this amcunts to about 3 V in all. When the circuit is not driven, it consumes about 1 mA, and is therefore eminently suitable for building into portable, battery-operated equipment.

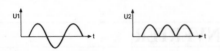

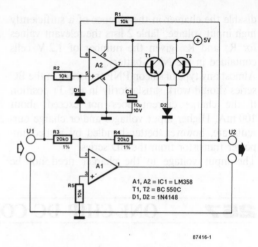

A1, A2 = IC1 = LM358
T1, T2 = BC 550C
D1, D2 = 1N4148

87416-1

259   SIMPLE NICD CHARGER

Dry batteries have one major disadvantage: they go flat. Rechargeable types, such as NiCd cells, also suffer from this drawback, but they can at least be recharged. Sometimes even a fifteen minute charge is sufficient to give enough life to, say, an electronic flash battery.
A NiCd charger is, in essence, nothing but a sophisticated current source. The present design contains four such sources with a common control switch, but each with a separate LED that lights as soon as a battery is connected to it.
In position 1, the sources each provide a current of about 90 mA; in positions 2 and 3 values of between 100 and 300 mA as required. Note, however, that with charging currents above about 200 mA the transistors must be fitted on suitable heat sinks.

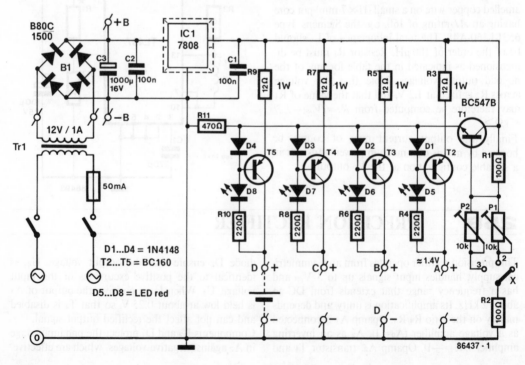

B80C 1500

IC1 7808

C3 1000µ 16V
C2 100n
C1 100n

R9 12Ω 1W
R7 12Ω 1W
R5 12Ω 1W
R3 12Ω 1W

BC547B
T1

12V / 1A
Tr1

50mA

R11 470Ω

D4 T5
D3 T4
D2 T3
D1 T2

R1 100Ω

D8
D7
D6
D5

R10 220Ω
R8 220Ω
R6 220Ω
R4 220Ω

P2 P1
10k 10k

D1...D4 = 1N4148
T2...T5 = BC160

≈1.4V

D +
C +
B +
A +

X

D5...D8 = LED red

D

R2 100Ω

86437 - 1

On stability considerations, it is advisable to mount diodes D₁ to D₄ incl. in good thermal contact with the relevant transistors.

Terminals +B and −B enable the circuit to operate from a 12 V DC source, such as a car battery, in situations where a mains supply is not available.

Modern NiCd cells can be given a fast charge without any problems. The present unit can charge Type AA (=HP7=R6) cells in about 8 hours (position 1=90 mA); Type C (=HP11=R14) cells in 10-14 hours (position 2=180 mA); and Type D (=HP2=R20) in 20 hours (position 3=200 mA).

260   SIMPLE ZERO CROSSING DETECTOR

Zero crossing detectors are often contained in rather complex circuits, or they are part of an integrated circuit, the rest of which is not required. Basically, such a detector is required to give a pulse every time the mains voltage passes through the zero potential. The detector proposed here is very simple indeed: the mains voltage is transformed down, rectified in D₁, and smoothed by C₁ to give a direct voltage of 17 V. Part of the mains voltage is taken from across R₂ and used to drive transistors T₁...T₃ During positive half cycles T₁ conducts and T₂ and T₃ are off, whereas negative half cycles switch on T₂ and T₃ while T₁ is off. When the momentary voltage across R₂ lies between +0.6 V and −0.6 V, none of the transistors conducts, so that the output voltage is high. In this way, a short positive pulse is produced every time the mains voltage passes through zero potential. Since operation is direct

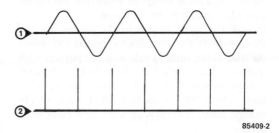

85409-2

from the mains, there is no phase shift caused by the usual isolating transformer.

Where the direct voltage output of the circuit is used for supplying external circuits, attention should be paid to the current required by those circuits and the rating of the transformer. It may also be necessary to increase the value of C₁.

Finally, remember that the circuit and, therefore, any external units are connected direct to the mains!

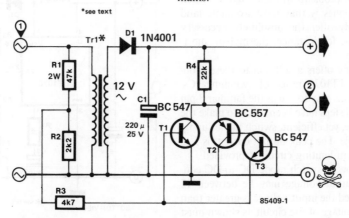

85409-1

261   SUPPLY PROTECTION

The use of external mains voltage adaptors for cassette recorders, portable radios, home computers, pocket calculators, and so on, is common practice since the typical enclosure sizes of this type of electronic equipment either does not allow the incor-

poration of a mains supply, or the device has been primarily intended for battery operation.

Unfortunately, the degree of idiosyncrasy among manufacturers of adaptors is rather high; a standard for adaptor output voltage and output polarity is definitely hard to find. It may, therefore, be quite risky to power, say, the home computer from an adaptor which is not tailored to this (expensive) piece of electronic equipment.

Here is a simple circuit to prevent a lot of trouble; its extremely low cost fully justifies incorporation in any equipment operated from an external DC supply. The supply protection consists of a mere four parts and a fuse, which may already be incorporated in the equipment. The zener diode is selected to have a zener voltage of about one volt higher than the equipment supply voltage.

In case the input voltage to the circuit has the wrong polarity, the zener diode conducts and causes the triac to fire, since its gate is driven positive with respect to MT2; the current flow through the triac is sufficiently high to look like a short-circuit to the fuse, which duly melts and breaks the supply voltage, before damage is inflicted upon equipment parts.

Operation of the circuit in an overvoltage condition is even simpler, since in that case the zener also supplies the gate of the triac with a firing voltage.

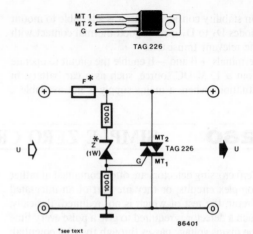

Obviously, if everything is in perfect order, the protection circuit is as if non-existent to the equipment it is part of, because it introduces no additional voltage drop. Finally, the only modification to the circuit for use in positive-earth equipment involves insertion of the fuse in the negative-supply line.

262   SWITCH MODE POWER SUPPLY

One of the major problems in the design of switch mode power supplies is that most available (and suitable) ICs only offer the absolutely necessary facilities and not, for instance, thermal or short-circuit protection.

Linear Technology offers a solution to these problems with their LT1070 range of switching ICs. These devices are as easy to use as the familiar 3-pin regulator ICs. All steps have been taken to make the design of a simple, yet efficient, switch mode supply as easy as possible. The peak output current is 5 to 9 A, and a current-limiting circuit is provided.

The diagram shows a switch mode DC-to-DC converter, whose output voltage may lie between 12 and 48 V, provided the input voltage is greater than 3 V. The input voltage of the circuit as shown must always be lower than the output voltage. It is, however, possible to modify the circuit to obtain an output voltage that is lower than the input voltage. One of the modifications is replacing L1 by a suitable transformer.

The output current is dependent on the value of the input voltage. For an input voltage of 3 V, the output power is 10 watts maximum. Our prototype, operating from 3 V, delivered about 50 mA at 48 V,

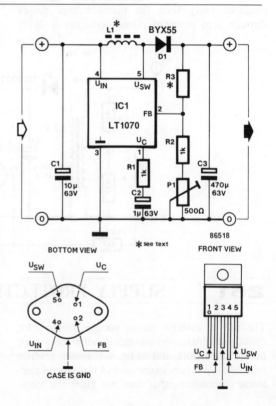

while at an input voltage of 24 V the output current was over 1 A.

In the construction, account must be taken of high peak currents: all connections should, therefore, be short, and the input and output lines should be SWG20 (0.8 mm ∅) or thicker. This also applies to the earth connections.

It should also be noted that spikes are present on the output voltage. If necessary, these may be eliminated by an LC filter, the inductance of which has the same value as L_1, and the capacitance is between 10 and 100 μF. The quality of the capacitor is of importance because of the required low series resistance for RF signals.

263   VARIABLE 3 A POWER SUPPLY

As far as construction is concerned, this is a real mini power supply, but it can deliver up to 3 A at an output voltage of 1.25...25 V. Note, however, that integrated voltage regulator IC_1 has on-chip overload protection that comes into operation when the dissipation in the device reaches 30 W. The ADJ(ust) pin of the regulator is connected to the junction of potential divider R_1-P_1 The output voltage, U_o, is calculated from

$$U_o = [1.25 \ (1 \ + \ P_1/R_1)] \ V$$

where P_1 and R_1 are in ohms (the value of P_1 is measured between the wiper and the junction with R_1, i.e., 0...2.5 kΩ).

Capacitor C_1 is a conventional filter capacitor, while C_2 and C_3 improve the regulation. Protection diodes D_1 and D_2 ensure that at switch-off the potential at the output of IC_1 is more positive than that at its input. The value of R_1 has been chosen to ensure that the minimum load current through IC_1 is about 3.5 A.

It is essential that IC_1 is mounted on a heat sink rated at about 1 K/W — do not scrimp on the heat conducting paste!

When only low output voltages are needed, it makes sense to use a mains transformer with a lower secondary voltage (for U_o = 5 V, the secondary voltage should be 9 V). When a 24 V secondary is used, and the required output voltage is 1.25 V, the maximum output current is 1 A, otherwise the maximum dissipation of the LM 350 is exceeded, and the internal protection will switch off the regulator. When the secondary voltage is 9 V, and U_o = 1.25 V, the maximum load current amounts to 2.5 A.

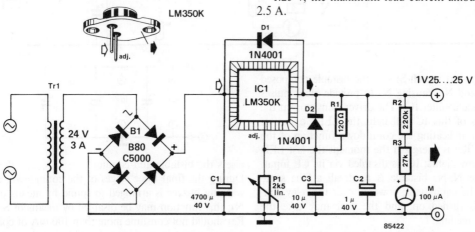

264   VISIBLE POWER-ON DELAY

While in the process of repairing or testing electronic equipment, it is often desired to have more time available for hooking up an oscilloscope probe or test lead to the part in question, after power has been applied.

This circuit gives you plenty of time to reach any component in the circuit, since the equipment is only switched on after a fixed interval following depression of the start button.

The basic operation of the circuit is as follows. Ac-

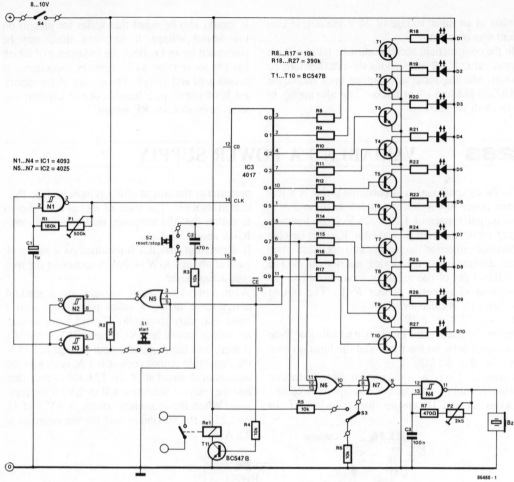

R8...R17 = 10k
R18...R27 = 390k

T1...T10 = BC547B

N1...N4 = IC1 = 4093
N5...N7 = IC2 = 4025

IC3
4017

86488 - 1

tivating start switch S_1 sets the bistable composed of N_2 and N_3, causing N_3 to provide clock pulses to decade counter IC_3. The driver transistors at the outputs of this IC will light the LEDs one after another, indicating the countdown function of the circuit. Re_1 is energized the moment the last LED in the row lights; IC_3 is disabled via its $\overline{CE}$ input, and the N_2-N_3 bistable is reset, all at the same time. The equipment, powered over the relay contacts, is turned on, and the user may take the desired reading.

The power-on interval may be restarted or interrupted during countdown by depressing S_2, which

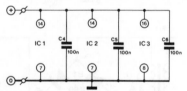

resets the bistable and counter.

During the final three stages of the countdown, a warning buzzer is arranged to sound by means of N_4; this function may be disabled by means of S_3. Re_1 should not consume more than 100 mA of coil current, while its contact(s) should be rated to suit the load to be switched.

265   VOLTAGE INVERTER

Here is a circuit that produces a negative voltage from a positive one, for instance, from $+5$ V to -10 V. The output voltage, U_o, is determined from

$$U_o = -1.2(R_1/R_2 + 1) \quad [V]$$

As in other, similar circuits, the maximum output current depends on the ratio between input and output voltage and is calculated from

$$I_{o(max)} = 500/(R_1/R_2 + 1) \quad [mA]$$

The choke is readily made with a 17.5 mm pot core on which 85 turns of 0.2 mm² enamelled copper wire are close-wound.

The maximum input voltage to the IC is 15 V. Efficiency is of the order of 60 per cent.

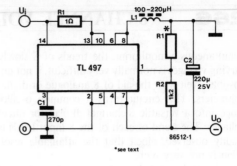

266   8-CHANNEL VOLTAGE DISPLAY

Simultaneously monitoring the trends of 8 slowly varying voltages is normally very difficult, if not impossible, even with the aid of 8 analogue or digital voltmeters. This circuit turns a common oscilloscope into a versatile 8-channel display for direct voltages. The trend of each of the 8 input levels is readily observed, albeit that the attainable resolution is not very high.

The circuit diagram shows the use of an 8-channel analogue multiplexer, IC_1, which is the electronic version of an 8-way rotary switch with contacts X_0-X_7 and pole Y. The relevant channel is selected by applying an binary code to the A-B-C inputs. Example: binary code 011 (A-B-C) enables channel 7 ($X_6 \rightarrow Y$). The A-B-C inputs of IC_1 are driven from three successive outputs of binary counter IC_2, which is set to oscillate at about 50 kHz with the aid of P_1 As the counter is not reset, the binary state of outputs Q_5, Q_6 and Q_7 steps from 0 to 7 in a cyclic manner. Each of the direct voltages at input terminals 1 to 8 is therefore briefly connected to the Y input of the oscilloscope. All eight input levels can be seen simultaneously by setting the timebase of the scope in accordance with the time it takes the counter to output states 0 through 7 on the Q_5-Q_6-Q_7 outputs. The correct starting time for the oscilloscope trace is ensured by using the Q_8 output of the counter to supply the trigger pulse. Diodes D_1 and D_2 provide for some space between adjacent bars on the display, and create a horizontal reference line. The timebase on the scope should be set to 0.5 ms/div, and triggering should occur on the

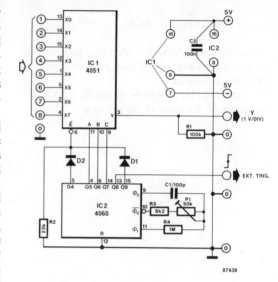

positive edge of the external signal. Set the vertical sensitivity to 1 V/div. The input range of this circuit is from —4 V to + 4 V, and connected channels are terminated in about 100K.

Adjusting the 8-channel voltage display is straightforward. Simply select the previously mentioned scope settings, and adjust P_1 to make all 8 channels visible over the full width of the scope screen—see the accompanying photograph.

The circuit has a modest current demand of less than 5 mA from a simple ± 5 V supply, or from two 4.5 V flatpack batteries.

267   AUDIO TESTER

A simple millivoltmeter and an equally simple sine wave generator are ideal instruments for checking and testing audio equipment. The audio tester combines the two, as shown in figure 1, where A_1 and A_2 form the millivoltmeter circuit, while the sine wave generator is built from A_3 and A_4.

As the audio tester is supplied (asymmetrically) from a 9 V battery, this supply must be halved for the operational amplifiers. This is essentially done by zener diode D_7. This zener is biased by R_6, and the reference voltage is taken from the junction of diodes D_8-D_9 via resistor R_7. The reference voltage is, therefore, about 5.3 V. The constant voltage drop across the two diodes is applied across preset P_3

which serves to negate the offset voltage of A_2 (enabling the millivoltmeter to be calibrated to zero). The input signal is applied across high pass filter C_1/R_1 to the non-inverting input of A_1. For all practical purposes, this sets the input impedance at 1 MΩ. Note that the circuit is fully driven with an input signal of 50 mV$_{rms}$. Higher inputs necessitate a voltage divider at the input or a reduction in gain in A_1 by dropping the value of R_3. When this resistor is reduced to 6k8, for instance, the gain of A_1 is 2, and the input sensitivity is 275 mV$_{rms}$.

Full-scale deflection of the meter is set by P_1 Opamp A, together with diodes $D_3 \ldots D_6$, functions as an active full-wave rectifier. The meter is connec-

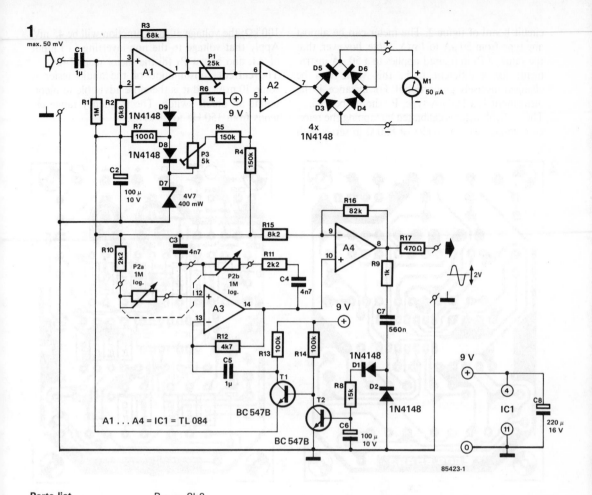

85423-1

Parts list

Resistors:

R_1 = 1 M
R_2 = 6k8
R_3 = 68 k
R_4, R_5 = 150 k
R_6, R_9 = 1 k
R_7 = 100
R_8 = 15 k
R_{10}, R_{11} = 2k2
R_{12} = 4k7
R_{13}, R_{14} = 100 k
R_{15} = 8k2
R_{16} = 82 k
R_{17} = 470 Ω
P_1 = 25 k preset (see text)
P_2 = 1 M stereo preset, log.
P_3 = 5 k preset

Capacitors:

C_1, C_5 = 1 μ metallized plastic foil
C_2, C_6 = 100 μ/10 V
C_3, C_4 = 4n7
C_7 = 560 n
C_8 = 220 μ/16 V

Semiconductors:

$D_1 \ldots D_6, D_8, D_9$ = 1N4148
D_7 = zener diode 4V7/0,4 W
T_1, T_2 = BC 547B
IC_1 = TL084

Miscellaneous:

M1 = moving coil meter, 50 μA (see text)
PP3 (9 V) battery with dual miniature clip
SPST on/off switch (optional — see text)
PCB 84923

ted in of the diagonals of the diode bridge. To ensure that even small AC voltages can be measured, the potentials at both inputs of A_2 must be absolutely equal. Because of this, a small offset voltage is applied to the non-inverting input via R_5.

The sine wave generator is essentially a Wien bridge oscillator, A_2, whose frequency determining compo-

nents are P_2 C_3, and C_4. To ensure stable operation, an active feedback loop takes part of the output signal of buffer amplifier A_4, rectifies this (D_1, D_2) and applies the consequent DC voltage to the inverting input of A_3 via buffer stages T_1 and T_2. The output voltage of the generator section is 2 V_{pp}. The audio tester is best constructed on the printed circuit board of figure 2. The meter can be almost any type from 50 μA to 1 mA. Note, however, that the value of P_1 in figure 1 applies to a 50 μA instrument; for a different f.s.d., this value can be changed inversely proportional. For instance, if the instrument is a 500 μA type, P_1 should be 2k5.

The millivoltmeter is calibrated by tapping the reference voltage with a divider of 820 Ω in series with 100 kΩ: the voltage at their junction will be 45 mV. Apply that voltage to the non-inverting (+) input of A1, and adjust P_1 till the meter reads "45".

The current consumption of the audio tester is some 10 mA, and it is therefore advisable to incorporate an on/off switch. The frequency range extends from 150 Hz to 20 kHz.

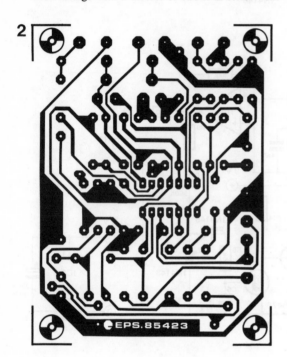

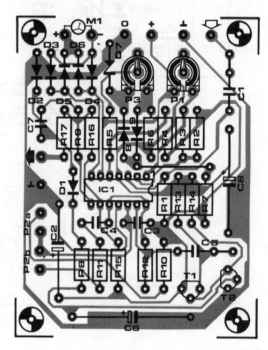

268   AUTOMATIC SWITCH OFF

If you are one of the many who frequently forget to switch off their digital multimeter, this circuit is for you.

When this little circuit, which is intended to be incorporated in the multimeter, is switched on, capacitor C_1 is connected to the +9 V line via D_1. Since C_1 is discharged, the gate of T_3 is also at +9 V which causes T_3 and T_2 to conduct. The meter is then switched on.

Capacitor C_1 slowly charges via R_2. After about 2 or 3 minutes, the potential at the gate of T_3 becomes too low to keep the FET in conduction. Transistor T_2 then also switches off, and the battery is disconnected from the multimeter.

Transistor T_1 ensures that when the multimeter is switched off manually, capacitor C_1 is discharged.

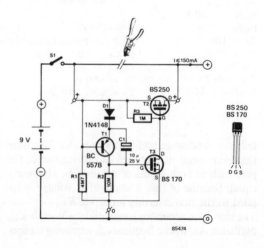

When the multimeter on/off switch, S_1, is opened, a base current will flow to the negative terminal of C_1 via R_1 and R_2. Transistor T_1 then conducts and discharges C_1. The circuit is thus immediately ready for use again. Without T_1, there would have to be a delay of a few minutes before the circuit could be switched on again.

The circuit is best built on a small piece of vero board and then fitted between the on/off switch and the meter itself.

A final tip: T_2 could be replaced by a Darlington, such as a BC516, in which case a $1\,M\Omega$ resistor would have to be inserted in the connection to the drain of T_3. This arrangement would have the advantage that the BC516 is more easily obtainable than the BS250, but the disadvantage of causing a slightly larger voltage drop across the circuit: 0.8 V as compared with less than 0.1 V when a BS250 is used. The current in both cases is 10 mA.

269   CALIBRATION GENERATOR

A calibration generator is of particular use with many older generation receivers, which have no, or a poor, frequency read-out. However, the RF section of these receivers is invariably far superior to that of most modern models, and consequently there are still many of these 'oldies' in use.

The circuit in the accompanying diagram provides calibration signals at multiples of 100 kHz and 1 MHz, all of which are available simultaneously, so that no switching is necessary.

The output signal of the crystal oscillator, T_1, is divided by 10 in IC_1. Astable N_1 operates at a fre-

quency of around 22 Hz, which is low enough to allow zero beat tuning even in SSB operation. The 100 kHz harmonics sound (on AM) like a sort of woodpecker.

Astable N_3 operates at about 1.5 kHz and is gated with the 22 Hz signal. Consequently, the 1 MHz signal appears for 22 ms as a carrier wave, which is modulated with the 1.5 kHz signal during the next 22 ms. This signal is also easily tuned for zero beat. The circuit is usable up to 30 MHz when CMOS devices are used, and up to around 300 MHz with HCMOS ICs.

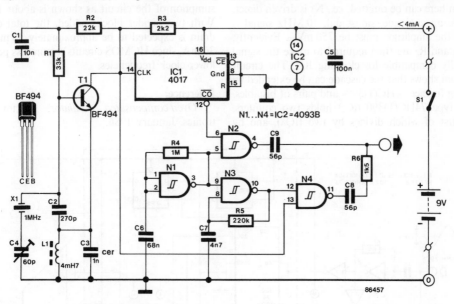

270   CRYSTAL TESTER

Many electronics hobbyists have crystals lying about, but don't know whether these are still working all right. The crystal tester described here will

quickly show whether a crystal can be used or should be discarded.

Transistor T_1 and the crystal under test form an oscillator. Capacitors C_1 and C_2 form a voltage divider in the oscillator circuit. If the crystal is in good order, the oscillator will work. Its output voltage is then rectified and smoothed by D_1 and C_4 respectively. The resulting direct voltage at the base of T_2 is sufficient to switch this transistor on, so that the LED lights.

The circuit is suitable for use with crystals of a frequency between 100 kHz and 30 MHz. Current consumption is about 50 mA.

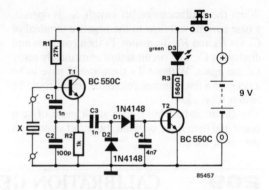

271   DIVIDER CASCADE

This circuit can be driven either with an analogue, or a digital precision 10 MHz signal for dividing down to a number of commonly used timebase periods. The oscillator proposed in [1] is particularly suitable for driving the present cascade, since it offers excellent stability thanks to the use of 1 10 MHz quartz crystal fitted in an electronically controlled oven. It should be noted, however, that its output is digitally compatible, so that components R_1-C_1 and R_2 at the input of the circuit shown here can be omitted, i.e., N_1 is driven direct. Where an analogue, sinusoidal, 10 MHz signal is used, the amplitude must be 750 mV$_{pp}$. Evidently, R_1-C_1 and R_2 are then required to make the signal digitally compatible for clocking IC_3. The circuit diagram shows that the cascade can be extended by adding further 74HC(T)390s and pairs of bistables. The Type 74HC(T)390 (IC_3) holds two counters, the first of which divides by two ($1Q_A$), and by

5 ($1Q_C$). Bistable FF_1 is driven with the $1Q_D$ output, and outputs the :10 signal, which is also applied to the CLK inputs of the second counter in IC_3. This also divides by 2 and 5, while FF_2 gives a total division factor of 100 in the first block of the cascade. The use of decade counters results in output periods commonly used for an oscilloscope timebase. Counters and bistables may be added to obtain relatively long, yet accurately defined, periods for specific applications. The current consumption of the circuit as shown is about 12 mA. With two divider blocks added, the total current drain is expected to be approximately 25 mA, not 36 mA, since HCMOS circuits require less power at lower clock frequencies.

Reference:
[1] *Oven-compensated oscillator*. Elektor Electronics, January 1986.

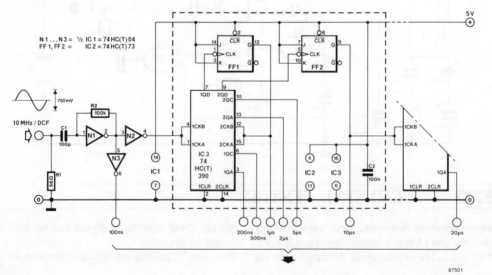

FAST VOLTAGE-CONTROLLED PULSE GENERATOR

Certain measuring and process control applications require pulse generator sections which are to operate over a large frequency range and must, therefore, produce a signal with very low pulse width. It is for this reason that the proposed circuit uses high-speed complementary MOS (HCMOS) type gates; the prototype typically produced an output pulse width of 20 ns over the frequency range of several hundred hertz to 25 MHz.

The combination IC_1-T_1 is a voltage-controlled current source which discharges C_2. The fast charging of this capacitor is effected through the voltage at

the output of Schmitt trigger N_1-R_3-D_1. The lower frequency limit of the proposed circuit mainly depends on the offset voltage of opamp IC_1. In order to enable setting the lower frequency limit, T_1 must be arranged so as not to draw any current at an input voltage of 0V; to this end, offset preset P_1 should be correctly adjusted. Finally, the output pulse width may be widened by increasing the capacitance of C_2; this will not alter the attainable sweep range.

Literature: E Abbel, Electronic Design 18 (1984), pp 270-271.

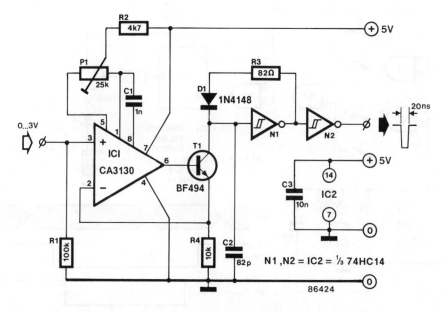

FAULTFINDING PROBE FOR μPs

Anyone who has ever tried to faultfind in a microprocessor system with a test probe will have experienced the uselessness of it. This is because the signals at the address, data, and control buses are constantly — and rapidly — changing. This means that it is not just the signal level that is important, but also the instant the signals are present. For faultfinding properly, you need a logic analyser, which is capable of indicating several signals simultaneously.

If you have no logic analyser, the probe presented

here may provide the solution. Strictly speaking, this is nothing more than a bistable multivibrator (FF₁). Data are simply read direct and cause D₁ to light or stay out, depending on the state of FF₁. The bistable only reads at the instant its clock input (pin 3) switches from low to high).

The clock signal is thus the key for all measurements carried out with the probe and that means it must be chosen with some care for every test. Suppose you have to check whether a certain portion of memory is all right. The $\overline{CE}$ signal in the memory is then connected to the QUAL input of the probe. Switch S4 must be closed, because $\overline{CE}$ is active low. The probe can then only read data during a $\overline{CE}$ of the RAM under test. The CLK input of the probe is connected to the $\overline{RD}$ signal of the memory. Reading must then be carried out during the trailing, i.e., the positive-going, edge. Switch S1 must, therefore, be closed. Reading is effected by, for instance, a PEEK command in BASIC. Diode D1 will then light in accordance with the signal emanating from the RAM during this process.

Be careful that this BASIC is not used by the RAM section being tested, because then there will be more than one read process and the probe will only retain the last of these. There is no easy solution in that case, but often it will be possible with the aid

of a monitor to make the microcomputer execute only one command in machine language.

To keep the probe small, DIL (dual in line) switches are used in the S1...S4 positions. Note that only S1 or S2 and S3 or S4 should be closed simultaneously at any one time.

LS type ICs may be used, but as these put a relatively high load on the circuit during tests, HCT types are better. These are fully compatible with the LS types but have high impedance inputs. HC types should only be used where systems are already executed entirely in CMOS; the supply voltage can then be higher than 5 V.

Current consumption of the circuit is small: 10 mA for the LED and and 5 mA for the ICs (if these are TTL).

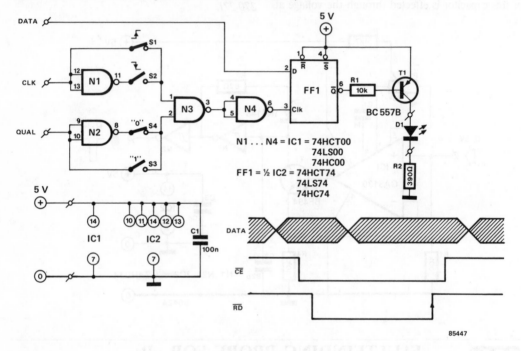

85447

---

274   FUNCTION GENERATOR

This is a downright simple design for an AF function generator that supplies a rectangular and triangular signal, and can be fed from a single 9 V supply. The signal generator proper is a Type TLC272 dual CMOS opamp from Texas Instruments. This chip is remarkable for its low current consumption and wide operating range.

The circuit is essentially composed of two functional parts. Opamp A1 is connected to function as a Schmitt-trigger whose toggle point is set to 4.5 V,

while A2 is an integrator that converts the rectangular signal from A1 into a triangular waveform. The oscillation frequency of the circuit is fixed solely by the ratio R/C and can be calculated from $f_0 = R_2/4RR_1C$. Resistor R may be replaced by the combination of the 10K resistor and 100K potentiometer as shown to effect continuous adjustment of the output frequency within the AF signal band. The generator should not be terminated in less than 10K.

304

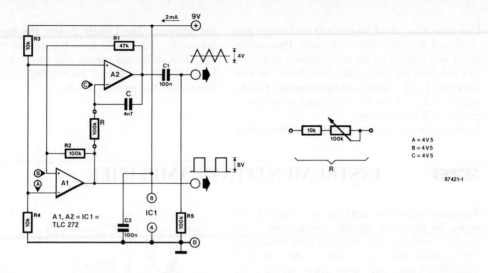

275   GHZ PRESCALER

In the *1.2 GHz input stage* (February 1985) for the microprocessor-controlled frequency counter, we used an SB8755 prescaler in the IC_7 position. This IC, which divides the 100...1200 MHz signal at input C by 512, is perfect for the purpose, but is rather expensive. Just recently, another prescaler, which is much cheaper and more sensitive, has come onto the market: the U665B from Telefunken. The U665B is a 1024 prescaler with integral pre-amplifier. Its sensitivity is better than 10 mV$_{rms}$ for frequencies between 80 MHz and 900 MHz. It is fully usable up to 1200 MHz, but its sensitivity drops to about 30...40 mV$_{rms}$ at that frequency.

To fit the U665B onto the PCB, first remove existing IC_7, IC_8, and P_3. No other components should be removed because, although they may look superfluous, they are needed for the interconnection between the component and track sides of the board.

The new IC is fitted so that its pin 1 coincides with pin 8 of the previous IC_7. Next, solder capacitors

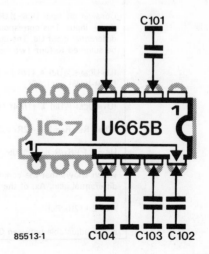

C_{101}, C_{102}, C_{103}, and C_{104} direct to the relevant pins of the new IC and to the earth plane. Then, solder pins 4 and 6 direct to the earth plane and place a wire link between pin 8 of the U665B and the hole where pin 1 of IC_7 used to be (see drawing). Finally, solder a wire link between the holes where pins 1 and 11 of IC_8 used to be.
So much for the hardware; now something about the software. The U665B divides the input frequency by 1024, while $IC_7 + IC_8$ divided by only 512. This difference means that one byte in the EPROM must be altered: address \$627 reads \$09; this should be amended to \$0A.

---

276   INSTRUMENTATION AMPLIFIER

This instrumentation amplifier was originally designed for the serial digitizer described in [1], but should be suitable for many other applications also. The amplifier makes it possible to use a relatively long, interference-free, connection between the transducer or sensor and the digitizer input.

The theoretical basis for the circuit is summarized in the accompanying Table. It is seen that the common mode rejection of the amplifier serves to suppress interference. In practice, however, the low drive margins of the inputs and outputs of the opamps impose some limitations. Both suggested types have PNP input transistors capable of handling input voltages between 0 and U_b-1.5 V. The output of the OP-220 can deliver voltages between 0 and U_b-1 V, that of the LM358 between 0 and U_b-1.5 V.

The current consumption of the opamps is low at about 150 µA for the OP-220, and 1 mA for the LM358, while the slew rate is about 0.04 V/µs and 0.4 V/µs respectively. For optimum accuracy it is recommended to use high stability (1%) resistors in positions R_1-R_5 inclusive.

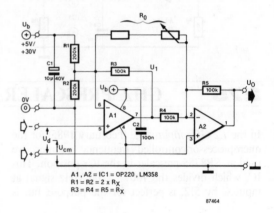

A1, A2 = IC1 = OP220, LM358
R1 = R2 = 2 x R_X
R3 = R4 = R5 = R_X

87464

PMI Application

Reference:
[1] *Universal peripheral equipment (2): Serial Digitizer*. Elektor Electronics, September 1986 p. 23 ff.

Micropower instrumentation amplifier
Consider an input UCM- ½Ud at the − input of the circuit, and UCM + ½Ud at the + input. This corresponds to a common-mode input UCM, and a differential input Ud. The currents at the inverting input of each opamp can be summed to form two equations:
$(U_b-UCM + \frac{1}{2}U_d) \bullet (1/R_1) + (U_d/R_0) + (U_1 + \frac{1}{2}U_d) \bullet (1/R_3) =$ $(UCM-\frac{1}{2}U_d) \bullet (1/R_2)$ (1)
$(U_1 = UCM-\frac{1}{2}U_d) \bullet (1/R_4) + U_o-\frac{1}{2}U_d) \bullet (1/R_5) = U_d/R_0$ (2)
When $R_1 = R_2 = 2R_3 = 2R_4 = 2R_5 = 2R_x$, (1) and (2) can be combined to
$U_o = 2(1 + R_x/R_0)U_d + \frac{1}{2}U_b$
which shows that the common mode input (UCM) has been rejected. The differential gain, Ax, of the circuit is therefore
$A_x = 2 + (2R_x/R_0)$
and is adjustable between 0 and 1,000 by varying Ro.

The video signal transmitted by most TV broadcast stations is rather complex. For most tests and experiments, however, a fairly simple signal will suffice. The circuit presented here provides a small, inexpensive source of line synchronizing pulses and line bar.

The first of the three timers in the diagram provides 4.7 μs sync pulses. It is arranged as an astable multivibrator with a period of 64 μs. The rising (here: negative-going) edge of the sync pulse triggers a second timer. The width of the output pulse of this timer determines the position of the line bar. The line bar proper is provided by the third timer. To obtain a usable video signal, the sync and bar signals must be added, which takes place in R_4-R_5-R_6. The resistor network is followed by a buffer that ensures an output impedance of 75 ohms. The unit can,

therefore, be connected direct to a standard video input. The sync and bar signals occupy 40 per cent and 60 per cent of the composite signal respectively. Calibration is carried out by connecting the unit to a monitor or, via a modulator, to a normal TV receiver. Presets P_1, P_2, and P_3 are set to the centre of their travel. Turn P_1 to obtain a still picture. If the sync pulse is too wide, it will be visible at the left-hand side of the picture. The pulse may be narrowed with the aid of P_2, after which P_1 may need a small re-adjustment.

Where an oscilloscope is available, P_2 can initially be set to obtain 4.7 μs pulses at the output (pin 3) of IC_1. Then, the total period is set to 64 μs with the aid of P_1

The line bar is centred with P_3: as its width is fixed, this completes the calibration.

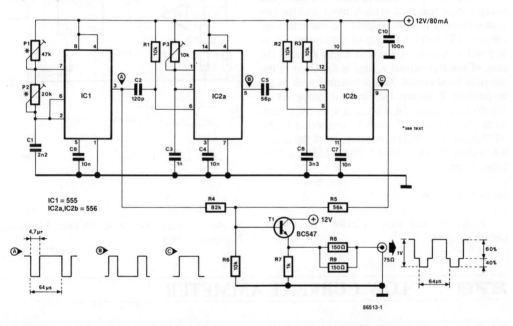

IC1 = 555
IC2a,IC2b = 556

This circuit outputs a logarithmic signal for driving the VCO input on the Elektor Electronics Function Generator [1], but can be used for other generators as well. Usually, the exponential function is derived from the (temperature-sensitive) B-E junction in a transistor, but this design uses a simple R-C network and an opamp to generate the logarithmic sweep.

With reference to the circuit diagram, U_s is applied to the generator's VCO input, while U_{sync} is used for triggering an oscilloscope on the positive signal edge. Contrary to the Elektor Electronics Sweep Generator in [2], the timebase of the scope is used for the horizontal deflection, so that the horizontal (frequency) axis has a logarithmic scale. The sweep range is 1:100 (U_{vco} = 0.1—10 V). Opamp IC_2 is dimensioned for a gain of 2 (R_3-R_4) and generates an sweep voltage, U_s, with the aid of network P_3/P_4-R_1-C_1/C_2:

$$U_s = U_1 \exp(t/R_1 C_1) \text{ when}$$
$$U_1 \le U_s \le U_2.$$

When U_s reaches level U_2, the bistable in IC_3 is reset. Capacitor C_1 (or C_2) is then discharged via R_2 and the discharge input on the 555 (or 7555) until $U_s = U_1$, causing IC_3 to be set and the next sweep period to commence. The output of the monostable supplies the trigger signal for the oscilloscope.

To adjust the circuit, set the function generator to 100 Hz; external frequency. Connect the VCO input to the wiper of P_1 (do not forget the ground connection), and adjust this preset for an output frequency of 100 Hz. Next, connect the VCO input to the wiper of P_2, and adjust this preset for an output frequency of 10 kHz. Proceed with connecting the oscilloscope, set to 10 ms/div., external trigger. The sweep voltage is applied to the Y input, and the vertical sensitivity is adjusted until the maximum excursion of U_s reaches the top of the display. Set S_1 to position A (sweep 0.1 s), and adjust P_3 until the peak of the exponential voltage is displayed in the top right-hand corner. This is repeated with S_1 set to position B (sweep 1 s), and the scope set to 100 mV/div. (adjust P_4). This completes the adjustment procedure, and U_s can be connected to the VCO input. The current consumption of the circuit is less than 25 mA or 15 mA with a 555 or a 7555 fitted, respectively.

References:

(1) *Function generator.* Elektor Electronics, December 1984.

(2) *Audio sweep generator.* Elektor Electronics, November 1985.

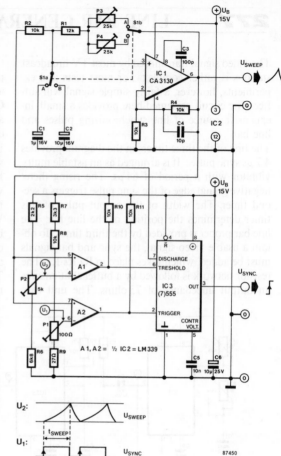

---

279   LOW CURRENT AMMETER

This 7-range ammeter measures currents between a few pA to 100 μA without using precision resistors with very high values. The circuit is set up around a current mirror T_{1a}-T_{1b}. The input current is mirrored in this transistor pair, and the current through T_{1b} is greater than the input current by a factor set with S_1. Meter M_1 is a 100 μA fsd type for displaying the measured value. The effective series voltage drop at the input terminals of the instrument is only 500 μV because the voltage across the

inputs of A_1 is forced to virtually nought.

The accuracy of the ammeter depends mainly on the components used. Depending on the required precision, certain components may be replaced by types with a better specification. The Type LF411 opamp used in the A_1 position, for example, can be replaced with the Type OP-41 to achieve a tenfold reduction in the input bias current, and hence an improvement in the final accuracy of the instrument. Transistor pair T_{1a}-T_{1b} may be replaced by a Type MAT-02, and the voltage reference set up with

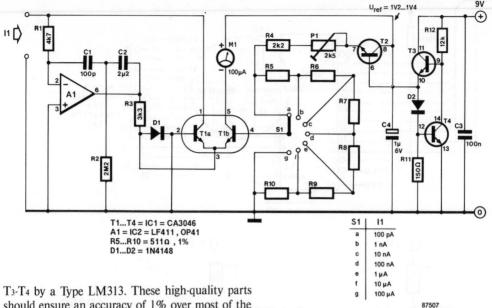

T1...T4 = IC1 = CA3046
A1 = IC2 = LF411 , OP41
R5...R10 = 511Ω , 1%
D1...D2 = 1N4148

U_ref = 1V2...1V4

9V

S1	I1
a	100 pA
b	1 nA
c	10 nA
d	100 nA
e	1 µA
f	10 µA
g	100 µA

87507

T3-T4 by a Type LM313. These high-quality parts should ensure an accuracy of 1% over most of the range. The meter is calibrated in the 1 µA range. Preset P1 is adjusted for full scale deflection of M1 at an input current of 1 µA.

When it is intended to make a printed circuit board for the pico ammeter, it should be borne in mind that two 2.5 cm long, parallel running, copper tracks spaced 1.25 mm and etched on a high quality epoxy/

glass carrier represent a leakage resistance of about 100 GΩ. This corresponds to a leakage current of 150 pA at a voltage difference of 15 V. Evidently, the PCB for the present ammeter should be

thoroughly cleaned to rule out leakage current through residual moisture or resin. Also note that the

insulation of standard test leads is likely to make reliable measuring of currents smaller than 1 pA impossible. The only way to overcome this difficulty is to use dry air or PTFE (Teflon).

Source: *PMI Linear and Conversion Applications Handbook.*

280   MEASURING WITH THE BBC MICRO

The BBC micro, one of the best value-for-money computers on the market, can be used for a variety of applications thanks to the various interfaces provided as standard. The four analogue inputs, each with a resolution of 10 bits, make it particularly suitable for measuring all kinds of processes.

There is unfortunately one drawback: the rather poor reference voltage associated with the analogue inputs. That voltage is obtained from three normal diodes connected in series. The alternative described here has been in use in our BBC micro for some time.

Diodes D6...D8 in the diagram provide a reference voltage of 1.8 V, which is fine for use with a joystick interface, but will not do where absolute values are to be measured. The three diodes are, therefore, re-

placed by one zener diode, a 2.5 V type LM336Z. This diode deviates no more than 1.8 mV over the temperature range of 0...70 °C; its long-term stability is better than 20 p.p.m. at 25 °C. Its internal resistance is 0.4 Ω, which makes it ideal for our purpose. Moreover, it is easily fitted into the micro without the need for any alterations other than the removal of D6...D8. The micro remains, of course, fully compatible with existing software.

Cut off the adjust terminal from the LM336Z, and unsolder D6...D8 from the computer. Solder the anode and cathode of the zener to the cathode connection of D6 and the anode connection of D8 respectively. A good-quality small soldering iron is indispensable here!

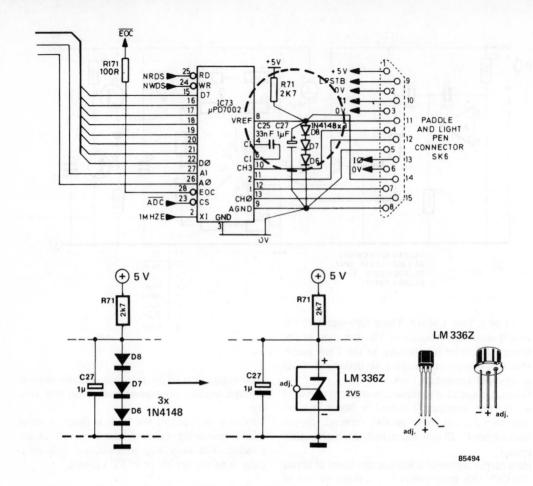

281   METER AMPLIFIER

A meter amplifier is intended for use between a sensor or other measuring device, such as a probe, and the indicator. It is characterized by a high input impedance, typically 1 MΩ, and a differential input. A differential input ensures that the output signal cannot be affected by hum or noise on the meter leads.

The input signals are buffered by differential amplifiers A_1 and A_2. The 22 pF capacitors in the C_1 and C_2 positions obviate any tendency to oscillate. The output of opamp A_3 is a function of the difference between the two input signals. Opamp A_4 serves to compensate for any offset and also to set the amplification at exactly 1. The bandwidth of the circuit as shown is not less than 100 kHz, and the phase shift is 0°.

As already mentioned, the amplifier may be used with any sensor, for instance, in computer control of the central heating, or to monitor the ambient temperature in rooms. It can also be used with a multimeter or oscilloscope.

The peak-to-peak level of the input signal should not exceed about 80 per cent of the supply voltage. Current consumption is not greater than 25 mA at a supply voltage of ±18 V.

Calibrate the unit by adjusting P_2 under no-signal conditions for zero output, and setting the amplification to exactly 1 with P_1 If you aim at perfection, use 1 per cent resistors.

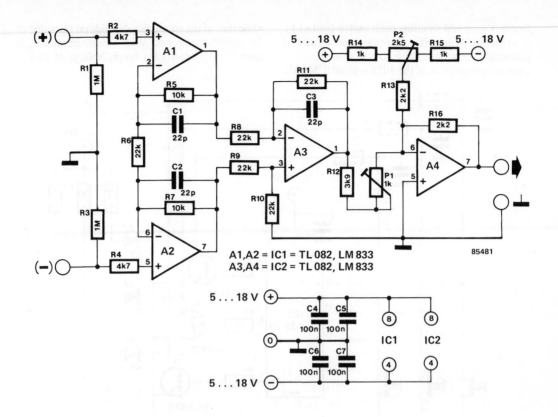

A1,A2 = IC1 = TL 082, LM 833
A3,A4 = IC2 = TL 082, LM 833

85481

282   METERING SELECTOR

When just one meter is used to measure the voltage of three different sources, it is, of course, possible to use a three position rotary switch to select any one of the sources. However, care must be taken here, because the switch must break before make, otherwise two sources are interconnected and this is normally highly undesirable.

Any electronic equivalent of the rotary switch must, of course, also break before make. Unfortunately, transistors have the property of switching on much faster than switching off. For example, a well-driven BC 547 takes a couple of μs to switch off, but far less than that to switch on.

The present circuit circumnavigates these potential troubles by using the output level as criterion, whereby a 4028 serves as the referee. The 4028 is a one-of-ten active high decoder which drives one of three transistors, $T_1 \ldots T_3$. Let us assume that T_1 is on: its collector voltage is low, and so is input A of the 4028. The other two collectors are high, and so are inputs B and C of the decoder. The 4028

therefore sees binary code 6 (110) at its input and this causes pin 6 to go logic high, so that T_1 is driven hard.

When in this condition another key, for instance, S_2, is pressed, a wrong code, i.e., 4 (100), ensues. Output 4 of the 4028 is, however, not connected, T_1 switches off, but T_2 is not yet driven. Only after T_1 has actually switched off, and its collector goes high, does 5 (101) arise at the input of the 4028: T_2 will then be driven.

In practice, the voltage at the collector may be used to control a CMOS switch that arranges the change over of the meter or the sound channel. It is also possible to replace the collector resistor by a suitable relay, but this would, of course, introduce even longer delay times (of the order of milliseconds). In that case, the feedback to the input must be effected by a separate contact of the relay, but there is then, of course, absolute certainty that switching is correct!

Another variant is including a resistance in each

311

feedback loop and shunting each switch contact by a capacitor. This *RC* network will ensure a reasonable delay during the change over. Current consumption of the 4028 is small (CMOS!),

while that of the transistors depends on the value of the collector resistors. With values as shown, it amounts to 18 mA for a supply voltage of 10 V.

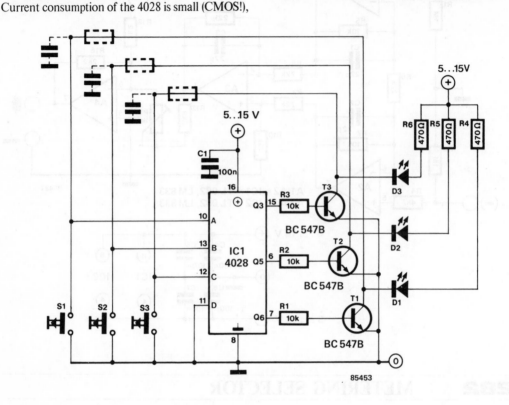

85453

283   NOISE GENERATOR

Noise is normally defined as unwanted electrical signals spread over a relatively flat, wide frequency spectrum. In most equipment, great care is taken to reduce the amount of noise to a minimum, resulting in a low noise factor.

None the less, noise is useful for measuring the behaviour of a circuit under varying input conditions. A noise generator is used, for instance, for measurements on coaxial cables, microwave links, and RTTY (radio teletype) and CW (continuous wave = radio telegraphy) decoders. The present circuit may also be used to imitate the sound of wind, mosquitoes, bees, and other buzzing insects.

The circuit consists of a relaxation oscillator, IC1, which is provided with positive and negative feedback via P_1-R_2 and P_3-P_2-R_3-C_1 respectively. Zener diode D_1 functions as noise source. The amplification of the noise is determined by the setting of

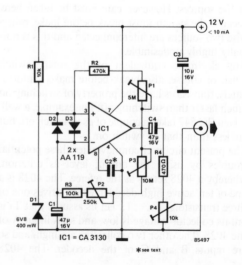

P_3 (coarse) and P_2 (fine). The setting of P_1 determines the noise bandwidth: a small effective value results in a narrow band, and increasing values cause wider bands.

Due to the negative feedback, the opamp also functions as a low-pass filter: a small feedback factor results in a low roll-off frequency. The pass band of the opamp also depends on the value of C_2: a value of 47 n causes a noise similar to the buzzing of a mosquito or bee. Diodes D_2 and D_3 serve as input limiters. The output level of the generator can be adjusted with P_4

Current consumption is not greater than 10 mA at 12 V.

284   OPAMP TESTER

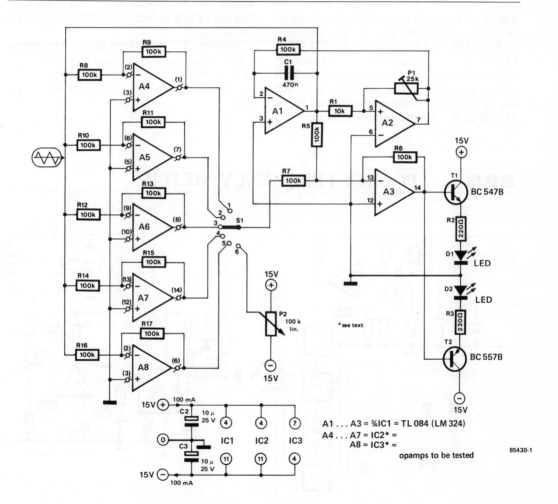

A1 ... A3 = ¾ IC1 = TL 084 (LM 324)
A4 ... A7 = IC2* =
A8 = IC3* =
opamps to be tested

85430-1

All types of operational amplifier can be functionally checked with the tester proposed here.

The principle of the tester is quite simple: a triangular voltage is applied to the inverting (—) input of the specimen. This voltage is, of course, inverted. If then the inverted and the original triangular voltage are added, the result should be zero. Any deviations from this are taken as a malfunction which is indicated by one of two light-emitting diodes (LEDs). The tester has, of course, a self test facility so that the error-free operation of it can be readily ascertained.

Opamps A_1 and A_2 form a triangular pulse generator. Opamp A_1 operates as an integrator: capacitor C_1 is charged, and as soon as the voltage across it reaches the threshold value of Schmitt trigger A_2, resistor R_4 is connected to earth, and C_1 discharges until the voltage across it reaches the second threshold of A_2, when the process repeats itself.

Opamp A_3 functions as the summing stage whose output is fed to two transistors that drive LEDs. The specimens are connected as inverters in either positions $Ap_1 \ldots Ap_4$ or Ap_5. In the design it was assumed that the most frequently encountered opamps are contained in a 14-pin DIL housing (as, for instance, the TL 084 used for $A_1 \ldots A_3$), or in an 8-pin DIL package (such as the LM 355 or LM 387). For different packages, the specimen connections in figure 1 should be modified accordingly. When a specimen is defect, the output of A_3 consists of a triangular voltage superimposed on the (DC) offset. This is sufficient to bias the drive tran-

sistors and one or both LEDs flash in rhythm with the triangular voltage. The frequency of that signal is about 10 Hz, and this can be altered to some extent by changing the value of R_4 and/or C_1.

It is clear that the voltage at the output of A_3 must be greater than ± 0.6 V, otherwise the bias for the transistors is too small. Preset P_1 should therefore be adjusted so that the LEDs just do not light when an opamp that is known to work correctly is inserted in the relevant specimen position.

The self test function is easily checked: when P_2 is turned from one extreme of its travel to the other, first one LED, then both, and finally the other LED should light.

In positions $1 \ldots 4$ of switch S_1, the four opamps contained in, say, a TL 084 can be tested sequentially; in position 5, the single opamp contained in, say, an LM 355; and position 6 is the self test setting.

285   POCKET FREQUENCY METER

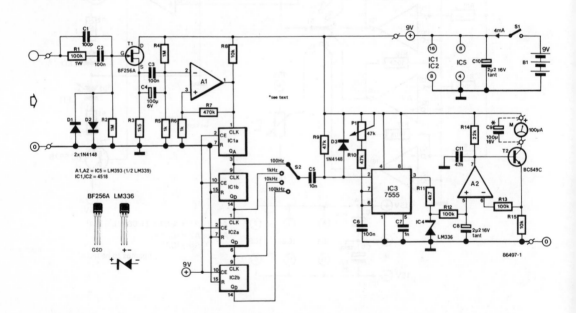

This easy to construct circuit meets the demand for a simple, yet versatile battery operated frequency meter which can interpret signals with a minimum rms voltage of 10 mV and a maximum frequency of 100 kHz. The quiescent current consumption of the meter circuit is only 4 mA, which ensures a long life

for the 9 V battery. Also of interest is the fact that the circuit continues to work normally with battery voltages down to about 5 V. The meter input is protected up to 250 V AC.

From the circuit diagram it is seen that the input signal is applied to the gate of T_1 via R_1 and C_2. C_1

is an additional speed-up capacitor to improve the response at higher frequencies, while anti-parallel connected diodes D_1 and D_2 protect the FET gate from high voltage surges. T_1 functions as a buffer, preceding Schmitt trigger A_1, which has been dimensioned for a relatively low hysteresis of about 18 mV to prevent the overall sensitivity being too strongly degraded. The output of A_1 is fed direct to divide-by-two counter IC_{1a}, which is followed by three cascaded divide-by-ten IC sections. S_2 selects the divisor and hence the relevant frequency range. Whatever range is selected, a frequency of 50 Hz at the pole of S_2 corresponds to a full scale reading on moving coil meter M.

The signal at the pole of S_2 is used to trigger the monostable built around the Type 7555 low-power precision timer. The correct operation of this circuit section can only be achieved if the time period of the monostable is less than half that of the full scale frequency, i.e. $\frac{1}{2}(1/50)s = 10\ ms$. Therefore, a monostable time of 8 ms is used in the proposed configuration.

The output signal from IC_3 has a duty factor which is proportional to the input signal frequency. The pulses from IC_3 are levelled at 2.5 V_{pp} by IC_4, before being integrated by R_{12} and C_8 to produce a direct voltage which is proportional to the input frequency. The circuit around A_2 and T_2 is a simple voltage-to-current converter with the 100 μA moving coil meter connected in the collector supply line to T_2. C_9 may be added to stabilize the read-out at the lower end of the scale.

Though a Type LM393 opamp has been used, the less expensive Type LM339 also works all right, provided the inputs of the unused opamps contained in this chip are tied to the positive supply rail to minimize their power consumption.

The frequency meter is so sensitive that merely touching the input terminal with a finger causes the meter to read the mains frequency. This is, incidentally, a convenient method of calibration, since P_1 may be set to give a reading in accordance with the local mains frequency, which is usually stable within 1%.

286   PROGRAMMABLE BAUD-RATE GENERATOR

Only some computers, e.g., the Samson 65, enable you to reprogram the ACIA (asynchronous communications interface adapter), or whatever your serial interface may be, if you want to connect a printer and a modem to your computer. With most other micros, you have to use an additional circuit like the one proposed here.

The circuit is based on a presettable, synchronous down counter, a CMOS IC type 40103. Another CMOS IC, type 4060B, serves as a crystal controlled clock generator. The crystal frequency, f_x, is 2.4576 MHz, while the clock, f_c, is 153.6 kHz. The output frequency, f_o, of the generator is determined from

$f_o = [153.6/(N + 1)]$ kHz

where N is the decimal equivalent of the number that is input to the J0...J7 terminals of the 40103 (see table).

The number N is provided by the computer and from there written into, and stored by, the 74LS374. The table gives various baud rates (also for RTTY — radio teletype) and the corresponding decimal and hexadecimal numbers. If you want to shift the baud range upwards, select a higher value output of

baud-rate	N (dec)	N (hex)
4800	1	01
2400	3	03
1200	7	07
600	15	0F
300	31	1F
150	63	3F
110	86	56
100	95	5F
75	127	7F
57	167	A7
50	191	BF
45,45	210	D2

the 4060B: for instance, output Q5 for a maximum rate of 9600, output Q6 for a maximum rate of 19200, and so on. As for every one of these steps the output frequency is doubled, the relevant value of f_o must be used in the formula given above; i.e., 307.2 kHz when Q5 is used, 614.4 kHz when Q6 is used, and so on.

The address decoder in the circuit diagram is arranged for a Z80 computer, as can readily be seen from the control signals, but this is purely taken as an example. The signal from the data bus is applied to the 74LS374 at the leading edge of the $\overline{STROBE}$ pulse at the output of the decoder. The articles *address decoding* and *memory timing* in the January and February 1984 issues of *Elektor Electronics* respectively contain all the necessary information for the design of an address decoder for any type of computer.

The address decoder in the diagram is shown for the decoding of the hexadecimal address F0. Many versions of BASIC on Z80 computers permit the programming of the baud-rate generator with the instruction

OUT 240, N

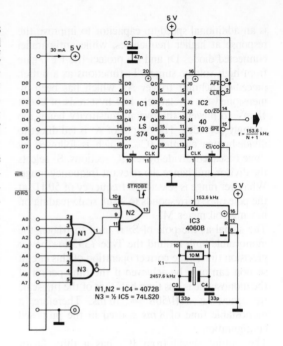

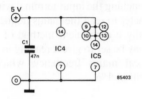

287   RECTANGULAR PULSE GENERATOR

The excellent properties of counter/divider IC type 4059 have, so far, not been given the prominence in *Elektor Electronics* they deserve. One of these

properties is the provision of divide ratios anywhere between 3 and 15 999 depending on the logic level at inputs $J_1 \dots J_{16}$ and the setting of switches

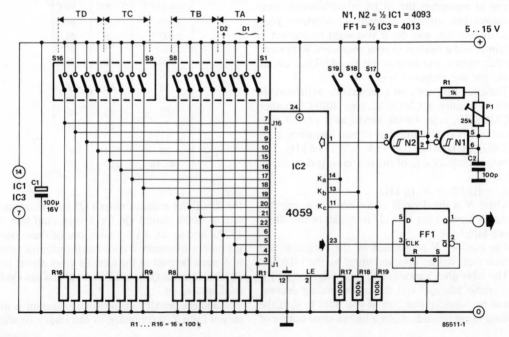

$S_{17} \ldots S_{19}$.

The 4059 is clocked by a relaxation oscillator, N_1-N_2, which could have been a crystal-controlled type instead of the one shown in figure 1.

The dual-D bistable type 4013 at the output is essential because the width of the pulses at pin 23 of the 4059 is comparable to the clock frequency. The bistable ensures that the pulses emanating from pin 23 are reshaped into rectangular form. The Q output of the bistable is, of course, half the frequency of the wave train at pin 23 of the divider. Inputs $J_1 \ldots J_{16}$ of IC_2 are divided into groups of four. The binary information at these inputs is called $T_A \ldots T_D$. Inputs $J_1 \ldots J_4$ are further subdivided into D_1 and D_2. In total there are, therefore, five data inputs, of which the smallest, D_2, is only one bit wide. Furthermore, the 4059 has three mode control inputs, $K_a \ldots K_c$, whose composition results in a factor K as shown in table 1. If $K=10$, input D_1 becomes four bits wide: J_4 then forms part of D_1! The divisor, n, is then calculated from:

$$n = 10^3 T_D + 10^2 T_C + 10 T_B + D_1$$

In all other cases,

$$n = K(10^3 D_2 + 10^2 T_D + 10 T_C + T_B) + D_1$$

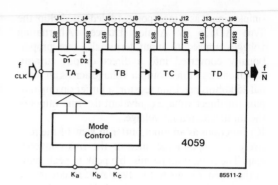

The 4059 can be programmed by computer, by hand, or with the aid of an up-or-down counter. The generator can be used in electrophonics, in measuring techniques, as timer, and even as a digital phase-locked loop frequency synthesizer in FM tuners.

The circuit operates from a 4…15 V supply and current consumption is small.

288   RMS-TO-DC CONVERTER

For some obscure reason, establishing the root-mean-square (rms) value of an alternating voltage seems to be among the least familiar procedures for many an electronics hobbyist; measuring the alternating voltage may be easy, but deciding on the relevant unit expressing quantity — rms, mean, or peak-to-peak value — is quite another matter. Since the rms value of an alternating voltage is the most frequently used of the above mentioned three, some convenient means of obtaining that value without calculations may be of interest in practical measuring techniques.

The rms value of an alternating voltage U across a resistor R equals the direct voltage causing the same dissipation level in R.

Example: a 50% duty factor, $1\,V_{pp}$ rectangular voltage across a resistor R. Find the rms level of this voltage.

The mean dissipation in R, caused by this periodic signal equals

$$\tfrac{1}{2}\,(U_{pp})^2/R = 1/(2R) \qquad \text{[W]}$$

The direct voltage causing the same dissipation has a level of

$\tfrac{1}{2}\sqrt{2} \approx 0.71$ V, since $P = (\tfrac{1}{2}\sqrt{2})^2/R = 1/(2R)$[W].

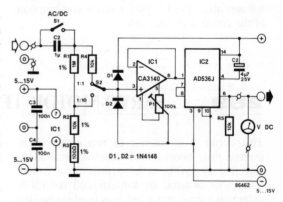

This is also the conversion factor for obtaining the rms value from the peak-to-peak value, since

$$U_{rms} = \sqrt{\tfrac{1}{2}U_{pp}^2} = \tfrac{1}{2}\sqrt{2}\,U_{pp} \approx 0.71 U_{pp}\,[\text{V}]$$

therefore $U_{pp} \approx 1.41 U_{rms}$ in this example.

Although moving coil meters measure the mean value of the rectified (pulsating) input voltage, they are calibrated in terms of rms voltages. Therefore, the calibration is only valid for sinusoidal voltages. The proposed rms-to-DC converter is a relatively simple circuit as it incorporates a dedicated chip, the Type AD536 by Analog Devices. Alternating voltages applied to input terminal 1 are proportionally converted into a direct output current, which causes a direct output voltage across an internal 25 kohms precision resistor; a buffer opamp outputs the direct voltage equivalent (i.e. rms value) of the input alternating voltage.

IC$_1$ functions as an input buffer in view of the relatively low input impedance of the rms converter chip. The maximum permissible peak-to-peak value of the input voltage to the Type AD536 equals the symmetrical supply voltage level; D$_1$ and D$_2$ have been added to protect IC$_1$ against accepting input voltage levels in excess of the $\pm$ supply voltage. S$_2$ functions as a $\times 1/\times 10$ input attenuation selector to enable high voltage measurements; the function of S$_1$ is to block any DC components in the input signal to the converter. It is useful to realize that the rms value of a composite (AC + DC) signal is calculated from

$$U_{rms} = \sqrt{U_{DC}^2 + U_{AC}^2}.$$

Preset P$_1$ should be turned to obtain 0 V with respect to ground at terminal 6 of IC$_2$ with no input signal applied and S$_2$ set to the $\times 1$ position.

The converter achieves an accuracy of 1% for input voltage levels lower than 100 mV and input frequencies up to about 6 kHz. For signals up to 1 V, the bandwidth is expected to be of the order of 40 kHz, while 100 kHz may be attained with input voltages above the 1 V level. Current consumption of the circuit is about 5 mA.

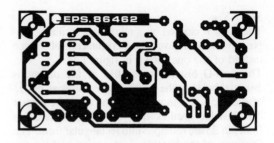

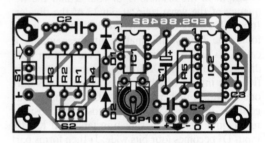

Parts list

Resistors:
R$_1$ = 1M; 1%
R$_2$ = 10k; 1%
R$_3$ = 100Ω; 1%
R$_4$; R$_5$ = 10k
P$_1$ = 100k preset

Capacitors:
C$_1$ = 4.7μ; 25 V electrolytic
C$_2$ = 1μ; MKT
C$_3$; C$_4$ = 100n

Semiconductors:
D$_1$; D$_2$ = 1N4148
IC$_1$ = CA3140
IC$_2$ = AD536J

Miscellaneous:
S$_1$ = miniature switch
S$_2$ = toggle switch
PCB Type 86462

---

289   SERVO-MOTOR TESTER

This circuit is of interest to two categories of readers; first, model aircraft/boat/train enthusiasts objecting to having to leave their radio control transmitter switched on for extended periods in order that a servo-motor and associated mechanical parts can be made to function as desired; secondly, constructors of computer-controlled robots incorporating servo-motors. The latter field of interest is a typical combination of mechanics and electronics plus software, and it is sometimes urgently required to be able to keep them apart as the specific parts of the robot have been prepared for testing, which, arguably, should be possible to do without having to write special programs to this end on the computer. The proposed servo-motor test unit is, as can be

seen from the circuit diagram, a downright simple design based on the use of Type 555 or 7555 timer chips connected in a cascade arrangement which can be expanded further to drive more than two servos at a time, if desired; it is readily seen that the second and third stages of the circuit are identical. The first timer, IC$_1$, serves as an astable multivibrator whose output pulse period time is determined with $T = 0.693(R_1 + R_2)C$. The indicated values for the relevant timing parts therefore provide a pulse period time of about 20 ms at pin 3 of IC$_1$. The rising edge of this square wave triggers monostable IC$_2$, whose output pulse width may be set with P$_1$; the given series connection of P$_1$ and R$_4$ ensures a large enough pulse width range for

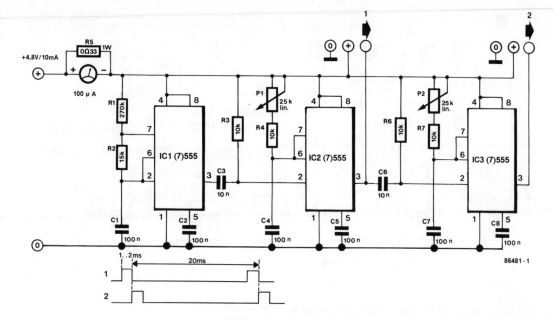

most types of servo-motor, which typically require activation pulse widths of the order of 1...2 ms. The second servo control stage is identical to the set-up around IC2, and up to eight triggered 555 stages, each with its own pulse width control, may be cascaded in this way.

It is suggested to fit each of the servo control potentiometers with a simple scale in order to have a relative indication regarding the motor's lateral or angular position.

The ammeter in series with the positive supply line offers an indication about the total current consumption of the servos, and it is thus readily detected when one or more have got stuck in their movement. The test circuit itself does not contribute much to the total current consumption indicated on the meter; some 3 mA is required for each Type 555 timer in the row, while the use of low power Type 7555 equivalents should reduce this figure even further. It is, therefore, perfectly feasible to make the tester into a portable, battery-operated unit, powered by four penlight type NiCd batteries.

290   SIMPLE SWEEP GENERATOR

The sweep generator is an indispensable piece of measuring equipment for testing the frequency response of AF amplifiers, filters, and loudspeaker systems. At the heart of this design is the well-known Type XR2206 function generator chip from EXAR. It is seen to the right on the circuit diagram, in a standard application with 3 capacitors and a rotary switch for selecting the frequency range, and a potentiometer, P_5, for adjusting the amplitude of the output signal. The signal frequency is a function of the current drawn from pin 7 on the XR2206:

$$f_0 = 320I/C \ [Hz]$$

where I is in milli-amperes, and C is in micro-farads.

It should be noted that pin 7 is internally kept at 3 V, which is available at pin 10 also.

The left-hand part of the circuit comprises the sawtooth generator, IC_1, and a buffer, IC_2. The former is set up as an integrator, whose sweep period depends on the voltage at terminal C. Potentiometer P_2 enables setting the sweep period between 0.01 and 10 seconds; the maximum duration is adjusted with P_4. The sawtooth voltage at pin 6 of IC_1 has an amplitude of 5 V_{pp}, and can be used to drive the horizontal deflection (X) input of an oscilloscope via terminal K. The amplitude of the sawtooth voltage is determined by the zener voltage of D_1 and the base-emitter voltage of T_2, which is briefly turned off when the output of IC_1 exceeds

319

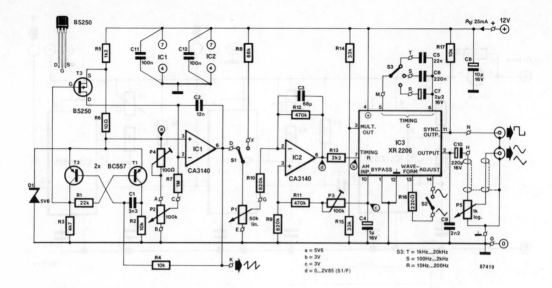

5 V. The collector of this transistor is then pulled to ground via R_3, so that T_1 is switched into conduction. The integrator is reset by making the — input of IC_1 positive with respect to the + input with the aid of T_3, R_5 and R_6.

Capacitor C_1 serves to lengthen the on-time for T_1 and T_3 to ensure that the flyback of the sawtooth is finished.

Potentiometer P_1 is a voltage divider to define the sawtooth amplitude, and hence the sweep range, while S_1 makes it possible to turn off the sweep function (position F).

Opamp IC_2 is configured as a buffer stage for inverting and attenuating the sawtooth voltage, to which a direct voltage is added also. The output of IC_2 carries a sawtooth voltage with an amplitude between 0 and 2.85 V, or a direct voltage between the same limits when S_1 is set to position F. Bearing in mind that the reference voltage of IC_3 is 3 V, the current through R_{13}, and hence the output frequency, can be varied by a factor 20, which is the maximum attainable deviation factor in all 3 frequency ranges. The frequency scale can be calibrated with the aid of P_3.

Parts list

Resistors (±5%):
$R_1 = 22K$
$R_2; R_4; R_{17} = 10K$
$R_3 = 4K7$
$R_5 = 1K2$
$R_6 = 10R$
$R_7 = 1M0$
$R_8 = 68K$
$R_9; R_{10} = 820K$
$R_{11}; R_{12} = 470K$
$R_{13} = 2K2$
$R_{14}; R_{15} = 33K$
$R_{16} = 220R$
$P_1 = 50K$ linear potentiometer
$P_2 = 100K$ linear potentiometer
$P_3 = 100K$ preset
$P_4 = 100R$ preset
$P_5 = 1K0$ logarithmic potentiometer

Capacitors:
$C_1 = 3n3$
$C_2 = 12n$
$C_3 = 68p$
$C_4 = 1\mu$; 16 V; radial
$C_5 = 22n$
$C_6 = 220n$
$C_7 = 2\mu2$; 16 V; radial
$C_8 = 10\mu$; 16 V; radial
$C_9 = 2n2$
$C_{10} = 220\mu$; 16 V; radial
$C_{11}; C_{12} = 100n$

Semiconductors:
$D_1 =$ zenerdiode 5V6; 400 mW
$T_1; T_2 = BC557$
$T_3 = BS250$
$IC_1; IC_2 = CA3140$
$IC_3 = XR2206$

Miscellaneous:
$S_1 =$ miniature SPDT switch.
$S_2 =$ miniature SPST switch.

$S_3 = $ 1 pole, 3-way rotary switch.
PCB Type EPS87419

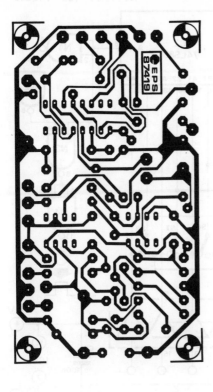
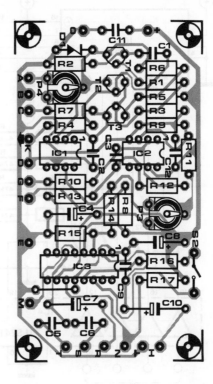

291   SIMPLIFIED WORD COMPARATOR

Primarily intended as a trigger source for an oscillo-scope in the testing of digital circuits, the compara-tor is a derivative of the *word recognizer and delayed trigger* published in the July/August 1981 issue of *Elektor Electronics*.

When an 8-bit binary word is recognized during a comparison with a pre-determined value, the pres-ent circuit issues a short trigger pulse. In contrast to the original circuit, the present one has no provision for either a delayed trigger pulse or an external trig-ger input. None the less, the comparator remains an almost indispensable aid in the testing of digital cir-cuits.

The unit is based on two four-bit comparators, IC_1 and IC_2. The reference level for them can be set sep-arately with switches $S_1 \ldots S_4$ and $S_5 \ldots S_8$ respect-ively. With these switches set as drawn, inputs A and B are interconnected: this is the don't care pos-ition. With a switch set to its centre position, a high reference level is obtained, while when it is set to the

extreme right position, a low reference level is ob-tained.

When all A and B inputs agree, the $A = B$ output of IC_2 goes logic high. Gates $N_1 \ldots N_4$ suppress short spurious pulses that arise during the stabilization of the comparator inputs.

The size of the binary word can be increased by cascading two or more comparators. Account must then be taken of the transit delay which amounts to 24 ns per comparator. In some tests this may lead to an unacceptable delay if several comparators are used.

The current consumption is about 60 mA per com-parator: 32 mA is drawn by the LS241, and 10 mA by the LS85. This enables the current consumption of multiple comparators to be calculated quite eas-ily.

Note that each additional IC must be separately decoupled by a 100 n capacitor.

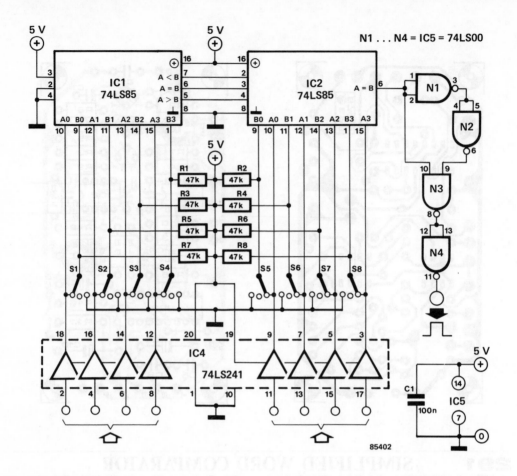

N1 ... N4 = IC5 = 74LS00

85402

292   TWO-TONE RF TEST OSCILLATOR

This test oscillator is useful to ensure optimum operation of RF amplifier stages designed to work on the short-wave bands. Based on two crystal oscilators, it provides considerable output power (10 to 100 mW) to enable measuring intermodulation characteristics of high level and RF power stages. The quartz crystals used here not only serve as the frequency determining elements (2...20 MHz), but also as output filters to prevent one generated signal being lost in the other oscillator. With this in mind, tapped inductors L_1 and L_2 ensure freedom of mutual interference when the oscillator is used for frequencies higher than 10 MHz. Both inductors are wound as 12 turns of enamelled copper wire with a centre tap, on either a small balun or a suitably rated core with an air gap. Outputs of equal

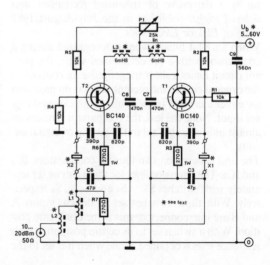

amplitude can be obtained by adjusting P_1. The test oscillator consumes about 250 mA from a 60 V supply. This means that both transistors should be fitted with a heat-sink, and that chokes L_3 and L_4 should be capable of carrying about 150 mA.

293   VARIABLE WIEN BRIDGE OSCILLATOR

A Wien bridge oscillator can be made variable by using two frequency determining parts that are varied simultaneously at high tracking accuracy. High-quality tracking potentiometers or variable capacitors are, however, expensive and difficult to obtain. To avoid having to use such a component, this oscillator was designed to operate with a single potentiometer. The output frequency, f_o, is calculated from

$$f_o = 1/(2\pi RC\sqrt{\alpha})$$

where $R = R_2 = R_3 = R_4 = R_6$, $C = C_1 = C_2$, and $\alpha = (P_1 + R_1)R$. Preset P_2 allows adjusting the overall amplification such that the output signal has a reasonably stable amplitude (3.5 V_{pp} max.) over the entire frequency range.

The stated components allow the frequency to be adjusted between 350 Hz and 3.5 kHz. Other frequency ranges are readily defined with the aid of the above formula, although it should be noted that the upper frequency limit is determined mainly by the gain-bandwidth product of the opamps Type OP-221 and TLC272. The current consumption of the oscillator depends on the type of opamp used. The following values were measured: OP-221: 0.5 mA; TLC272: 2 mA; TL072: 2 mA. The construction of the oscillator should present very few problems since a ready-made circuit board is available.

(PMI Application)

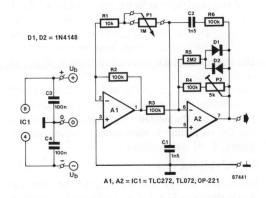

Parts list

Resistors ($\pm 5\%$):

R_1 = 10K
$R_2;R_3;R_4;R_6$ = 100K
R_5 = 2M2
P_1 = 1M0 linear potentiometer
P_2 = 5k0 preset

Capacitors:

$C_1;C_2$ = 1n5
$C_3;C_4$ = 100n

Semiconductors:

$D_1;D_2$ = 1N4148
IC_1 = TLC272 or TL072 or OP-221

Miscellaneous:

PCB Type 87441

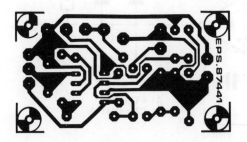

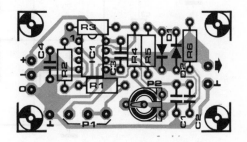

This AF oscillator can be built with only one active component, and draws so little current that it is conveniently fed from a 9 V (PP3) battery.

The basic circuit of the Wien bridge oscillator is shown in Fig. 1. The oscillator consists of two sections, namely the opamp plus R_3-R_4 which determine the amplification factor, and positive feedback network C_1-R_1-C_2-R_2 which enables the circuit to oscillate. This network is composed of a low-pass section R_2//C_2, and a high pass section R_1+C_1. The phase difference incurred in these is nulled at the frequency of oscillation, when the filters form a pure ohmic potential divider with an attenuation of 3. Therefore, the opamp must have an amplification of 3, to keep the overall amplification at unity, so that the oscillation is maintained. The output frequency, f_o, of the oscillator is

$$f_o = 1/(2\pi\sqrt{R_1 R_2 C_1 C_2}) \qquad [Hz]$$

but only if $R_1 \approx R_2$ and $C_1 \approx C_2$. In the practical design shown in Fig. 2, the oscillation frequency is about 1,000 Hz.

Both the inverting and the inverting input of the opamp in Fig. 1 must be held at half the supply voltage to ensure minimum current consumption if the oscillator is to be fed from a battery. Figure 2 shows how this is realized in the practical version of the Wien bridge oscillator. Here, resistors R_2 and R_3 from Fig. 1 are seen as R_{2a}-R_{2b} and R_{3a}-R_{3b}, respectively, connected as voltage dividers. This can be done with impunity, because the voltage source is a virtual short circuit for alternating voltages, and there is also C_3 as an effective decoupling device. For an alternating voltage, therefore, the resistors

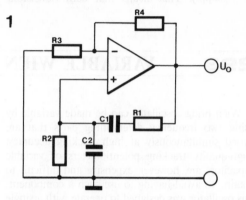

1

are parallel combinations. Evidently, R_{2a}, R_{2b}, R_{3a}, and R_{3b} have two times the calculated resistance of the respective components R_2 and R_3 in Fig. 1. The amplification of the opamp is adjustable with P_1, which should be set for reliable oscillation at virtually no distortion of the output sine wave. When the oscillator is properly aligned, the distortion should be less than 0.1%.

The use of the Type TLC271 CMOS operational amplifier results in a current consumption of only 0.32 mA at $U_o = 6\ V_{pp}$. It is possible to use a special low-power opamp such as the type OP-22 biased with a resistance of 1 MΩ to reduce the current consumption to 0.1 mA. However, this will cause the oscillation frequency to be limited to 1,000 Hz, due to the reduced slew rate at very low bias settings, which in turn give rise to a strong increase in the distortion level.

PMI Application Note AB111.

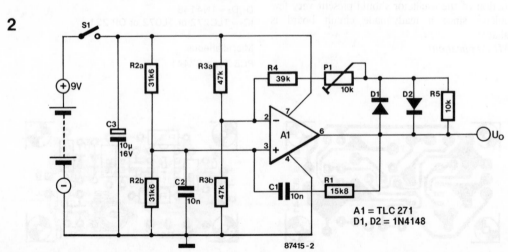

2

A1 = TLC 271
D1, D2 = 1N4148

87415-2

295   RF MODULE FOR INDOOR UNIT

The series of articles on satellite TV reception, started in the September 1986 issue of *Elektor Electronics*, has met a great deal of interest from our readers. Many have successfully ventured out into the world of centimetre waves and SHF construction methods, and are proud to watch the pictures produced by a home-made Indoor Unit [1].

The construction and alignment of the RF input stage and the local oscillators is undoubtedly the most difficult phase of the project. However, an attractive alternative is now available for those constructors hesitant about their skills in dealing with very high frequency components and techniques. The Type HL ECS51 is a ready-made, tunable, 950-1750 MHz to 480 MHz converter of Taiwanese origin, and is eminently suitable for taking over the previously mentioned functions on the RF board (Type EPS 86082-1). The module is tuned with a voltage between 0 and 20 V, and requires no band (H/L) switch. It has a connection for applying the LNB supply voltage, which is carried to the LNB via the downlead cable as usual. The module itself is conveniently fed from 12 VDC, and consumes about 100 mA. Its RF input is a Type F socket.

Figure 1 shows the ready connection of the module to the RF board in the IDU. Module pin 3 is the AGC input, which is grounded here to achieve maximum gain. A 56 kΩ resistor is fitted in series with the existing +33 V tuning voltage rail to ensure the correct maximum input to pin 5. The IF output on the module accepts a common phono plug, to which a short length of thin (RG174) coax cable is soldered for connecting to the short track between pin 3 and 4 of MX₁ on the RF board. Coupling capacitor C₇ should be left in place, but MX₁, the RF input stage, and both local oscillators may be omitted, since the module takes over their function. In case the RF board is already complete, it is recommended to remove MX₁, R₃ and band selector S₁. The screen between the RF input stage and the local oscillators may also be omitted, but not the remaining screens on the board.

Before aligning the "modular" Indoor Unit, the intermediate frequency requires lowering from 610 to 480 MHz. The VCO in the SL1451 PLL can be tuned to the new centre frequency by increasing the inductance of L₈. This is easiest to do by making a new inductor as shown in Fig. 2. Use about 5 cm of silver plated, ∅ 1 mm (SWG20) wire to make the single turn inductor, ensuring that the underside of it is just above the PCB surface.

The alignment procedure of the module-based In-

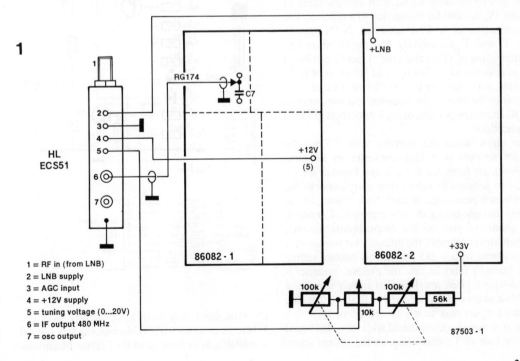

1

HL
ECS51

1 = RF in (from LNB)
2 = LNB supply
3 = AGC input
4 = +12V supply
5 = tuning voltage (0...20V)
6 = IF output 480 MHz
7 = osc output

door Unit is essentially identical to that set forth on page 54 in Part 2 of [1]. The reference there to *TV channel 36 (600 MHz)* should then be read as *TV channel 21/22 (approx. 480 MHz)*. The IF band-filters can be tuned to the new frequency when the respective trimmers are set for nearly maximum capacitance.

Finally, a note on the results obtained with the module in combination with the RF board as described here: the original, completed, and properly aligned RF board with the BFG65, local oscillators, and MX₁ fitted gives a slightly better performance when relatively weak signals (C/N ≤ 12 dB) are being received. This is mainly due to its noise figure being lower than that of the HL ECS51 module, which is specified for no less than 15 dB in this

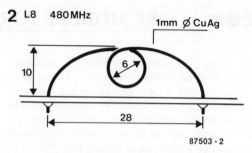

2 L8   480 MHz

1mm ∅ CuAg

87503 - 2

respect. None the less, the module gives good results with relatively strong input signals.

Literature reference:
[1] Indoor Unit for Satellite TV Reception Parts 1-3; *Elektor Electronics*, October 1986 and following issues.

296   RGB-TO-MONOCHROME VIDEO COMBINER

This circuit offers impeccable monochrome images when driven by the digital RGB and sync signals of a high-resolution graphics card such as the one featured in *Elektor Electronics*, issues from November 1985 to March 1986.

Transistor T₂ in the video combiner/buffer ensures a short-circuit proof, 75Ω impedance monochrome and composite video signal with an rms value of about 1V, as usual for connection to a monitor. The combination of a PNP and an NPN transistor, T₁ and T₂ respectively, for amplification and combination of video and sync typically exhibits a good response to the fast rise and fall times of these signals, and thus enables sufficient picture definition in the case of, for instance, text presentation at 80 characters per line, or high-resolution graphics applications.

The input circuit arrangement with T₁ and the mixer resistors is a D/A converter in its most rudimentary form; the R, G, B, and I signals are applied to resistors at values that correspond to the luminance percentage of each basic colour, to the effect that any colour shade is represented as one of 16 shades of grey on the monochrome monitor. Where this is desirable, the intensity bit resistor may be replaced with a 2k5 preset; this enables setting the intensity ratio. In case the present combiner is used with a video interface that merely supplies a video and sync signal, or merely RGB signals, the unused inputs may simply be left open.

The sync signals are combined with the video signal at the base of T₂; depending on the system setup,

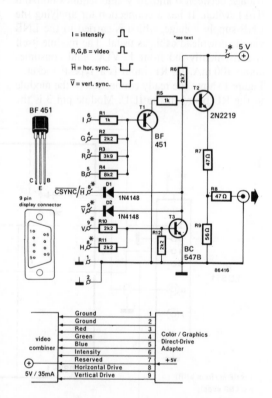

video combiner	Ground	1	
	Ground	2	
	Red	3	
	Green	4	Color / Graphics
	Blue	5	Direct-Drive
	Intensity	6	Adapter
	Reserved	7	+5V
5V / 35mA	Horizontal Drive	8	
	Vertical Drive	9	

the sync input may have to be slightly modified. Where an inverted CSYNC (composite sync) signal is available, as in the case of the Elektor Electronics graphics card, all parts relevant to the sync inputs may be dispensed with, except for D1. Resistors R5 and R6 determine the black level of the composite video signal, to which the sync component is added by D1, which is capable of lowering the base voltage of T2 to a value, lower than the black level. Diode D2 allows separate, inverted sync signals to be applied to the combiner, and T3, R10, R12 and R11 may be added for video systems that output a positive-going, separate sync.

The combiner may also be used with the video-

interface incorporated in the IBM PC (see *Elektor Electronics*, May 1985 issue); if this computer is equipped with a monochrome video board, the sync mixer only requires D2, R11, R12, and T3. The IBM colour board requires the addition of R10, whereas D2 may be left out. Figure 2 shows how the video combiner is typically connected to the IBM colour board. Note the use of the 'reserved' line (7) for the +5V supply voltage of the combiner circuit.

297   SCART SWITCH

This circuit is not really a technical novelty, but it has its practical uses. If, for instance, it is desired to connect a video recorder AND a computer permanently to the SCART socket at the back of a modern television set, it will be found that that is impossible. All that can be done is to connect either the video recorder or the computer. But the proposed SCART switch offers a solution to this problem. The switch is constructed from a small (110 × 60 × 30 mm) metal case, a six-pole change-

over switch, two SCART sockets, one SCART plug, and a length of screened coaxial cable. Suitable holes should be provided in the case to receive the two sockets, a cable outlet, and the switch. The various components are connected together as shown in the accompanying diagram. The SCART plug is connected at the free end of the cable, which should not be longer than 1 metre. The connections to the sockets and plug are also identified in the table.

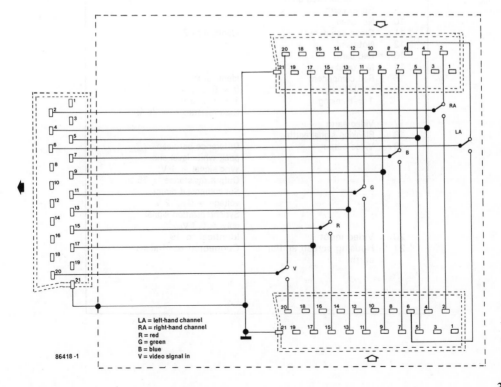

LA = left-hand channel
RA = right-hand channel
R = red
G = green
B = blue
V = video signal in

86418 -1

The completed switch should find a home beside, under, or on top of the TV set: the SCART plug is inserted into the SCART socket at the back of the set. The two SCART sockets on the case are then used to receive the computer and video recorder respectively. From then on, it is a simple matter of switching between recorder and computer!

SCART connector

Pin	Function	Level
1	Audio output (right-hand) or channel 2	0.5 V for output impedances ≥ 1 kΩ
2	Audio output (right-hand) or channel 2	0.5 V for input impedances ≤ 10 kΩ
3	Audio output (left-hand) or channel 1 or mono	0.5 V for output impedances ≤ 1 kΩ
4	Audio earth	
5	Blue earth	
6	Audio input (left-hand) or channel 1 or mono	0.5 V for input impedances ≥ 10 kΩ
7	Blue component	Difference between peak value and blanking signal level = 0.7 V; load impedance = 75 Ω; superimposed direct voltage = 0...2 V
8	Switching voltage: 0 = TV reception 1 = operation of associated units	0 = 0...2 V 1 = 9.5...12 V
9	Green earth	
10	Not used	
11	Green component	Identical to 7
12	Not used	
13	Red earth	
14	Not used	
15	Red component	Identical to 7
16	Blanking signal 1 = blanking	0 = 0...0.4 V 1 = 1...3 V Load resistance = 75 Ω
17	Video earth	
18	Blanking signal earth	
19	Video output	Difference between peak white level and sync signal = 1 V; Output resistance = 75 Ω; Superimposed direct voltage = 0...2 V Synchronization signal only = 0.3 V_{pp}
20	Video input	Identical to 19
21	Housing screen and/or earth	Connected to chassis

Many monitors have separate inputs for the line (horizontal) and field synchronization pulses. If your computer only provides composite sync pulses, the circuit described here makes it possible to split the composite sync signal, $\overline{CSYNC}$, into proper line, $\overline{HS}$, and field, $\overline{VS}$, pulses.

It is possible to feed the $\overline{CSYNC}$ as line sync pulses direct to the monitor, which is the reason that the $\overline{CSYNC}$ input is connected direct to the $\overline{HS}$ output terminal.

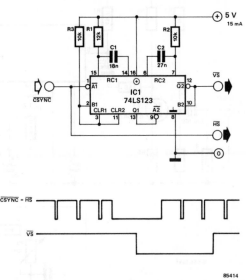

To derive the field sync pulses from the composite signal, a dual retriggerable monostable type 74LS123 is needed. The first mono period is slightly longer than the distance between two line sync pulses. As the monostable is retriggered by each line sync pulse, it only resets in the absence of a line sync pulse, that is, at the onset of a blanking interval. The first monostable then triggers the second, which generates a $\overline{VS}$ pulse at its $\overline{Q}$ output. When the second mono period has lapsed, the first monostable has already been provided with more line sync pulses, so that monostable 2 is not triggered again until the next blanked interval. The overall result is that all line sync pulses are suppressed, while monostable 2 provides field sync pulses.

Many monitor chassis currently offered by computer surplus stores have separate inputs for horizontal and vertical synchronization signals. Most home micros, however, have a composite video output, so that some form of interfacing is required to drive these bargain monitors.

The Type TBA950-2 is a sync separator chip which is frequently encountered on TV chassis. In its standard application circuit, it requires to be driven by a flyback signal derived from the output of the line frequency oscillator. Without this signal, which is applied to pin 10, the sync pulse would end up somewhere among the picture lines. To be able to use the TBA950-2 in the present application, the horizontal pulse is slightly shifted with the aid of a double monostable multivibrator, IC2.

The operation of the circuit should be clear from the accompanying timing diagram. The output pulse from the TBA950 is fairly wide (26 μs), and its positive edge triggers the first MMV (Q1), whose negative output pulse transition in turn triggers the second MMV in the 4538 package. The line sync pulse for the monitor is available positive and negative at IC2 outputs Q2 and $\overline{Q2}$, respectively.

Adjust the circuit as follows: set P2 to the centre of its travel, and adjust the frequency control, P1, such that the image is stable. Next, position the image by adjusting P3. If the correct position can not be obtained, the phase control, P2, must be carefully readjusted, followed by P3. The vertical sync pulse is available at pin 7 of the TBA950-2. Finally, the dashed resistors and diodes are required if the monitor inputs are designed to accept signals with a peak-to-peak amplitude of 5 V.

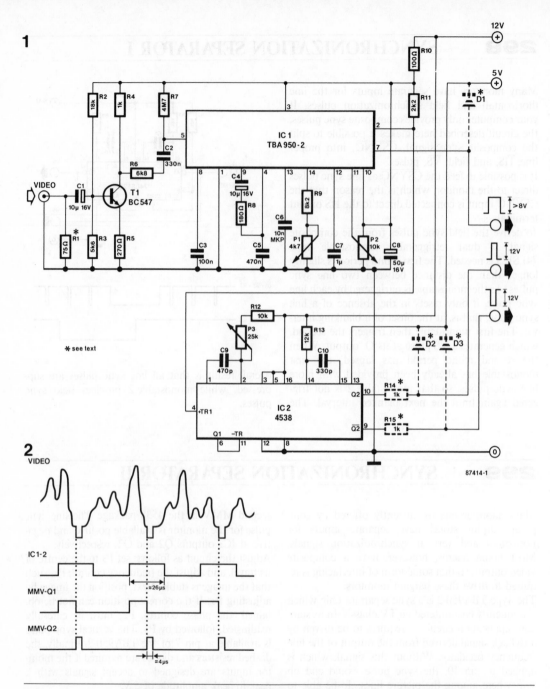

1

2
VIDEO

IC1-2

MMV-Q1

MMV-Q2

≈26µs

≈4µs

87414-1

VIDEO AMPLIFIER FOR B/W TELEVISION SETS

It appears that the use of portable, mains operated television receivers as monitor in a computer system has become very popular. The article *use your TV*

receiver as a monitor (Elektor Electronics, November 1984) described an all-embracing amplifier, but here we propose a much simpler one.

To raise the standard video signal of 1 V$_{pp}$ to the level required by the television receiver, a preamplifier with a bandwidth of not less than 10 MHz is required. With careful construction of the present amplifier, this bandwidth is guaranteed, and should actually be of the order of close to 20 MHz. With a supply voltage of 12 V, the direct-voltage output is 4 V. If different supply voltages are used, the DC output is retained at that level by suitably altering the values of R_1 and R_2 (which form a voltage divider). However, the supply voltage should not be lower than 10 V, nor higher than 15 V. The amplification depends on the ratio $R_7 : R_8$; if higher amplification is needed, the value of R_7 should be increased.

The respectable bandwidth is achieved by low value base and collector resistors: with this arrangement, even audio transistors may be used in this, essentially HF, circuit. In any case, the cut-off frequency of a BC 547 is 300 MHz, and that of a BC 557 is 150 MHz.

The input impedance is strictly determined by R_3;

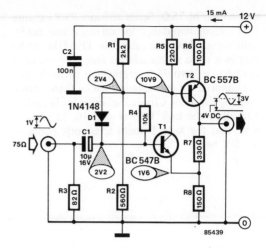

its value of 82 Ω is near enough the required impedance, but if you really want to be a purist, there are 75 Ω resistors available at some stockists, or you can connect a 100 Ω resistor in parallel with a 330 Ω one.

301   VIDEO BUFFER/REPEATER

This universal video amplifier is intended as a buffer/repeater in a long coaxial cable to keep the signal at a reasonable level. Its gain is about 6 dB. The circuit is built from readily available components: some transistors and a few others.

The circuit consists of a two-stage amplifier, T_1 and T_2, and an emitter follower that functions as impedance converter. The bandwidth at —3 dB is not less than 20 MHz. Current consumption at a supply voltage of 12 V amounts to about 20 mA. The power supply needs to be regulated to prevent lines and other noise on the screen.

The buffer/repeater is very suitable for being combined with the *video selector* featured elsewhere in

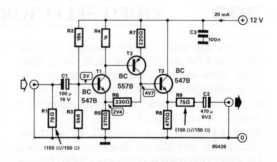

this issue. The present circuit, with R_1 omitted, is then used as a buffer for the output of the inverter. Its input impedance is then around 4 kΩ.

302   VIDEO DISTRIBUTION AMPLIFIER

The Type TEA5114 from Thomson-CSF comprises three electronic switches followed by a buffer/amplifier. Normally the voltage amplification is 2 (6 dB). When the input voltage exceeds 1.2 V$_{pp}$, or when

the output voltage exceeds 1.5 V$_{pp}$, an internal selector reduces the amplification to unity (0 dB). The threshold of 1.2 V$_{pp}$ is created with the aid of voltage divider R_4-R_5, which also forms the input

termination of 75 Ω. Series resistors R_1-R_3 ensure
75 Ω output impedance for driving video equipment via standard coax cable. The TEA5114 can be
used as a video source selector also, provided each
input has its own 75 Ω termination network. The
non-connected inputs should then be fitted with a
coupling capacitor. Channel selection is effected by
controlling the logic level at pins 10, 12 and 15.
Note that the logic 1 (high) level corresponds to
+2.5 V here.

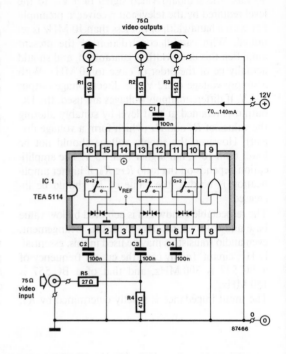

303　　　VIDEO SELECTOR

It is sometimes useful, or even necessary, to use the
same screen for more than one video source. Some
simple video selectors used for this purpose suffer
rather badly from crosstalk. The present circuit does
not have this drawback: the unused channel(s) is
shorted out with a switch.

When CH(annel) 1 is switched in, electronic
switches ES_1 and ES_2 are closed and ES_4 is open.
The other channel(s) is effectively choked because
ES_5 and ES_6 are both open and any residual
crosstalk is shorted to earth by ES_8. Each channel
uses its own IC so that there is no risk of cross channel interference via the chips.

As the switches have a certain impedance in the on
state, there will be some losses when the output is
terminated into 75 Ω. It is, therefore, best to buffer
the output; for instance, with the *video
buffer/repeater* described elsewhere in this issue.

The input of the video selector must be terminated
into 75 Ω. The —3 dB bandwidth is about 8 MHz.
Current consumption amounts to 1...2 mA depending on the supply voltage. A high supply
voltage is preferable, because the electronic switches
then have the lowest impedance in the on state.

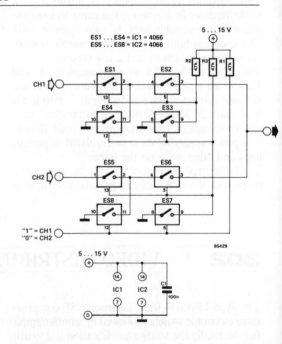